The Fundamentals of
X-ray and Radium Physics

The Fundamentals of X-ray and Radium Physics

By **JOSEPH SELMAN, M.D.**

Director, School for X-ray Technicians
Tyler Junior College
Chief of Radiology, Mother Frances Hospital
Director, Radiology Department
Medical Center Hospital
Consultant in Radiology, East Texas Tuberculosis Hospital
Tyler, Texas

CHARLES C THOMAS • **PUBLISHER**
Springfield · Illinois · U.S.A.

CHARLES C THOMAS · PUBLISHER
BANNERSTONE HOUSE
301–327 East Lawrence Avenue, Springfield, Illinois, U.S.A.

Published simultaneously in the British Commonwealth of Nations by
BLACKWELL SCIENTIFIC PUBLICATIONS, LTD., OXFORD, ENGLAND

Published simultaneously in Canada by
THE RYERSON PRESS, TORONTO

Printed in the United States of America

Dedicated to my wife

PREFACE

It is obvious to anyone who has had experience in teaching radiologic physics to student x-ray technicians that the majority of students have had poor preparation for this course of study. Those students who may have been exposed to physics and mathematics in high school often retain so little knowledge of these subjects that they must learn anew even the simplest principles. The student x-ray technician with a background of college training in the sciences is indeed a rarity.

Many teachers devoted to the training of student x-ray technicians have long recognized the dearth of textbooks in physics designed for technicians. A desirable textbook of this type must lead the student, as painlessly as possible, from the most elementary considerations all the way to radiologic physics, a task which is by no means simple. The subject matter must be presented in great detail in order that the student may derive a more complete understanding of it. At the same time, the text must be as non-mathematical as possible and couched in language that is readily comprehensible.

On the basis of lecture notes and other data used in the instruction of student technicians over a period of years, the author has written the present book with the primary purpose of simplifying for the student x-ray technician the subject of radiologic physics in all its theoretical and practical aspects as it confronts the technician. With this aim in view, basic principles of physics and chemistry are emphasized and presented in greatest possible detail. At the same time, the simplest available terminology is employed in order to avoid a language barrier to the comprehension of these important principles. In accordance with the familiar pedagogic rule of repetition, the more significant physical principles are repeated, presented from various standpoints, and correlated wherever possible throughout the text.

Recognizing the value of visual aids to education, the author has made free use of numerous line drawings to facilitate the study of the text. Tables have been included only to emphasize certain points rather than as a source of reference for specific data. Throughout the book, fundamental principles are stressed, and if these are grasped by the student, he is then in a better position to understand the specific data furnished by the manufacturer for the equipment or supplies in use in his radiology department.

Mathematics of the simplest type is employed only where deemed essential to the understanding of fundamental principles. A summary of elementary mathematics introduces the book so that the student's memory can be more easily refreshed. It embodies all of the mathematical principles that are to appear in later chapters, so that if the first chapter is mastered the student should encounter no difficulty with the algebra and geometry employed in subsequent chapters.

There has been included a somewhat detailed consideration of the intimate structure of matter, and some space has been devoted to the quantum theory. This may be criticized by those teachers who feel that too much emphasis is already being placed on physics in the students' overburdened curriculum. However, it is felt, in view of the great strides that have been made in atomic physics in the last few years and the growing importance of radioactive isotopes, that the student should have at least a minimum concept of atomic structure and atomic energy.

The material has been so organized that certain sections may be omitted at the instructor's discretion without seriously interfering with the continuity of the text. On the other hand, these more advanced considerations will appeal to the student technician fortunate enough to have a better-than-average scientific background.

Although it has been pointed out repeatedly that this book has been conceived primarily for the student x-ray technician, it is felt that it will also be of distinct advantage to the resident in radiology who is just entering upon his period of training and needs an introductory textbook to prepare him for more advanced reading as his knowledge of the subject develops.

With some exceptions, the author makes no claim to originality, but it is impossible to mention by name the thousands of radiologists, physicists, and technicians who have developed the science of radiology to its present high position. Grateful acknowledgement is hereby accorded to the following who so kindly took time from their busy curriculum to review certain sections of the text and offered invaluable suggestions and criticisms: T. W. Bonner, PhD., Professor of Physics at the Rice Institute; Otto Glasser, PhD., Professor of Biophysics at the Cleveland Clinic Foundation; and Mr. W. S. Cornwell and his associates at the Eastman Kodak Company. The illustrations were prepared from the author's sketches by Mr. Howard Marlin, Tyler, Texas. The manuscript typing was ably executed by Miss Betty Presley of Tyler, Texas.

The author appreciates the kindness of the Machlett Laboratories, Inc., and of the General Electric X-ray Corporation for furnishing the basic drawings of their x-ray and valve tubes; and of the Eastman Kodak Company, E. I. du Pont de Nemours, Inc., and Ansco for the data on x-ray films, film processing, and screens. Finally, the author is grateful to the publisher, Mr. Charles C Thomas, for his encouragement, patience, cooperation, and sound advice.

JOSEPH SELMAN, M.D.

Tyler, Texas

CONTENTS

The Fundamentals of
X-ray and Radium Physics

CHAPTER *1* SIMPLIFIED MATHEMATICS

All branches of science require, for their proper understanding, the ability to employ mathematics. Since the student x-ray technician is really embarking on a scientific career, he must be acquainted with at least those elementary mathematical principles that will facilitate his mastery of the various phases of radiologic physics.

It is taken for granted that the student technician has had no less than the elementary courses in high school mathematics. The present section is intended to refresh the student's mind on the simple arithmetic, algebra, and geometry that are essential for the proper understanding of physical principles. If the technician will try to forget any fears that he may have acquired in the past regarding mathematics, he will have little or no difficulty with this subject. Every technician should have an easy, working knowledge of the simple mathematics to be presented here, so that he may readily solve any problems that may arise in his day-to-day work; for example, conversion of radiographic distances, reading tube rating charts, determining film coverage at various distances with various size cones, and many similar problems.

The discussion will be subdivided into several parts: (1) arithmetic, (2) algebra, (3) ratio and proportion, (4) geometry, and (5) graphs and charts. Only the most elementary considerations will be included.

ARITHMETIC

Arithmetic is the science of calculation by the use of numbers. It is assumed that the student has fair ability in addition, subtraction, multiplication, and division.

Fractions

The manipulation of fractions may be hazy in the student's mind so that a brief review is in order. *A fraction is defined as a part of*

3

a whole number. For instance, $\frac{1}{2}$, $\frac{1}{3}$, $\frac{2}{5}$ are fractions. The fraction $\frac{3}{5}$ may be read "three divided by five," and represented also as $3 \div 5$.

Note that a fraction consists of one whole number divided by another such that they are not evenly divisible. Thus, $\frac{3}{5}$ is a fraction, whereas $\frac{4}{2}$ is not a fraction since $4 \div 2 = 2$.

The parts of a fraction have definite names. The number above the line is called the *numerator* and the number below the line the *denominator.* In the fraction $\frac{3}{5}$, 3 is the numerator and 5 is the denominator.

If the numerator is smaller than the denominator, as in $\frac{3}{5}$, we have a *proper fraction.* If the numerator is larger than the denominator, as $\frac{5}{3}$, it is called an *improper fraction,* because $5 \div 3 = 1\frac{2}{3}$, which is really a whole number plus a fraction.

In *adding* fractions, all of which have the *same* denominator, one adds all the numerators together and places the sum over the denominator:

$$\frac{2}{7} + \frac{3}{7} + \frac{6}{7} + \frac{5}{7} = \frac{2+3+6+5}{7} = \frac{16}{7}$$

$$\frac{16}{7} = 2\frac{2}{7}$$

Subtraction of fractions having the same denominator follows the same rule:

$$\frac{6}{7} - \frac{4}{7} = \frac{6-4}{7} = \frac{2}{7}$$

If a series of fractions is to be added or subtracted, and the denominators are *different,* then the *least common denominator* must be found. This is the smallest number which is exactly divisible by all the denominators. Thus,

$$\frac{1}{2} + \frac{2}{3} - \frac{3}{4} = ? \qquad \text{(a)}$$

Find the smallest number which is divided exactly by each denominator. This number is 12. Place 12 in the denominator of a new fraction:

$$\frac{\qquad}{12} \qquad \text{(b)}$$

Divide the denominator of each of the fractions in (a) into 12, and then multiply the answer by the numerator of that fraction; the result is then placed in the numerator of the new fraction (b):

$$\frac{6+8-9}{12} = \frac{5}{12}$$

When numbers are multiplied, it is said that one *takes their product*. In multiplying fractions, take the product of the numerator and place it over the product of the denominator and then simplify this new fraction:

$$\frac{4}{5} \times \frac{3}{10} = \frac{4 \times 3}{5 \times 10} = \frac{12}{50}$$

The resulting fraction can be simplified by dividing the numerator and the denominator by the *same* number, in this case, 2:

$\frac{12}{50} = \frac{6}{25}$, which cannot be further simplified.

It should be noted that when the numerator and the denominator are both multiplied by the same number, or both divided by the same number, the value of the fraction does not change. For instance,

$$\frac{3}{5} \times \frac{2}{2} = \frac{6}{10}, \text{ is the same as}$$

$$\frac{3}{5} \times 1 = \frac{3}{5}.$$

When two fractions are to be divided, as $\frac{4}{5} \div \frac{3}{7}$, the fraction that is to be divided is the *dividend,* and the fraction that does the dividing is called the *divisor.* In this case, $\frac{4}{5}$ is the dividend and $\frac{3}{7}$ the divisor. To work this type of problem, the rule is to invert the divisor (called "taking the reciprocal") and multiply the dividend by it:

$$\frac{4}{5} \div \frac{3}{7}$$

$$\frac{4}{5} \times \frac{7}{3} = \frac{28}{15} = 1\frac{13}{15}$$

Per Cent

A special form of fraction is *per cent*. It is represented by the sign %, and indicates that the number standing with it is to be divided by 100. Thus $95\% = {}^{95}\!/_{100}$. One cannot use percentages as such in mathematical computations, but must convert the percentage to a fraction or a decimal. For instance,

$$150 \times 40\% \text{ is changed to}$$
$$150 \times {}^{40}\!/_{100} \text{ or } 150 \times \tfrac{2}{5}$$
$$\text{or } 150 \times 0.40.$$

Decimals

A simplified method of representing fractions is embodied in the decimal system. A *decimal* is a proper fraction whose denominator is 10, or 10 raised to some power such as 100, 1000, 10,000, etc. The denominator is symbolized by a dot placed in a certain position. For example, the decimal 0.2 means the same as $\tfrac{2}{10}$; 0.02 means the same as $\tfrac{2}{100}$; 0.002 means $\tfrac{2}{1000}$, etc. Decimal numbers can be multiplied or divided the same as whole numbers, but care must be exercised in placing the decimal point in the proper position:

$$
\begin{array}{r}
2.24 \\
\times 1.25 \\
\hline
1120 \\
448 \\
224 \\
\hline
2.8000
\end{array}
$$

Note that one adds the total number of digits to the right of the decimal points in the numbers being multiplied, which in this case turns out to be 4. Then one points off 4 places from the right in the answer and that is the correct position for the decimal point. In scientific work, the decimal system is used almost exclusively in preference to conventional fractions.

ALGEBRA

The word *algebra* is derived from the Arabic language. It is that branch of mathematics which deals with the relationship of quantities by the use of letters or symbols. It is really mathematical shorthand. Ordinarily, the symbols used in algebra are the letters of the alphabet.

The manipulation of these letters is identical with the manipulation of numbers, and need not mystify the student. In algebra, the fundamental operations are addition, subtraction, multiplication, and division. There are fractions, equations, and proportions just as in arithmetic. Algebra is of value in giving us a method of finding an unknown quantity when the relationship of certain known quantities is understood.

The symbols for manipulation of algebraic letters are the same as those used in arithmetic:

$+$ (plus) add
$-$ (minus) subtract
$\times$ (times) multiply
$\div$ (divided by) divide
$=$ equals

Since one uses letters in place of numbers, a definite answer cannot be found immediately, so that one must introduce the concept *equation*. This is defined as the expression of the equality of two or more quantities. For example, a is an unknown quantity, and b is another unknown quantity. Suppose they are to be added; there will result a third unknown quantity, let us say c. This can be expressed in the form of an equation.

$$a + b = c.$$

If now, we learn that a is 4, and b is 5, then, substituting these values in the equation,

$$4 + 5 = c$$
$$9 = c$$
$$\text{or, } c = 9$$

Similarly, we can subtract algebraic quantities. Suppose one wishes to subtract an unknown quantity, y, from an unknown quantity, x. The answer will be another unknown, let us say z. The equation is:

$$x - y = z$$

If it is learned that x is 7 and y is 4, then, substituting these values in the equation,

$$7 - 4 = z$$
$$3 = z$$
$$\text{or, } z = 3$$

It should be pointed out that in algebra, negative numbers are permissible. For instance, in the equation $x - y = z$, if x is 8 and y is 11, then

$$8 - 11 = z$$
$$-3 = z$$
$$\text{or, } z = -3$$

Multiplication and division in algebra are also similar to the arithmetic procedures:

$$a \times b = c$$

If a is 2 and b is 3, then

$$2 \times 3 = c$$
$$6 = c$$
$$\text{or, } c = 6$$

In algebra, when two or more symbols are multiplied, the $\times$ sign is usually omitted; thus, $a \times b$ is written ab. When two symbols are divided, they are written as a fraction; thus, $a \div b$ is represented a/b.

When two negative quantities are multiplied, the answer is positive; $-a \times -b = ab$. When two negative quantities are divided, the answer is positive; $-a/-b = a/b$. When a positive and a negative quantity are multiplied or divided, the answer is negative; thus, $a \times -b = -ab$, and $a/-b = -a/b$.

In handling an algebraic expression consisting of a group of terms one must perform the indicated multiplication and division first, and then carry out the indicated addition and subtraction. An example will clarify this:

$$ab + c/d - f$$

Let $a = 2, b = 3, c = 4, d = 8,$ and $f = 5$. Substituting in the expression,

$$2 \times 3 + \frac{4}{8} - 5 = ?$$

Performing *multiplication and division first,*

$$6 + \frac{4}{8} - 5 = ?$$

Then, performing addition and subtraction,

$$6\frac{4}{8} - 5 = 1\frac{4}{8} = 1\frac{1}{2}$$

A parenthesis inclosing a group of terms indicates that all of the terms inside the parenthesis are to be multiplied by the term outside the parenthesis. Thus, in the expression

$$6\,(8-4+3\times 2) =$$
$$6\,(8-4+6) =$$
$$6\times 10 = 60$$

The handling of simple algebraic equations such as the technician will have to deal with, is quite easy if the fundamental rules are learned. In studying this phase of mathematics, the technician can simplify his task by frequently testing the rules by the substitution of numbers to show that the rules really work. A simple equation is the following:

$$a + b = c + d$$

In this equation, $a + b$ is called the *left member,* and $c + d$ is called the *right member.* Each letter is called a *term.* If any quantity is added to one member of the equation, the same quantity must be added to the other member in order for this to remain a true equation. Similarly, if any quantity is subtracted from one member, the same quantity must be subtracted from the other member. This is greatly simplified if one pictures the equation as being a see-saw. If people of equal weight are placed at each end, the board will remain horizontal—the equation is balanced. If a second person is now added to one end of the see-saw, a person of similar weight must be added to the other end in order to keep the board level. This is illustrated in Figure 1.

Returning again to the simple equation:

$$a + b = c + d$$

If any three of the terms are known, the fourth can be found. Suppose, a is 3, b is 4, c is 1 and d is unknown. Substituting these values in the equation,

$$3 + 4 = 1 + d$$

How can d be found? It is necessary to rearrange the equation so that d is alone, that is, the only term in its member. In this case,

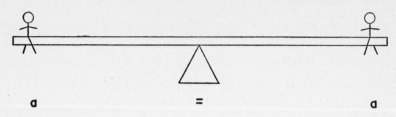

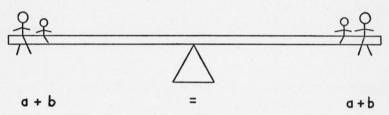

Figure 1. Analogy of algebraic equation to a see-saw.

1 must be moved from the right member to the left, but a definite rule must be followed: *If a term is transposed from one member of an equation to the other member, it assumes the opposite sign.* Following this rule, 1 becomes a minus 1 when moved to the left member. Thus,

$$3 + 4 - 1 = d$$
$$6 = d$$
$$\text{or, } d = 6$$

Usually, in algebraic calculations, the terms are rearranged before their numerical values are substituted. In this case,

$$a + b = c + d$$

Since d is unknown, c must be transposed to the left member:

$$a + b - c = d$$
$$\text{or, } d = a + b - c$$

since reversing both members of an equation does not alter its balance.

In algebraic equations in which terms are related by multiplication or division, a rule analogous to transposition applies. For example, in equation

$$x = y/z$$

if x and z are known, the equation is solved for y by first moving z from the right member to the left. Since z in the right member is a "divided by," it becomes a "multiplied by" in the left member and

$$zx = y$$
$$\text{or,} \quad y = zx$$

The rule in this case is simplified thus: *if the denominator of one member of an equation is moved, it enters the numerator of the other member.* If the numerator of one member of an equation is moved, it enters the denominator of the other member.

If in the equation $x = y/z$, x and y are known, z is solved as follows: move z into the numerator of the opposite member,

$$xz = y$$

Then move x into the denominator of the right member, and

$$z = y/x \qquad (1)$$

The above rule can be readily tested. Suppose that y is 12, and x is 3. Substituting in equation (1),

$$z = \frac{12}{3}$$
$$z = 4$$
$$4 = \frac{12}{3} \qquad (2)$$

If we wish to move 3, it must be placed in the numerator of the left member of the equation,

$$4 \times 3 = 12 \qquad (3)$$

Note that the numerical equation (3) balances.

Now, referring again to equation (2), suppose we wish to move 12. It must be placed in the denominator of the left member:

$$\frac{4}{12} = \frac{1}{3}$$

Again, it is evident that the equation balances. Thus, we see that the rule is valid in this case, and it could be shown mathematically that it applies equally in all cases.

RATIO AND PROPORTION

A *ratio* is a fixed relationship between two quantities. It simply indicates how many times one quantity is bigger or smaller than another quantity. It has essentially the same meaning as a fraction. The symbol that expresses a ratio is the colon (:). Thus, $a:b$ is read "a is to b." Or, $5:6$ is read "5 is to 6." These ratio forms can be equally well represented as fractions:

$$a:b \text{ is the same as } a/b$$
$$5:6 \text{ is the same as } \frac{5}{6}$$

The meaning of ratio is very important for the technician. Furthermore, ratios enter into the concept of *proportion*. A proportion is defined as an expression showing that two given ratios are equal. Thus, we may have an algebraic proportion,

$$a:b :: c:d \qquad (1)$$

which is read "a is to b as c is to d." This can be expressed more simply in fraction form,

$$a/b = c/d \qquad (2)$$

The same idea can also be presented numerically. Thus,

$$3:6 :: 4:8$$
$$\text{or } \frac{3}{6} = \frac{4}{8}$$

If any three terms of a proportion are known, the fourth may be solved, in either of two ways. Suppose in proportion (1) a is 2, b is 4, d is 8, and c is unknown. Substituting these numbers in the proportion,

$$2:4 :: c:8$$

The rule for solving a proportion is that the product of the means (the inner two terms, in this case 4 and c) is equal to the product of the extremes (the first and last terms, in this case 2 and 8). Therefore,

$$4c = 2 \times 8$$
$$4c = 16$$
$$c = 4$$

A second, and simpler method which requires no special rules, is to form the fractions:

$$\frac{2}{4} = \frac{c}{8}$$

Transfer 8 to the numerator of the left member,

$$\frac{2 \times 8}{4} = c$$

$$c = \frac{16}{4} = 4$$

There are two general types of proportions that are of interest in radiography.

1. *Direct proportion.* In this type, one quantity varies in the same direction as some other quantity on which it depends. For example, if we say "*a* is proportional to *b*," it means that if *b* is doubled, *a* is automatically doubled; if *b* is tripled, *a* is tripled, etc. In order to represent this in a more mathematical sense, let us assume that the quantity a_1 exists when b_1 exists; now if b_1 is changed to b_2, then a_1 becomes a_2. Thus,

$$a_1 : b_1 :: a_2 : b_2$$

The numbers below the letters are called "subscripts" and have no significance except to label a_2 as being different from a_1. Such a direct proportion is solved by either of the two methods described above.

2. *Inverse proportion.* In this type, one quantity varies in an opposite direction as another quantity on which it depends. Thus, if we say "*a* is inversely proportional to *b*," it means that if *b* is doubled *a* is halved, if *b* is tripled, *a* is divided by 3, etc. Such a proportion is set up as follows:

$$a_1 : \frac{1}{b_1} :: a_2 : \frac{1}{b_2}$$

Multiplying the two means, and then the two extremes,

$$\frac{a_1}{b_2} = \frac{a_2}{b_1} \qquad (3)$$

A numerical example may help to clarify this. Suppose that when b_1 is 4, a_1 is 2; if *a* is inversely proportional to *b*, what will a_1 become if b_1 is changed to 8? In this case, a_2 is the unknown, and b_2 is 8. Substituting in equation (3),

$$\frac{2}{8} = \frac{a_2}{4}$$

$$a_2 = \frac{8}{8} = 1$$

Thus, *a* is halved when *b* is doubled.

GEOMETRY

Geometry is that branch of mathematics which deals with figures in space. A few of the more elementary rules will be listed in order to refresh the student's memory.

1. A *line* is the shortest distance between two points, under ordinary conditions. A line has only one dimension, length.

2. A *rectangle* is a geometric figure made up of four lines which meet at right angles. The opposite sides are equal. The sum of the lengths of the four sides is called the *perimeter*. The area of a rectangle is the product of two adjacent sides. Thus, in Figure 2 the perimeter is the sum $a + b + a + b = 2a + 2b$. The area is $a \times b$ which is more simply represented by ab.

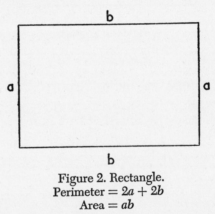

Figure 2. Rectangle.
Perimeter $= 2a + 2b$
Area $= ab$

3. A *square* is a special rectangle in which all four sides are equal. Therefore, the area of a square equals the square of one side. This is shown in Figure 3.

4. A *triangle* is a geometric figure made up of three lines that intersect at their ends. The perimeter of a triangle is the sum of the three sides. The area of a triangle is ½ the base times the altitude (the altitude is the perpendicular distance from the apex to the base). This is shown in Figure 4.

5. A *circle* is a closed curved line which is everywhere at an equal distance from one point called the center. The length of a circle is called the *circumference*, which is equal to the diameter

times a constant called π (pi). The diameter is a straight line passing through the center and cutting the circle at two points. Pi is a constant, always equal to $3\frac{1}{7}$ (approximately). The *area* of

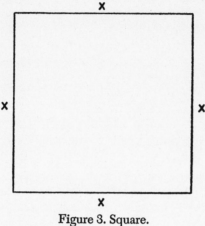

Figure 3. Square.
Perimeter $= 4x$
Area $= x \times x = x^2$

a circle equals π times the radius squared. The radius is a line drawn from the circle to its center. These relationships can be understood more easily by referring to Figure 5.

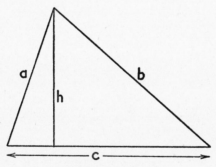

Figure 4. Triangle.
Perimeter $= a + b + c$
Area $= \frac{1}{2}ch$

One geometrical problem that is of great importance in radiology, and which is closely related to ratio and proportion, is the relationship of *similar triangles*. These are triangles which have the same shape, although they may vary in size. *In similar tri-*

angles the corresponding sides are directly proportional. All of the corresponding angles are equal, as would be expected since the shapes of similar triangles are the same.

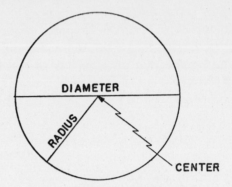

Figure 5. Circle.
Circumference $= \pi \times$ diameter $= \pi d$
Area $= \pi \times$ radius^2 $= \pi r^2$

In Figure 6 are shown two similar triangles. The corresponding sides are proportional, which means that

$$a : A :: b : B, \text{ or}$$
$$a : A :: c : C, \text{ or}$$
$$b : B :: c : C.$$

Note that the corresponding angles are equal.

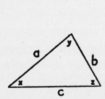 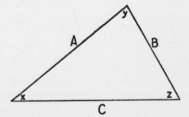

Figure 6. Similar triangles. $a:A::b:B::c:C$ because the corresponding sides are *proportional.* The corresponding angles are *equal.*

If we have a triangle and then draw a line across it parallel to the base, there will result two similar triangles, one partly superimposed on the other. This is revealed in Figure 7. Line *BE* has been drawn parallel to the base *CD*. Then, triangle *ABE* is similar to triangle *ACD* and their corresponding sides are proportional. This type of problem is simplified by considering the two triangles as being completely separated as in Figure 6.

A thorough comprehension of the theorem of similar triangles is essential to the understanding of photographic and radiographic projection. Let us assume that an object is placed in a beam of light which comes from a point source (see Figure 8). The shadow image of the object is allowed to fall on a surface which is parallel

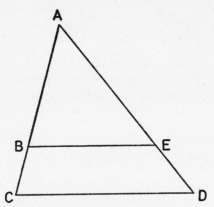

Figure 7. Similar triangles. *BE* is parallel to *CD*. Triangle *ABE* is similar to triangle *ACD*. Therefore,
AB:AC::AE:AD:BE::CD.

to the long axis of the object. Note that the image is larger than the object. If the distances of the object and of the image from the source of light are known, and if the size of the object is known, then the size of the image can be determined from the similarity of triangles *ABC* and *ADE*. We can set up the proportion,

$$\frac{\text{image size}}{\text{object size}} = \frac{\text{image distance}}{\text{object distance}}$$

Substituting the known values in the equation, we can predict the size of the image by solving the equation. Note that if any three of the values are known, the fourth can be readily obtained from the same equation. This same principle applies in radiography, as will be shown in Chapter 18.

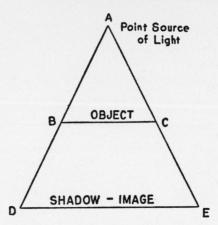

Figure 8. Projection of the shadow image of an object by a point source of light.

GRAPHS AND CHARTS

For practical purposes, graphs and charts may be considered as diagrams that represent the relationship of two things, one of which depends on the other. The dependent factor is called the *dependent variable*. The factor which changes independently is called the *independent variable*.

When data are accumulated, showing how one factor changes with a change in some other factor, they can be written in the form of a table, or they can be represented graphically. Tables are often less convenient to read than are graphs. The technician should not be frightened by the sight of a graph since it merely represents a simplified table and is very easy to read if the habit is cultivated.

The ease of construction and interpretation of a sample graph should readily dispel any fear that the technician may have inherited from his school days. As an example, it is found by practical experience that the optimum developing time for x-ray film varies inversely as the temperature of the developing solution; that is, as the temperature is increased the developing time must be decreased. By actual test with a certain developer, the data in Table I are obtained. This information can now be charted on graph paper. The temperature, which is the independent variable,

TABLE I

TIME-TEMPERATURE DEVELOPMENT DATA

Temperature in F	*Developing Time in Min.*
60	5¼
62	4½
64	3¾
65	3½
68	3
70	2¾
72	2½
75	2

is plotted along the horizontal axis of the graph. The developing time, which is the dependent variable, is charted on the vertical axis, as shown in Figure 9. To introduce the above data into the chart, take the first temperature listed in the table and locate it on the horizontal axis. Trace vertically upwards from this point to the horizontal line corresponding to the correct developing time, and mark the intersection with an x. Repeat this for all the values in the table, and then draw a line connecting the x's.

Having constructed the graph, how does one read it? Suppose the temperature is found to be 65 F, and one wishes to determine the correct developing time. Locate 65 F on the horizontal line and trace vertically upwards to the intersection with the *graph line;* from this point of intersection trace horizontally to the vertical axis on the left, where the correct developing time can be read. This is shown in Figure 10, where the tracing lines are shown as broken lines with arrows. It is evident that the horizontal tracing line meets the vertical axis at approximately 3½ minutes, which is the correct developing time at this temperature. Thus, a properly constructed graph can show us the developing time for temperature readings that did not appear in the original table, a process called *interpolation.*

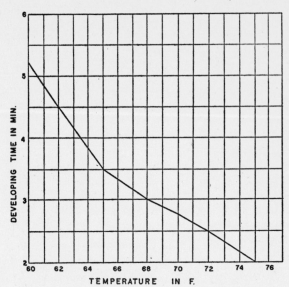

Figure 9. Time-temperature development graph.

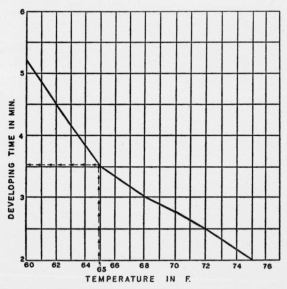

Figure 10. Method of using a time-temperature developing graph. Select the correct temperature on the horizontal axis, in this case 65 F. Follow vertically upwards, as shown by the arrows, to the graph line. Then follow horizontally to the time axis where the correct developing time in this case is seen to be 3½ min.

QUESTIONS AND PROBLEMS

1. Reduce the following fractions:
    (a) $\frac{4}{8}$
    (b) $\frac{9}{12}$
    (c) $\frac{10}{15}$
    (d) $\frac{4}{5}$
    (e) $\frac{14}{16}$
2. Solve the following problems:
    (a) $\frac{3}{5} + \frac{2}{5} + \frac{4}{5} =$
    (b) $\frac{2}{3} + \frac{3}{4} + \frac{3}{7} =$
    (c) $\frac{1}{2} + \frac{2}{3} + \frac{4}{5} =$
3. Divide as indicated:
    (a) $\frac{4}{5} \div \frac{3}{5}$
    (b) $\frac{4}{9} \div \frac{7}{16}$
    (c) $\frac{8}{9} \div \frac{3}{5}$
4. Mr. Jones has 100 bushels of potatoes and sells 75% of this crop. How many bushels does he have left?
5. If $a = b/c$, what is b in terms of a and c? What is c in terms of a and b?
6. Solve the following equations for the unknown term:
    (a) $x + 4 = 7 - 3 + 8$
    (b) $6 + 3 - 1 = 4 + 1 - a$
    (c) $6 + x - 4 = 3 + 1 - 2 - 7$
    (d) $x/3 = \frac{7}{9}$
    (e) $4/y = \dfrac{6 + 3}{10}$
    (f) $\dfrac{x + 4}{8} = 7 + 2 - 3$
7. What is meant by ratio? Proportion?
8. Solve the following proportions for the unknown quantity:
    (a) $a : 7 :: 2 : 21$
    (b) $3 : 9 :: x : 15$
    (c) $4 : 6 :: 7 : y$
9. The diameter of an x-ray beam is directly proportional to the distance from the tube target. If the diameter of the beam at a 20-in. distance is 10 cm, what will the diameter be at a 40-in. distance?
10. The exposure of a radiograph is directly proportional to the

time of exposure. What will happen to the exposure if the time is tripled?

11. What is the area of a circle having a diameter of 4 in.?

12. What is the area of a plot of ground measuring 20 ft. on one side and 30 ft. on the adjacent side?

13. Using the time-temperature graph in Figure 10, determine the proper developing time when the temperature is 64 F.

14. In order to make the exposure of a radiograph constant, the milliamperage is inversely proportional to the time of exposure. Suppose the quality of the radiograph is satisfactory with an exposure of 100 Ma at 1 sec, but we wish to use a faster technique of ¼ sec. What will the new milliamperage be at ¼ sec to give a radiograph of the same darkness?

CHAPTER 2 PHYSICS AND THE UNITS OF MEASUREMENT

Physics is an exact science. In dealing with a scientific subject, one must be careful to define all terms as precisely as possible. Each word must have an exact meaning. If this principle is adhered to, the study of science is greatly simplified, because we can better organize our ideas and convey them to others more clearly.

Since physics is a major subdivision of science, the latter should be defined first. *Science is organized and classified knowledge.* Natural phenomena are taking place around us constantly, which we may or may not be aware of. These do not constitute a science until sufficient information about them has been gathered by careful study, and these data have been grouped systematically and their interrelationships recognized.

What is *physics?* It may be defined as that field of science which deals with occurrences in inanimate nature, and is concerned with mechanics, heat, light, sound, and electricity. It is fundamental to all other sciences, and particularly to the study of the "why" and "how" of x-rays.

Science not only tries to describe and classify natural occurrences, but also attempts to correlate them by deriving certain principles known as *laws.* Scientific laws are based entirely on human experience, whether derived simply by observation of things around us or by laboratory experiments. Such laws state as clearly as possible, as far as we may know in our present state of knowledge, that certain events will always follow in the same order, or that certain facts will always be related in the same way. For example, we know that all bodies near the earth are attracted to the earth; this is a simple observation of the law of gravity.

Scientists are not satisfied with merely discovering the laws governing natural phenomena. They also attempt to correlate various laws in order to determine if they will fit into a *general pattern.* Thus, wherever possible, the laws of nature are tied together in such a way that a general idea, often in mathematical terms, expresses the operation of these laws. Such a broad, unified concept of the laws underlying certain natural phenomena is called a *theory.* This serves many useful purposes. It affords us a better insight into nature and also suggests new lines of scientific research, since it is common experience that no sooner is one problem in science solved, when numerous other ones present themselves. Theories help push back the curtains of ignorance and let in the light of knowledge.

One of the requirements of an exact science (as contrasted, for example, with some phases of biological science) is that it must not only classify human experience, but that it must also *measure it;* in other words, physics deals not only with the "how" of events, but also with "how much." This involves measurements, and in order that we may make our measurements intelligible to others, there must be chosen certain *standard units* which can be dealt with mathematically. These can be used not only in the description of natural phenomena with derivation of laws, or rules of nature, but can also be used to predict future events; for example, the astronomer can foretell when an eclipse of the sun will occur.

The units employed in physics are usually divided into two general types, the *fundamental units,* which are the simpler ones dealing with length, mass, and time, and the more complicated *derived units,* which are obtained by various combinations of the fundamental units.

Fundamental Units

Let us consider first the fundamental units. These are arbitrarily selected and named, but are so standardized that a given unit has the same meaning everywhere. There are at present two widely used systems of measurement, the English and the metric. In the exact sciences, the metric system is used internationally, and it will, therefore, be emphasized, but the more familiar equivalents in the English system units will also be indicated. The metric system is also known as the C.G.S. (or centimeter-gram-second) system.

1. *Length.* The unit of length in the metric system is the meter,

and its standard is defined as the distance between two scratches on a bar of platinum, kept near Paris at the International Bureau of Weights and Measures. It is roughly equal to a yard. Ordinarily, the meter can be subdivided into smaller units, such as centimeter ($\frac{1}{100}$ of a meter) and millimeter ($\frac{1}{1000}$ of a meter); or it can be multiplied to form a kilometer (1000 meters). In x-ray physics, we even have occasion to use very tiny fractions of these units; thus, the Ångstrom unit is $\frac{1}{100,000,000}$ of a centimeter. It is futile to memorize tables; if a few fundamental values are learned, they will prove useful.

1 meter = 100 cm (centimeters) = 1000 mm (millimeters)
1 Å (Ångstrom) = $\frac{1}{100,000,000}$ cm
1 km (kilometer) = 1,000 m (meters) = about 1,000 yards
1 in. = 2.54 cm

2. *Mass.* This refers to the amount of matter or substance in a body. It is usually determined by weighing the body, a procedure which determines the degree of attraction the earth has for the body. The more massive the body, the greater the attraction by the earth, and, therefore, the greater its weight. The unit of mass is the *kilogram,* which is the weight of a standard piece of platinum kept at the International Bureau of Standards. This is the standard unit, and all other kilograms are more or less exact copies of it. A more convenient unit is the *gram,* which is $\frac{1}{1000}$ of a kilogram.

1 kg (kilogram) = 1000 g (grams)
1 kg = 2.2 lbs.
28 g = 1 oz.

(The above discussion of mass and weight is not presented in strict accordance with physical principles, but has necessarily been simplified for our purposes.)

3. *Time.* This is a measure of the duration of events. We are all aware of the occurrence of events and the motion of objects, but to measure the duration of these with relation to our senses alone is very inaccurate. The standard unit of time is the *second* which is defined as $\frac{1}{86,400}$ of a mean solar day. In other words, it is a definite fraction of the average time it takes for the earth to make one rotation on its axis.

Derived Units

There are numerous derived units, but only those will be mentioned which have a practical bearing on x-ray physics.

1. *Area.* This is measurement of a given surface, and depends on length. Thus, a square or rectangle has an area equal to the product of two sides. The area of a circle equals the radius squared times π. This has been considered in detail in Figures 2, 3, 4, and 5 in Chapter 1. In the metric system, area is represented by square meters for large surfaces and square centimeters for small surfaces. Square centimeters can be abbreviated either as sq cm or cm^2.

2. *Volume.* This is a measure of the capacity of a container, and is also derived from length. The volume of a cube equals the product of three sides. In metric units, volume can be expressed in cubic centimeters (cc). One liter practically equals 1,000 cc and is approximately equivalent to one quart.

3. *Density.* This is the mass per unit volume of a substance, and may be expressed in g per cc.

4. *Specific Gravity.* This has *no units*. It is the ratio of the density of any material compared with the density of water. The density of water is 1.

5. *Velocity.* This is speed in a given direction, and can be expressed in cm per sec, or km per hr., or some other convenient unit. In everyday practice, the units are expressed in miles per hr. (English system).

6. *Temperature.* This is a measure of the average energy of motion of the molecules of matter. There are two systems in common use today. Among scientists, the centigrade system is used. In general daily use in this country is the Fahrenheit system. The following data show the difference between these systems:

CENTIGRADE   0 C = freezing point of water
100 C = boiling point of water

FAHRENHEIT   32 F = freezing point of water
212 F = boiling point of water

To change values from one system to the other, one may refer to tables, or the following formulas may be used:

$$C = \frac{5}{9}(F - 32)$$

$$F = \frac{9}{5}C + 32$$

QUESTIONS AND PROBLEMS

1. What is meant by "Science"? "Law"? "Theory"?
2. Why are standard units necessary?
3. With what do the fundamental units deal?
4. What is the metric system?
5. What is the unit of mass, and what is its standard?
6. What is the unit of time?
7. What is the approximate equivalent of 1 meter in the English system? One gram? One liter?
8. The temperature of a solution is 68 F. What is the equivalent temperature in centigrade units?
9. A patient is found to have a temperature of 40 C. What is his temperature in Fahrenheit units?

CHAPTER 3 THE PHYSICAL CONCEPT OF ENERGY

Force

All matter has in common a property called *inertia*. This may be defined as the tendency of a resting body to remain at rest, and the tendency of a body moving uniformly in a straight line to remain in motion. In order to set a resting body in motion, one must push or pull it; that is, one must apply a *force*. Conversely, in order to stop a moving body or change its direction, a push or pull must be applied. Thus, force may be simply considered as a push or pull applied to a body.

Work

If a force is made to act upon a body over a distance, *work* is done. For example, if a box is moved, a force is required in order to overcome the inertia of the body. This moving force multiplied by the distance the body is moved equals the work done. If the box is moved twice the distance, then twice as much work will be done. Work can be expressed in the following simple equation:

$$\text{work} = \text{force} \times \text{distance}$$

Energy

In a physical sense, work results from the expenditure of energy. What, then, is energy? *Energy may be defined as the actual or potential ability to do work.* It is obvious that work and energy must be measured in the same units, since a body cannot do more work than the energy it contains. There are two main types of energy:

1. *Kinetic Energy.* This is *energy of motion*, from the Greek word *kinetikos* = motion. Thus, the energy of a moving car or a rolling ball is called its kinetic energy.

2. *Potential Energy.* This is the energy a body has because of its position or its shape. For example, a car is parked on a hill. If

the brakes are released, the car will begin to move down the hill. It is logical to suppose that at the instant before the brakes were released, the car had *stored energy,* which became actual energy of movement, or kinetic energy, when the car began to move downhill. The wound-up spring in a clock is another example of stored or potential energy.

Thus, there are two main types of energy, kinetic energy (energy of movement) and potential energy (stored energy).

What is the relationship between potential energy and kinetic energy? This is readily determined by a simple example. Consider a ball placed on top of a hill. It has a certain amount of stored or potential energy. Where did this energy originate? A definite amount of work had to be performed to move the ball to its position on the hill. This work was done against the force of gravity, and is stored in the ball in the form of potential energy (see Figure 11). Now the ball is permitted to roll down the hill,

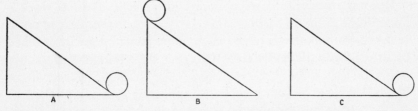

Figure 11. The relationship of potential energy to kinetic energy. In A the ball is at the foot of the hill. In B it has been pushed to the top of the hill, *external work* being required to accomplish this in overcoming the force of gravity. This work is stored in the ball as *potential energy.* In C the ball is allowed to roll down the hill, and the potential energy is thereby converted to *kinetic energy.* The external work = the potential energy = the kinetic energy.

and its potential energy is gradually converted to kinetic energy. As the potential energy decreases, the kinetic energy increases until finally the total kinetic energy equals the initial potential energy:

$$\text{stored energy} \longrightarrow \text{energy of motion}$$
$$\text{(P.E.)} \qquad\qquad \text{(K.E.)}$$

It should be noted that the ball has different values of potential energy along the slope of the hill, or in other words, the potential energy becomes smaller and smaller as the ball moves towards the bottom. If the potential energy at any point on the slope is now called an *energy level,* then it follows that the energy levels become lower and lower at successive points along the hill. This concept is very important, and will be considered later in the discussion of the energy levels of the electron orbits in the atom. As will be seen from Figure 12, the difference between any two

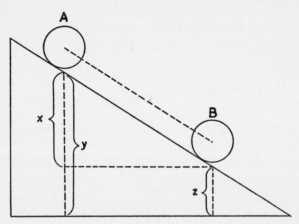

Figure 12. Potential energy at A — potential energy at B = kinetic energy from A to B; or, energy level at A — energy level at B = kinetic energy. If potential energy at A = *y*, and potential energy at B = *z*, then the difference in energy levels is *y* − *z* = *x*. Thus, *x* represents the amount of potential energy converted to kinetic energy when the ball moves from A to B.

energy levels equals the amount of energy that has been changed to kinetic energy. *The ball will not of its own accord move from a lower to a higher energy level; external work is required to accomplish this.* This is another way of saying that *energy will flow only from a higher to a lower level in the absence of outside work.*

It should be emphasized that work done to move the ball up the hill, equals the potential energy in the ball at the summit of the hill, equals the kinetic energy in the movement of the ball down to the bottom of the hill. This is the basic concept of the *law of conservation of energy.* This law, which is a simple expression of one type of human experience, states that *energy can be neither created nor destroyed, but various forms of energy can be changed to other forms. The total amount of energy in the universe is constant.*

What are the so-called *"forms of energy?"* They may be listed simply as mechanical, heat, light, electrical, and chemical. These can be changed from one form to the other. For example, an electric motor uses up electrical energy and produces mechanical energy which is almost equal to the used up electrical energy, any difference being due to the waste of some of the energy due to friction and production of heat. This can be expressed in a formula:

$$\text{electrical energy used by motor} = \text{mechanical energy} + \text{heat energy}$$

Another example is an electric battery which changes chemical energy to electrical energy. A steam engine converts the heat used in producing the steam, to mechanical energy. Any number of similar examples can be given. In all, however, the law of conservation of energy applies equally. Any energy disappearing in one form, appears in some other form and is never destroyed.

QUESTIONS

1. What is the physical concept of work?
2. Define energy. Force.
3. What is the difference between kinetic energy and potential energy?
4. Name the various forms of energy.
5. Define the law of conservation of energy. How is it proved?
6. What is the source of electrical energy in a battery?
7. Suppose that 1000 energy units of heat are applied to a steam turbine. What is the maximum number of energy units of electricity that can be obtained?

CHAPTER 4 MATTER, THE COMMON SUBSTANCE

I t is interesting to speculate on the fundamental structure of the material which composes the things about us. This has, indeed, occupied the mind of man from time immemorial, and the ancient Greek philosophers had very interesting concepts of this structure, some of which underlie even our highly advanced modern ideas.

One of the ways in which we can study a thing is to take it apart—the method of *analysis*. For instance, the only way in which one can determine the mechanism of a clock is first to take it apart and study its individual parts and their relationships to one another. If this has been done intelligently and successfully, the parts should be assembled again into a clock which functions exactly as it did before it was dismantled. This recombination of the parts is called *synthesis*.

Subdivisions of Matter

Let us apply now the method of analysis, based on logic and experiment, to the structure of matter. If a certain material, for example, a piece of rock salt, is broken into smaller and smaller pieces, there will eventually result the tiniest possible particle of salt, which still has the physical properties of the original chunk of rock salt; that is, it will have the same color, odor, taste, hardness, and other similar properties. This particle, much too small to be visible, is called a molecule of salt. *A molecule is the smallest subdivision of a substance which has the physical properties of that substance.* The closeness with which the molecules of a given body of matter are packed determines whether it will be a solid, a liquid, or a gas. The molecules are closest together in solids, and farthest apart in gases.

Suppose that the *molecule* of salt is to be subdivided further. This cannot be done by ordinary physical means, such as crushing it with a weight, because we are now dealing with another problem. The salt molecule is made up of two *atoms,* one of sodium and one of chlorine. These atoms are held together by strong electrochemical forces and therefore cannot be separated by ordinary physical means such as crushing. *The atom is the smallest unit of an element that can enter into a chemical reaction (or combination) with another element.*

It may have been noted that in the above discussion, two new terms were introduced. Since physics is an exact science, its language must also be exact, and so these two terms will be defined. The first is *substance, which is any material that has a definite, constant composition.* Thus, salt is a substance because it has constant composition, always consisting of a combination of sodium and chlorine atoms in equal numbers. Wood and air are not substances because their composition varies; they are called *mixtures.*

There are two main types of substances. The simpler ones are called *elements; an element cannot be decomposed into a simpler substance by ordinary means.* Examples of elements include sodium, iron, lead, oxygen, hydrogen, and chlorine.

More complex sustances are called *compounds, which are chemical unions of two or more elements in definite proportions.* Thus, salt is a *compound* of equal numbers of sodium and chlorine atoms in chemical combination; every molecule of salt contains one atom of sodium and one atom of chlorine. Note that a given material can be both a substance and a compound. Other compounds may be made up of combinations of many atoms, ranging into the thousands. Figure 13 illustrates the structure of matter down to the atomic level.

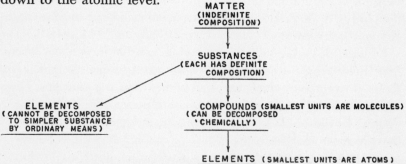

Figure 13. The schematic analysis of matter.

Atomic Structure

Suppose we attempt a further subdivision, namely, that of the atoms. The scientists have given us a highly satisfactory concept of atomic structure, as the result of many years of research in advanced physics, despite the fact that no one has, and no one probably ever will be able to peer inside an atom. The theory of atomic structure permits the explanation of practically all observed natural phenomena in atomic physics. (A theory is a set of principles that attempts to correlate observed natural phenomena.) Note that the structure of the atom is not a picture, but rather a diagram which attempts to correlate certain experimental observations that have been dealt with mathematically.

The most widely accepted theory of the makeup of the atom is that proposed by Niels Bohr in 1913, based, of course, on the work of his predecessors as well as on his own research. The atom is represented as a tiny solar system analogous to the sun with planets revolving about it (see Figure 14). In the atom, the sun is represented by the *nucleus* which is positively charged and contains practically all of the mass of the atom. Revolving around the nucleus, and corresponding to the planets, are the much lighter *orbital electrons,* which are elementary negative charges. *In a neutral atom, the number of orbital electrons exactly equals the number of positive charges in the nucleus.*

Every element has its own characteristic number of positive charges in the nucleus, and different atoms necessarily must have different total nuclear charges. The identity of the atom of a given element is maintained only if the nuclear charge is unchanged. If the charge is altered, as by modern atom-smashing machines, the element is transmuted into an entirely different element.

Of what does the *nucleus* of an atom consist? According to current theory, there are two main components of the nucleus. First, there are *protons,* which are elementary positive charges. These tiny particles of positive electricity are found, under ordinary conditions, in the nucleus only. However, methods are available to the physicist for liberating these particles from the nucleus. A proton weighs about 1838 times as much as an electron. Protons of all elements are identical, but *each element has its own charac-*

teristic number of protons in its nucleus. The second constituent of the nucleus is the *neutron,* which is a particle having no charge, but having practically the same mass as a proton. Thus, protons and neutrons impart mass to the nucleus but *only the protons contribute positive charges to the nucleus.* Other nuclear particles have been discovered in recent years; however, these will not be considered here.

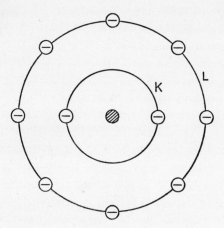

Figure 14. General atomic model according to the Bohr Theory. This shows the nucleus at the center surrounded by some of the orbits (paths) of the electrons. The K orbit can hold no more than 2 electrons, L no more than 8. The number of electrons that additional orbits can hold has been determined. The electrons revolve very rapidly in their orbits.

The so-called *orbits* are the paths around the nucleus in which electrons circulate in continual motion. The total number of electrons in these orbits (these are called planetary electrons) equals the number of positive charges in the nucleus. There is a definite number of electrons which is maximal for each orbit. Thus, there can be no more than 2 in the first orbit, 8 in the second, 8 in the third, and so on. The orbits are identified by letters of the alphabet, the innermost being called K, the next L, the third M, and so on (see Figure 14).

In summary, one can state that the atoms of various elements consist of the same building blocks: protons, neutrons, and electrons. Atoms differ from one another by virtue of differences in the combination of these same building blocks. The structure of an atom may be outlined as follows:

1. Nucleus—contains one or more:
   a. *Protons*—elementary positive particles, and
   b. *Neutrons*—elementary neutral particles having practically the same mass as the proton
2. Orbits—contain one or more:
   a. *Electrons*—elementary negative particles

The number of electrons in the orbits must equal the number of protons in the nucleus of a neutral atom.

Atomic Number

The question now arises as to what determines the identity of any element, making it distinctly different from any other element. The answer lies in the number and arrangement of the orbital electrons, or what amounts to the same thing, the number of nuclear protons. This number is characteristically the same for all atoms of a given element, and is different for the atoms of different elements. *The number of protons or positive charges in the nucleus of an atom is called its atomic number.* Thus, each element has its own characteristic atomic number and its own distinctive chemical properties.

Mass Number

What determines the mass of an atom? It has already been noted that practically the entire mass resides in the nucleus, and more specifically, in the nuclear protons and neutrons. Physicists have accepted these particles as the units of atomic mass and have designated the *total number of protons and neutrons in the nucleus as the mass number of an atom.* Now, it is to be emphasized that the *mass number* is not specific for any one element. It has been found that most elements, as they occur in nature, are a nearly constant mixture of atoms with different mass numbers because these atoms may differ in the number of nuclear *neutrons.* However, they must all have the same atomic number because

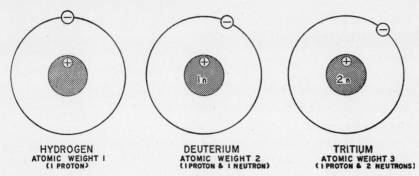

HYDROGEN
ATOMIC WEIGHT I
(I PROTON)

DEUTERIUM
ATOMIC WEIGHT 2
(I PROTON & I NEUTRON)

TRITIUM
ATOMIC WEIGHT 3
(I PROTON & 2 NEUTRONS)

Figure 15. Examples of isotopes. These elements all have the same atomic number, 1, but have different mass numbers or atomic weights. They are called isotopes of the same element, hydrogen. Their different mass numbers are due to the different numbers of neutrons in the nucleus. Tritium is an artificial isotope and is radioactive.

they have the same number of nuclear protons. Such *atoms of the same element that differ in mass number (but have identical atomic number) are called isotopes* (see Figure 15). It should be mentioned that the term "atomic weight" refers to the mass of an atom relative to the mass of oxygen isotope 16. For practical purposes, mass number and atomic weight are equal and these terms are often used interchangeably.

In summary, one can say that atomic number and mass number together specify the nuclear structure of any given atom, and the atomic number also indicates the number of external electrons.

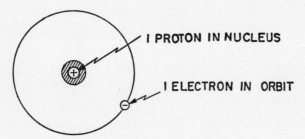

I PROTON IN NUCLEUS

I ELECTRON IN ORBIT

Figure 16. Atomic model of hydrogen.

The Periodic System

The preceding discussion will be made clearer by actual examples. All of the elements can be arranged in an orderly series, called the *periodic table,* from the lightest to the heaviest (on the basis of atomic weight), or from the lowest atomic number to the highest (see Table II). For instance, *hydrogen* is the simplest element, consisting of one proton in the nucleus and one electron outside circulating in its orbit. The atomic number of hydrogen is therefore 1, and the atomic weight or mass number is 1 (see Figure 16).

The next element in the periodic series is *helium* with 2 protons and 2 neutrons in the nucleus and 2 electrons in the orbit (see Figure 17). The atomic number of this element is 2 and the atomic weight 4.

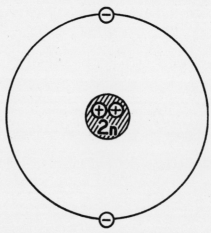

Figure 17. Atomic model of helium.

Lithium is the next element. It has atomic number 3, and one of its isotopes has an atomic weight of 7 (see Figure 18). Note that the first orbit has the maximum number of electrons, 2, and the third electron is in the next orbit. Thus, the K orbit of lithium has 2 electrons, and the L orbit one.

Chemical Behavior

If all the elements are arranged in table form, in order of increasing atomic number (periodic table), it will be found that there are *nine vertical groups* and *seven horizontal periods* (see Table II). The *groups* are families of elements which are found to have surprisingly similar chemical properties. In other words, they participate in chemical reactions in a similar fashion. The periods, on the other hand, consist of elements (horizontal rows) which have the same numbers of orbits around the nucleus and do not have similar chemical properties. This relationship of the various elements was first discovered by Mendeléef in 1870.

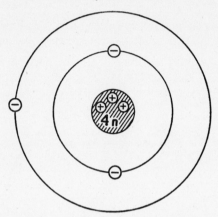

Figure 18. Atomic model of lithium.

Why do the elements in any vertical group behave similarly in a chemical sense? The answer lies in the number of electrons in their *outermost orbits*. For instance, lithium (Li), sodium (Na), and potassium (K) are seen in Table II to be members of the same family. Their atomic structure is shown in Figure 19. The neutrons are omitted here because they do not affect the discussion. It is seen from the diagram that although these elements

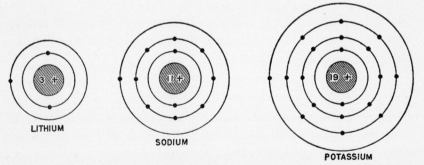

LITHIUM

SODIUM

POTASSIUM

Figure 19. Elements with valence of +1.

TABLE II

ATOMIC PERIODIC TABLE

The numbers above each element represent atomic weight.
The numbers below each element represent atomic number.

Period	Group 0	Group I	Group II	Group III	Group IV
0		1.008 **Hydrogen** (H) 1			
1	4.003 **Helium** (He) 2	6.940 Lithium (Li) 3	9.02 Beryllium (Be) 4	10.82 Boron (B) 5	12.01 **Carbon** (C) 6
2	20.183 Neon (Ne) 10	22.997 Sodium (Na) 11	24.32 Magnesium (Mg) 12	26.97 **Aluminum** (Al) 13	28.06 Silicon (Si) 14
3	39.994 Argon (A) 18	39.096 Potassium (K) 19	40.08 **Calcium** (Ca) 20	45.10 Scandium (Sc) 21	47.90 Titanium (Ti) 22
		63.57 **Copper** (Cu) 29	65.38 Zinc (Zn) 30	69.72 Gallium (Ga) 31	72.60 Germanium (Ge) 32
4	83.7 Krypton (Kr) 36	85.48 Rubidium (Rb) 37	87.63 Strontium (Sr) 38	88.92 Yttrium (Y) 39	91.22 Zirconium (Zr) 40
		107.88 **Silver** (Ag) 47	112.41 Cadmium (Cd) 48	118.70 Indium (In) 49	121.77 **Tin** (Sn) 50
5	131.3 Xenon (Xe) 54	132.9 Cesium (Cs) 55	137.4 **Barium** (Ba) 56	Rare Earths 57-71	178.6 Hafnium (Hf) 72
		197.2 **Gold** (Au) 79	200.6 Mercury (Hg) 80	204.4 Thallium (Tl) 81	207.2 **Lead** (Pb) 82
6	222. **Radon** (Rn) 86	224 Virginium (Vi) 87	226.05 **Radium** (Ra) 88	227.? Actinium (Ac) 89	232.1 **Thorium** (Th) 90

Group V	Group VI	Group VII	Group VIII		
14.008 Nitrogen (N) 7	16.000 **Oxygen (O)** 8	19.00 Fluorine (F) 9			
30.98 Phosphorus (P) 15	32.06 Sulfur (S) 16	35.457 Chlorine (Cl) 17			
50.95 Vanadium (V) 23	52.01 **Chromium (Cr)** 24	54.93 Manganese (Mn) 25	55.85 **Iron (Fe)** 26	58.94 **Cobalt (Co)** 27	58.69 **Nickel (Ni)** 28
74.91 Arsenic (As) 33	79.00 Selenium (Se) 34	79.92 Bromine (Br) 35			
92.91 Columbium (Cb) 41	96.0 **Molybdenum (Mo)** 42	? Technetium (Tc) 43	101.7 Ruthenium (Ru) 44	102.9 Rhodium (Rh) 45	106.7 Palladium (Pd) 46
127.6 Antimony (Sb) 51	126.93 Tellurium (Te) 52	126.92 **Iodine (I)** 53			
180.9 Tantalum (Ta) 73	183.9 **Tungsten (W)** 74	186.3 Rhenium (Re) 75	190.2 Osmium (Os) 76	193.1 **Iridium (Ir)** 77	195.2 **Platinum (Pt)** 78
209.0 **Bismuth (Bi)** 83	210. Polonium (Po) 84	211. Astatine (At) 85			
231.? Protoactinium (Pa) 91	238.1 **Uranium (U)** 92				

Elements that are of particular interest to the x-ray technician are in dark type.

have a different number of orbits, they have one thing in common: *the outermost orbit of each has one electron.* This determines the similarity of their chemical behavior.

Consider now the vertical group of elements: fluorine (F), chlorine (Cl), and bromine (Br) (see Figure 20). These ele-

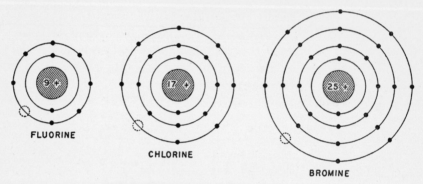

Figure 20. Elements with valence −1.

ments are seen to consist of different numbers of orbits, but are similar in that they all have one less electron in the outermost orbit than the number of electrons needed to fill the outermost orbit completely. These elements, too, resemble each other in their chemical properties.

The number of electrons in the outermost orbit is called *valence*. The elements of the type of lithium, sodium, and potassium have one electron in the outer orbit, and their valence is +1, because these elements can share that electron with an element which needs an electron to saturate its outer orbit. The elements in the fluorine, chlorine, bromine family, as described above, have one

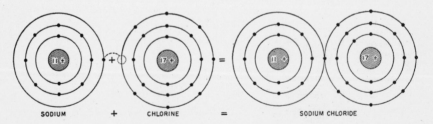

Figure 21. Combination of sodium and chlorine chemically to form sodium chloride.

less electron in the outer orbit than the number needed to saturate it. Their valence is —1. These elements can accept and share an electron from the lithium family. Figure 21 shows how sodium (valence +1) reacts with chlorine (valence —1) to form sodium chloride, a chemical compound, ordinary table salt. This is the basic explanation of chemical action. *The chemical properties of an element depend mainly on its valence.*

If an element has a valence of —2 (lacks 2 electrons to make its outer orbit complete), it can share an electron from two atoms of an element whose valence is +1. For example, hydrogen and oxygen combine to form water as follows:

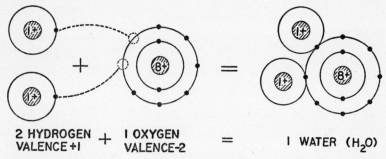

2 HYDROGEN + 1 OXYGEN = 1 WATER (H_2O)
VALENCE +1   VALENCE-2

Figure 22. Chemical combination of hydrogen and oxygen to form water.

It is interesting to note that if an element has all of its rings completely saturated, it will not enter into a chemical reaction since it cannot share an electron. Referring again to the periodic chart in Table II, one notes that there is such a family of elements which is known as the family of inert elements. The members of this family include helium, neon, argon, etc. This is illustrated in Figure 23.

The theory of chemical union just described, explains why elements always combine in *definite proportions.* Thus, sodium chloride is always formed by union of one atom of sodium and one atom of chlorine. Water is always formed by combination of one atom of oxygen with two atoms of hydrogen.

Fundamentally, *chemistry deals with reactions between atoms in the realm of the outer electron orbits. Modern physics is concerned mainly with the nucleus and the innermost electron orbits.*

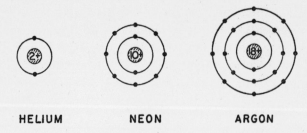

HELIUM   NEON   ARGON

Figure 23. Three members of the family of inert elements, with valence of 0. The outer orbit in each case
is completely filled with electrons. Therefore, these
elements do not enter into chemical reactions.

Ionization

If an electron is removed from one of the orbits of a neutral
atom, or if an electron is added to a neutral atom, the atom does
not lose its identity because it retains the same charge on its
nucleus and its atomic number is unaltered. However, the atom
is now electrically charged. Thus, if an electron is removed, the
atom becomes positively charged because one of its nuclear
charges is now unbalanced and the atom has an excess of positive
electricity. If an electron is *added* to a neutral atom, the atom
now has an excess of negative electricity and is negatively charged.
Such charged atoms will drift when placed in an electrical field, as
will be discussed later, and are called *ions* (from the Greek word
meaning "wanderer").

The production of ions from neutral atoms is called *ionization*.
This can be accomplished by the following methods:

1. *X-ray Bombardment of Matter.* X-ray energy displaces electrons from the atoms of the material which lies in the path of the
x-ray beam, and such atoms become positively charged, that is,
positive ions. The removed electrons may combine with neutral
atoms to produce negative ions, or the electrons may recombine
with positive ions to form neutral atoms.

2. *Electron Stream Bombardment of Matter.* The fast-moving
electrons in an electron beam, or the electrons released from atoms
by x-rays as in (1) may collide with orbital electrons of other
atoms and in turn displace them. The atom, after losing an elec-

tron in this manner, becomes positively charged, but it soon recaptures an electron and is neutralized. It is to be emphasized that ionization by x-rays or by fast electrons is of extremely short duration; the ions formed in this way become neutralized almost instantaneously.

3. *Spontaneous Breakdown of Radioactive Substances.* The rays emitted by the radium series, for example, can produce ionizing effects similar to those by x-rays.

4. *Light Ray Bombardment of Certain Elements.* When light falls on the surface of the metal, selenium, electrons are liberated from its atoms and these electrons are emitted from the surface of the metal. This principle is utilized in the photoelectric cell.

5. *Chemical Ionization.* When a salt such as sodium chloride is dissolved in water it becomes ionized, that is, it separates into sodium ions (Na^+) and chlorine ions (Cl^-). If the poles of a battery are connected to electrodes and these are immersed in the solution, the Na^+ ions will move towards the negative electrode (cathode) and the Cl^- ions will move towards the positive electrode (anode), as in Figure 24. This process of removal of the ions by electricity is called *electrolysis*.

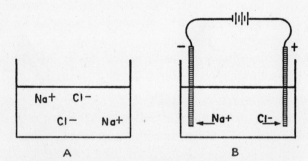

Figure 24. Chemical ionization and electrolysis. In A is shown a solution of ordinary salt (sodium chloride = NaCl) which has *ionized* to form equal numbers of Na^+ and Cl^- ions. In B a pair of electrodes has been immersed in the ionized salt; the Na^+ ions move towards the negative electrode (cathode) and the Cl^- ions drift towards the positive electrode (anode), a process called electrolysis.

The concept of ionization is extremely important. Many chemical reactions take place between ions in solutions. Ionization of air by x-rays is the basis of modern measurement of the intensity of an x-ray beam. Ionization of body tissues is believed to be the fundamental mode of action of roentgen and radium rays in therapy.

QUESTIONS

1. Define: element; compound; substance.
2. State briefly the Bohr concept of atomic structure.
3. Draw a model of the hydrogen atom and label the parts.
4. What constitutes the nucleus of an atom?
5. How does the weight of a proton compare with an electron?
6. A neutral atom has 12 electrons revolving in the orbits around the nucleus. What is its atomic number?
7. An atom has a nucleus containing 6 protons and 2 neutrons. What is its atomic number? Atomic weight?
8. Define "isotope," and give an example.
9. Why do elements combine chemically in fixed or definite proportions?
10. What is an ion? By what methods can ionization be produced?

CHAPTER *5* STATIC ELECTRICITY

Definition

In scientific language, static electricity is called *electrostatics,* which may be defined as *that branch of physics that deals with stationary or resting electric charges.*

It has previously been pointed out that all atoms have electrons surrounding a nucleus. The outer electrons are bound relatively loosely by the influence of the positively charged nucleus. If one or more of these electrons are removed, the atom is left with an excess of positive electricity and the atom is said to be positively charged. If the removed electron should become attached to a neutral atom, the latter will become negatively charged. Thus, there are only two kinds of electricity, positive and negative.

If the same principle is applied to a body of matter (which is, of course, made up of atoms), electrons may be removed or added to that body. This is known as *electrification,* and consists of the removal or addition of electrons to a body of matter by various means. An electrified or charged body has either an excess or a deficiency of electrons.

Methods of Electrification

How can we bring about electrification of a body? There are three methods available, some of which we have all noted in our daily experience.

1. *Electrification by Friction.* Most of us have observed that after walking over a woolen carpet, if we touch a metal doorknob a spark will jump between our hand and the metal. Again, we have noted that in combing our hair, we may hear a crackling sound, and the comb will seem to draw the hair to it. This is *electrification by friction,* that is, removal of electrons from one object by rubbing it with another object. This observation, interestingly enough, is the origin of the word *electricity.* It is said that the

ancient Greeks knew that if amber is rubbed with fur, it will then attract small bits of straw or leaves. They therefore named this amber material "elektron."

On the basis of the kind of charges developed by rubbing two objects together, it has been arbitrarily decided to call one *negative*, and the other *positive*. If a glass rod is rubbed with silk, some electrons are removed from the rod so that it becomes positively charged; this is *positive electrification*. The silk, of course, now has an excess of electrons and is negatively charged.

If a stick of amber is rubbed with fur, the amber picks up electrons and becomes negatively charged; this is *negative electrification*. It should be emphasized that friction is the simplest and most fundamental method of electrification.

Matter can be roughly classified on the basis of its ability to allow electrons to move freely through it. The materials in the first group are called *non-conductors or insulators* because electrons do not flow freely in them; they include amber, hard rubber, and glass. The materials in the second class are called *conductors* because they allow a relatively free flow of electrons; they are exemplified by *metals*, such as silver, copper, and aluminum. The next two types of electrification involve the use of such conducting or metallic bodies.

2. *Electrification by Contact.* If, after a body is charged by friction, it is allowed to touch an uncharged metallic object, the latter will then become charged. If the first object was negatively charged, it will give up some of its electrons to the metallic object and impart to it a negative charge. If, on the other hand, the first object had a positive charge, it will remove electrons from the metallic object and the latter will be positively charged. Thus, *we can conclude that a charged object confers the same kind of charge on any uncharged metallic body with which it comes in contact.*

3. *Electrification by Induction.* Every charged body has a zone around it in which its influence is exerted; this is called the *electrostatic field*. If an uncharged metallic object is brought into the electrostatic field of a charged object, there will be a shift in the electrons of the uncharged metal; this is the method of *electrification by induction*. Note that only the electrons move. In Figure 25,

if the negatively charged rod, B, is brought *near* the originally uncharged metal body A, but not touching it, the excess electrons on B will repel electrons on A distally, leaving the end of A nearest B positively charged. The reverse is also true; if B were a positively charged rod, the end of A nearest B would become negatively charged. When B, in either case, is removed from the vicinity of A, the electrons on A are redistributed to their original position and A is no longer charged.

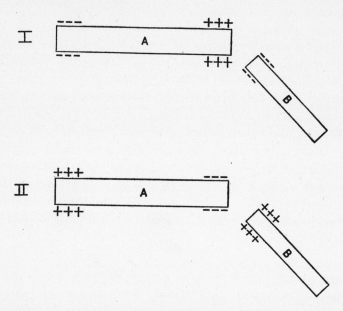

Figure 25. Temporary electrification by induction. A is a metallic rod. B is a charged body.

It is possible to charge a piece of metal by induction so that it will retain its charge even after the charging body has been removed. In Figure 26, A is shown first as it is affected by the electrostatic field of B. If, now, the negative end of A is connected temporarily to a water pipe (ground), the excess electrons will pass down to ground. If the ground connection is broken and B is *then* removed, A will remain positively charged. It must be emphasized that *in electrification by induction, the charged body confers the opposite kind of charge on the metallic body which is placed in its field.*

The above discussion introduces the concept of *ground*. The earth is considered to contain an almost infinite reservoir of electrons, and can also absorb an almost infinite number of electrons. Therefore, any possible charge can be neutralized if it is connected to ground by means of a conductor; if a positively charged body is connected to ground, electrons will move up to it and neutralize it. If a body that is negatively charged is connected to ground, the excess electrons will pass to ground and the body will

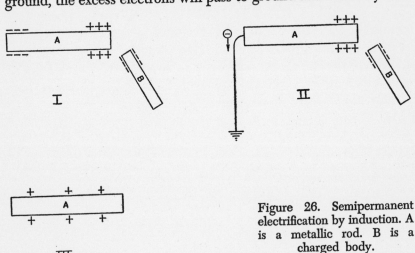

Figure 26. Semipermanent electrification by induction. A is a metallic rod. B is a charged body.

become neutral or uncharged. The symbol for ground is ⏚. Since all charged bodies are neutralized when connected to ground, or are brought to the same potential energy level as ground, we say that *ground potential equals zero.*

Laws of Electrostatics

There are four fundamental laws governing the phenomena of electrostatics.

1. *Like Charges Repel Each Other; Unlike Charges Attract.* If two bodies are charged negatively, they tend to remain separated from each other. If one is negative and the other is positive, they tend to attract each other (see Figure 27).

2. *Electric Charges Reside Only on External Surfaces of Conductors.* Thus, if a hollow metal ball is charged, all of the charges

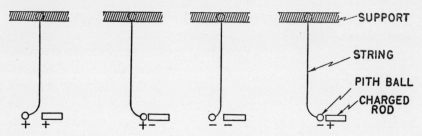

Figure 27. Like charges repel. Unlike charges attract.

are on the outside surface, while the inside remains uncharged, as is evident from Figure 28. The reason for this is that due to repulsion of the like charges, they get as far away from each other as possible, and the greatest possible distance exists between them if they are on the outside surface of the object.

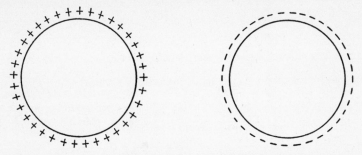

Figure 28. Electric charges tend to distribute themselves on the outer surface of a hollow metallic sphere.

3. *The Concentration of Charges on a Curved Surface of a Conductor is Greatest Where the Curvature is Greatest.* This is shown in Figure 29. The greatest possible concentration of charges is on a point, which obviously has an extremely high degree of curva-

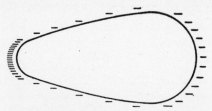

Figure 29. Electric charges tend to concentrate at the most pointed part of a metallic object.

ture; in fact, charges become so crowded on a point that they easily leak off through the atmosphere.

4. *Only Negative Charges (Electrons) Can Move in Solid Conductors.* The positive charges are relatively stationary, since they represent atoms which have had some of their outer electrons removed, and electrons are very much more mobile than atoms.

Electroscope

This is a device for detecting electric charges. Figure 30 shows the simplest type of such device. The electroscope may be charged

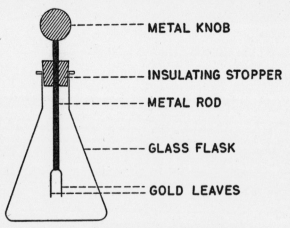

Figure 30. Gold leaf electroscope. When an electric charge is imparted to the electroscope, the leaves repel each other and spread apart.

by *contact* as shown in Figure 31. If the negatively charged rod is *touched* to the knob as in A, the knob, stem, and leaves become negatively charged and the leaves spread because they repel each other. If the rod is now removed as in B, the leaves remain separated and the electroscope is said to be negatively charged. On the other hand, if a positively charged rod is brought into contact with the knob of the electroscope, some electrons will move from the electroscope to the rod leaving the electroscope with a positive charge; the leaves will diverge just as they did before when they were negatively charged. The leaves will repel each other whenever they are similarly charged.

An electroscope can also be charged by *induction*. In Figure 32, a negatively charged rod is brought *near* (but not touching) the knob. It repels electrons of the knob down to the leaves and they spread. If the knob is now grounded, electrons pass to ground and the leaves collapse because they are now uncharged. If the ground

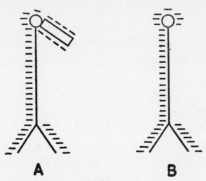

A   **B**

Figure 31. Charging an electroscope
by contact.

connection is broken and the rod is *then removed*, there is a deficiency of electrons in the electroscope (since some have been drawn off to ground), and the electroscope is positively charged; the leaves consequently diverge.

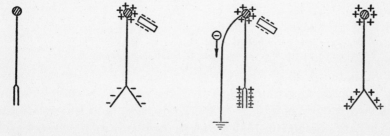

Figure 32. Charging an electroscope by induction. The successive steps
are indicated in the diagrams from left to right.

The electroscope can be used to detect electric charges, and also to determine if they are positive or negative. For example, if an electroscope is negatively charged and a positively charged body is brought near the knob, it will attract some of the electrons from the leaves up to the knob, and the leaves will come together. If an electroscope is negatively charged, and a negatively charged body is brought near the knob, some of the electrons from the knob will be repelled down to the already negative leaves and they will diverge even farther. Thus, we can deduce that if a charged body is brought near a similarly charged electroscope, the leaves will diverge farther. If a charged body is brought near an electroscope that has an opposite charge, the leaves will come together.

In general, the greater the charge the greater the divergence of the leaves. If the spread of the leaves is calibrated against a known charge, it can be used to determine the amount of an unknown charge.

A charged electroscope can be used to detect the presence of x-rays. The ionization of the air produced by x-rays or radium rays causes a discharge of the electroscope, and the leaves gradually come together. The rate of discharge, as shown by the speed with which the leaves collapse, is proportional to the degree of ionization of the air, and therefore to the intensity of the x-ray beam.

QUESTIONS

1. What is meant by electrification and by what three methods can it be accomplished?
2. What happens if two similarly charged bodies are brought close together?
3. How many kinds of electricity are there?
4. If a negatively charged object is touched to a neutral object, what kind of charge does the latter acquire?
5. State four laws of electrostatics.
6. Of what value is the electroscope in radiology? How does it work?
7. What is meant by an electrostatic field?

CHAPTER *6* *THE ELECTRIC CURRENT*

Definition

In the preceding chapter, the characteristics of stationary electric charges were considered. Under certain conditions, electric charges can be made to move through a suitable material, known as a *conductor*. *The science of electricity in motion is known as electrodynamics, or current electricity.*

The Nature of an Electric Current

Fundamentally, an electric current consists of electrons flowing along a metallic conductor. It should be recalled from an earlier chapter, that when anything moves it has kinetic energy. Therefore, it is evident that an *electric current,* resulting from the motion of electrons, must have *energy,* and the Law of Conservation of Energy applies. Thus, electrical energy can be converted to other forms, such as heat, mechanical, chemical, and so forth. Conversely, other forms of energy can be converted to electrical energy. These will be considered in greater detail later.

How do electrons move along a wire? It is believed that outer orbital electrons of the atoms of the wire metal move successively to the next atom along the surface of the wire. One electron does not move the full length of the wire in a continuous stream, but it may be pictured as colliding with an electron in front of it, which in turn moves forward, hitting the next electron.

Whenever anything moves, it is obvious that it must move over a certain path. *The electric circuit is defined as the path of an electric current.*

An electric current may also pass through certain solutions, as we have seen in Figure 24. This differs from conduction in a metal wire in that positive and negative ions in a solution carry the current in opposite directions, the positive ions moving towards the negative electrode (cathode) and the negative ions drifting towards the positive electrode (anode). In this chapter we will consider only the conduction of electrons in metallic conductors.

Sources of Current Electricity

It has already been pointed out that electricity in motion is a form of energy, and by the Law of Conservation of Energy it can not be produced except by conversion from some other form of energy. It is well known that in order to drive water through a pipe, one must utilize a pump or some other device for developing pressure. Similarly, devices are required to produce electrical pressure to drive an electric current through a circuit.

The two main sources of electric current are:

1. *Chemical.* This includes cells or batteries, which, by chemical reaction, convert chemical energy into electrical energy.

2. *Mechanical.* This is known as the dynamo or generator, which is capable of converting mechanical energy into electrical energy. Both will be considered more fully in later sections.

The Factors in the Simple Electric Circuit

In a simple electric circuit in which there is a steady flow of current in one direction (called direct current), there are three main factors involved. They can best be understood by comparing them in each instance with the corresponding factors involved in the flow of water through a pipe.

1. *Electromotive Force.* This is most often abbreviated as *emf*, and represents the *amount of electrical pressure generated in a battery or electric generator*. It is, in other words, the maximum difference in potential that can be developed between the terminals of a battery or generator. It is really a measure of the amount of work required to push electrons along an electric circuit. As the electric current flows through the circuit, there is a gradual fall of electrical potential along the circuit, just as in the case of water flowing through a pipe, the water pressure gradually becomes less farther and farther along the pipe. It would be well to reconsider, at this point, the section in Chapter 3 dealing with the difference in potential energy between two points on a hill, and the movement of a ball from a higher to a lower energy level. Similarly, the

electric current moves "down hill," so to speak, from a point of higher to a point of lower electrical potential, and the difference in energy level between the two points is known as the *potential difference*. This, incidentally, accounts for the definite direction in which a current moves at any particular instant.

What is the unit in which electromotive force (or potential difference) is measured? This is the *volt*, which was defined by the International Electrical Congress in 1893 as follows: *One volt is that electromotive force which will cause one ampere of current to flow in a conductor having a resistance of one ohm.* (This unit has recently been redefined by scientists, but is more complicated than the one stated here.)

2. *Current Strength.* This is the second factor involved in the consideration of electric circuits. The current *is really the amount of electricity flowing per second.* (In a water pipe, there is a definite amount of water flowing per second past a given point.) Since an electric current consists of a flow of electrons, the more electrons flowing per second the "stronger" the current, just as in the case of a stream of water, the more water flowing per second the stronger the current of water.

What is the unit of current strength? This is the *ampere,* which has been defined by the International Electrical Congress of 1893, as follows: *One ampere is that current strength which will deposit a standard weight of silver per second from a solution of silver nitrate by electrolysis* (to be exact, 0.001118 gram per second).

3. *Resistance.* This is the third factor in electric circuits and is a property of the materials making up the circuit itself. Electrical resistance *is that property of the circuit which acts as a hindrance to the flow of electricity.* As an analogy, when water flows in a pipe, there is resistance to its flow because of the friction of the molecules of water against the molecules of the pipe metal.

What is the unit of resistance? It is the *ohm,* which was defined by the International Electrical Congress of 1893 as follows: *One ohm is the resistance of a standard volume of mercury under standard conditions* (to be exact, it is the resistance to a steady current by a column of mercury weighing 14.4521g, having a length of 106.3 cm and a constant cross-sectional area, at O C).

On what does the resistance of a conductor depend? It depends on four things: (1) the material of which it is made; (2) its length; (3) its cross-sectional area; (4) its temperature. These four factors will now be considered in turn.

Certain materials are good *conductors* of electricity, best exemplified by metals such as copper and silver. Copper is not quite as good a conductor as silver, but since it is much cheaper it is very widely used in electric wires. Other materials, such as glass, wood, and plastics are non-conductors since they offer tremendous resistance to the flow of electricity. Such non-conducting materials are called *insulators* or *dielectrics*.

A long conductor, such as a long wire, has more resistance than a short one. In fact, the *resistance is directly proportional to the length of the conductor*.

A conductor with a large cross-sectional area has a lower resistance than one with a small cross-sectional area. A more precise way of expressing this idea is: *the resistance of a conductor is inversely proportional to the cross-sectional area*. Similarly, a water pipe having a large cross-sectional area offers less resistance than a small pipe.

With metallic conductors, the resistance becomes greater as the temperature rises.

Batteries or Cells

Consider now some of the types of *chemical devices* that are used as sources of electric current. There are two main types, the *dry cell* and the *wet cell*.

1. *Dry Cell.* This consists of a carbon rod immersed in a paste consisting of ammonium chloride, manganese dioxide, cellulose, and a small amount of water. These ingredients are contained in a zinc can, and the top is closed by a layer of asphalt varnish (see Figure 33). The dry cell is actually *moist*. Note that the carbon rod nowhere comes in contact with the zinc can. There is a chemical reaction which results in a potential difference being set up between the battery terminals or electrodes, that is, between the zinc and the carbon. The zinc becomes the negatively charged

electrode (cathode), while the carbon becomes the positive electrode (anode). A dry cell develops 1.5 volts. One of its main uses is in flashlights.

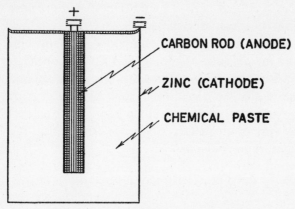

Figure 33. Construction of a "dry" cell.

2. *Wet Cell.* The most prevalent type today is the lead storage cell used in automobiles. It consists of a hard rubber or composition case containing sulfuric acid into which are immersed two electrodes. One is made of lead, which becomes negatively charged, while the other is made of lead oxide which becomes positively charged, as the result of a chemical reaction with the sulfuric acid. Each cell in a storage battery produces about 2 volts.

Elementary Electric Circuits

Certain fundamental principles have been presented and it is now possible to consider the simplest type of electric circuit. In this chapter, only a circuit with a *battery* as the source of electromotive force will be considered. This has a steady, direct current that flows *in one direction only*. The only hindrance to the flow of current in such a circuit is resistance, and this type of circuit is therefore known as a *resistance circuit.*

Essential Parts. The resistance circuit has three essential parts: (1) Battery, (2) Conductor, (3) Resistance. The circuit can be very easily represented by a diagram which will incidentally reveal some of the more common *symbols* used for this purpose (see Figure 34).

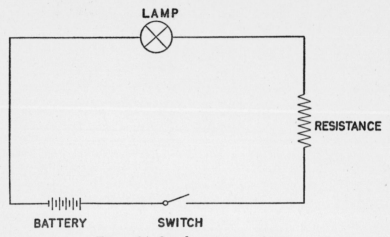

Figure 34. Simple resistance circuit.

Current flows only when the switch is *closed*. If the circuit is broken at any point, it is then called an *open circuit*. When the circuit is completed, it is called a *closed circuit*.

Polarity of Circuits. The current in a resistance circuit has a definite direction, but unfortunately, there has been confusion in the past because the early scientists, not having a clear concept of the nature of an electric current, assumed the wrong direction of flow. However, to avoid confusion this direction is still employed for practical purposes. It is called the *conventional direction* of flow and is assumed to be from the anode (positive terminal) through the external electric circuit to the cathode (negative terminal). The current in reality flows in the direction of the electron stream, that is, from the cathode through the external circuit to the anode. The student need not be confused by this if he will keep the following rule in mind: *the conventional direction of flow of an electric current is assumed to be opposite to the direction of electron flow in the circuit.* This is illustrated in Figure 35.

The conventional direction of flow must be used in practice because certain measuring devices or meters must be hooked into the circuit in a definite manner. These devices have *polarity;* that is, the two terminals on such a meter are labeled (+) and (−), and these must be connected so that the (+) terminal is on the

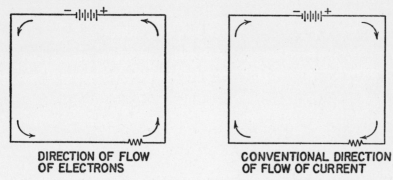

DIRECTION OF FLOW
OF ELECTRONS

CONVENTIONAL DIRECTION
OF FLOW OF CURRENT

Figure 35. The conventional direction of flow of the electric current is
opposite to the actual flow of the electrons.

(+) side of the circuit and the (−) terminal on the (−) side.
Otherwise, the meter may be ruined. Since these terminals are
marked on the basis of the conventional direction of flow of current, one can readily appreciate the need of keeping this point in
mind. In this text, unless otherwise indicated, the direction of
current flow will be the conventional direction.

Connection of Meters. Besides the necessity of attaching meters
by proper polarity, one must know also how to make the connection in the circuit.

A voltmeter measures voltage. It really determines the potential
drop across any two points in the circuit. Therefore, the voltmeter
is always connected in *parallel,* that is, it is placed in a small circuit
which is a branch of the main circuit, according to Figure 36. It
is obvious that if the voltmeter is attached successively between
various points in the circuit where the resistance may differ, the
potential drops will be different and the voltage readings on the
voltmeter will be different. Similarly, the drop in pressure between
any pair of points in a water pipe will be different if the bore of the
pipe is not uniform, there being a greater fall in pressure where the
pipe is narrower.

An ammeter (ampere + meter) measures the quantity of electricity flowing per second, or amperes. In a simple resistance circuit, the current flowing past all points in the circuit is the same.
Therefore, the ammeter is connected directly into the circuit, that
is, *in series* (see Figure 37).

Ammeters and voltmeters look alike externally and consist of a box enclosing the mechanism, with a glass window in which is seen a pointer that moves over a calibrated scale, as shown in

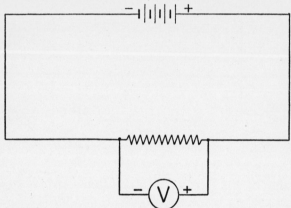

Figure 36. Correct connection of a voltmeter—in parallel.

Figure 38. The instrument is always labeled "Voltmeter" or "Ammeter." The construction of these devices will be described in a subsequent chapter.

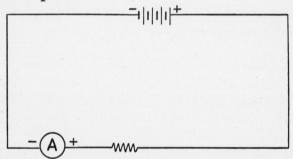

Figure 37. Correct connection of an ammeter—in series.

Ohm's Law

Ohm, a German physicist, discovered that when a steady direct current is flowing, there is a definite relationship between the voltage, amperage, and resistance in a resistance circuit. (That is, one in which resistance is the only obstacle to the flow of current, see above.) This is expressed in *Ohm's Law* which states

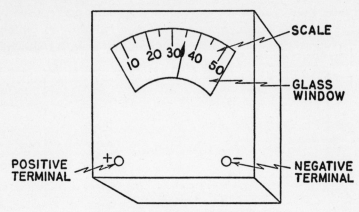

Figure 38. Voltmeter or ammeter.

that *the value of the current in a resistance circuit supplied by steady direct current is equal to the electromotive force divided by the resistance.* This may be expressed in the form of an equation:

$$I = \frac{V}{R}$$

where I = current in amperes
              V = emf in volts
              R = resistance in ohms

If any two of these values are known, the third may be found by substituting in the equation and solving for the unknown.

Two rules must be observed in applying this law:

1. When Ohm's Law is applied to a *portion of a circuit,* the current in that portion of the circuit equals the voltage across that portion of the circuit divided by the resistance of that portion of the circuit.

2. When Ohm's Law is applied to the *whole circuit,* the current in the circuit equals the total voltage across the circuit divided by the total resistance of the circuit.

Before citing examples of the application of Ohm's Law to electric circuits, it is necessary to study the different arrangements of the parts of a given electric circuit.

Series and Parallel Circuits

Electric appliances (toasters, flatirons, fans, etc.) and electric sources (batteries, generators) may be connected in a circuit in two principal ways. One is called a *series circuit, which may be defined as an electric circuit whose component parts are arranged in a row, so that the current passes consecutively through each part* (see Figure 39). The other arrangement is called a *parallel circuit, which is one in which the component parts are connected as branches of the main circuit so that the current is divided up among the branches* (see Figure 41).

1. *Series Circuit.* When electric appliances, which may be called *current-consuming devices,* are connected in series as shown in Figure 39, the total resistance is equal to the sum of the separate resistances. Thus, if R = total resistance of the whole circuit, and r_1, r_2, and r_3 represent the resistances of various current consuming devices connected in series, then,

$$R = r_1 + r_2 + r_3$$

Suppose in this case, $r_1 = 1$ ohm, $r_2 = 2$ ohms, and $r_3 = 3$ ohms, and the current in the circuit as measured by an ammeter is 15 amperes, what would the voltage be across the circuit? Applying *Ohm's Law,*

$$I = \frac{V}{R} \qquad (1)$$

therefore, $\qquad V = I\,R \qquad (2)$

Since $R = r_1 + r_2 + r_3$

$R = 1 + 2 + 3 = 6$ ohms.

Substituting in equation (2),

$$V = 15 \times 6 = 90 \text{ volts.}$$

This problem may be considered from a slightly different approach. Let us apply Ohm's Law to *each part* of the circuit. Then the voltage across r_1 is equal to Ir_1 or $15 \times 1 = 15$ volts. The voltage across r_2 is equal to Ir_2 or is $15 \times 2 = 30$ volts. The voltage across r_3 is equal to Ir_3 or $15 \times 3 = 45$ volts. The total voltage is $15 + 30 + 45 = 90$ volts, which is the same result obtained above by applying Ohm's Law to the entire circuit at once.

Certain important conclusions may be drawn from the above example. Note again that $V = I\,R$. What does this really mean? It means that the *voltage drop across a given resistance equals the current flowing through it multiplied by the resistance.* A definite amount of electrical pressure—voltage—is required to force the

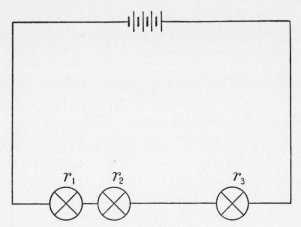

Figure 39. A circuit containing resistances (for example, lamps) in series.

current through the resistance. The greater the resistance, the more the electrical pressure required to force the current through, and therefore the greater the voltage drop. This leads to the concept of voltage not as a static entity, but rather as difference in potential between two points in an electric circuit. Thus, voltage drop and potential difference mean the same thing. It is evident that the voltage drop across an entire circuit can be no greater and no less than the sum of the voltage drops through each resistance connected in series. This has been proved in the example above.

If a group of *current-producing devices,* such as batteries, is connected in series, the *total voltage equals the sum of the voltages of each cell.* In such a circuit, the positive pole of one battery is connected to the negative pole of the next, as in Figure 40. If V is the total voltage, and v_1, v_2, v_3, and v_4 are the voltages of each cell, then

$$V = v_1 + v_2 + v_3 + v_4$$

The total current flowing in such a circuit can be determined from the total voltage and the total resistance by the simple application of Ohm's Law.

2. *Parallel Circuit.* When *current-consuming devices* are connected as branches of the main circuit, the total resistance is *not* equal to simple addition of the various resistances. Figure 41 shows a parallel circuit; careful comparison of A and B shows that the

circuits are essentially the same, despite the fact that they have been drawn somewhat differently. The law for this type of circuit states that the *voltage across each branch is the same; but the*

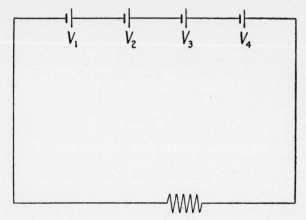

Figure 40. A circuit containing batteries in series.

current in the main line equals the sum of the currents in the various branches. Thus the voltage drop across r_1 is the same as that across r_2 and the same as that across r_3, and the voltage drop in each case is therefore equal to V. If the currents in the three

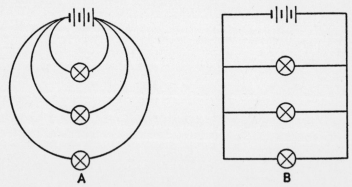

Figure 41. A and B are different methods of representing a parallel circuit. Note that they are fundamentally identical.

branches are 3, 5, and 8 amperes respectively, then the total current is $3 + 5 + 8 = 16$ amp.

What is the resistance of a circuit with several parallel branches? It is obvious that in such a circuit, the current is divided among the several branches or paths, so that the resistance would necessarily be lower than it would be in an undivided path. In other words, the *conductance* of a parallel circuit is greater than that of a series circuit. The conductance of a parallel circuit is equal to the sum of the conductances of the separate branches,

$$C = c_1 + c_2 + c_3 \qquad (1)$$

where C is the conductance of the entire circuit and c_1, c_2, and c_3 are the conductances of the separate branches. The conductance is defined as the reciprocal of the resistance, $1/R$.

$$C = \frac{1}{R}$$

Thus, if the resistance is doubled, the conductance is halved. If the resistance is halved, the conductance is doubled, etc.

To find the total resistance of a parallel circuit, substitute the values of resistance for those of conductance in equation (1),

$$\frac{1}{R} = \frac{1}{r_1} + \frac{1}{r_2} + \frac{1}{r_3} \qquad (2)$$

Thus, the total resistance of a parallel circuit can be found by the rule based on equation (2), *the reciprocal of the whole resistance equals the sum of the reciprocals of the separate resistances in a parallel circuit.* An example may help to clarify this law. If the resistances in the branches of a parallel circuit are 3, 6, and 9 ohms respectively, what is the total resistance of the circuit? Substituting the values of r in equation (2),

$$\frac{1}{R} = \frac{1}{3} + \frac{1}{6} + \frac{1}{9}$$
$$\frac{1}{R} = \frac{6 + 3 + 2}{18}$$
$$\frac{1}{R} = \frac{11}{18}$$

Inverting both sides of the equation

$$R = \frac{18}{11} = 1.55 \text{ ohms}$$

Note that the total resistance is less than any of the resistances in the individual branches.

It is interesting to observe, also, that the current divides among the branches so that the smallest current flows through the branch having the greatest resistance. Since V is equal in all branches, according to Ohm's Law, if r in a given branch is greater, i must be smaller, and vice versa.

With *current-producing devices* connected in parallel, the total voltage is the same as that of a single battery, if all the batteries are alike. Figure 42 shows this type of connection.

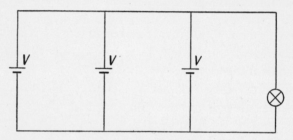

Figure 42. A circuit containing batteries connected in parallel.

The parallel circuit is the basic plan of all modern electrical wiring as used in homes, factories, and other buildings. If a series circuit were used in the home, for example, whenever an electric light bulb burned out the current to all the other lights would be interrupted. As additional appliances are added in a series circuit, each appliance gets less voltage since the total voltage drops must be divided among more appliances; thus, as more electric lights are added, all become dimmer.

In a parallel circuit, if one light bulb burns out, the others remain lighted since they are on branches of the main circuit. The more branches that are added, the lower the total resistance and the greater the total amperage. Thus, the more appliances added the greater is the total amperage flowing in the main circuit. When too many appliances are added, the amperage in the main line may become excessively great and the circuit is said to be *overloaded*. Under these conditions, the wiring system may become hot enough to ruin one or more appliances, and may even constitute a fire hazard. This danger can be avoided by the use of certain protective devices, the simplest of which is the *fuse*. This is connected into the circuit and contains a wire which melts when the amperage exceeds the safe maximum. The melting of the fuse wire breaks the circuit, thereby stopping the flow of current. Such a fuse, in which the protective wire has melted, is called a *blown fuse*. When two non-insulated wires carrying a current touch each other, they cause a *short circuit;* there is a marked fall in resistance and a corresponding rise in amperage which is usually sufficient to blow a fuse. The *circuit breaker,* another type of protective device, will be discussed in a later section.

Electric Condenser

We have already noted that electrical energy can be obtained from a chemical reaction in a dry or wet cell; in a sense, this may be considered as *stored electricity*. There is another method of storing electrical energy that does not depend on chemical changes. It may be recalled from the chapter on Static Electricity that when a conducting body is charged, the entire charge is distributed on the surface of the body. Such an electrically charged body *stores* electrical energy, provided that it is insulated so that the charge does not "leak" away. Under such circumstances, the charged object may be considered to be an *electric condenser*.

One of the simplest types of condensers is the *parallel-plate condenser,* consisting of a pair of flat metallic plates arranged parallel to each other and *separated* by a small space. This space may contain air, or may be filled with an insulating material, so that the plates at no time come in contact with each other. The operation of such a device is shown in Figure 43. When the con-

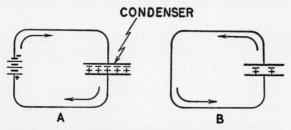

Figure 43. Parallel plate condenser. In A the condenser is connected to a battery and is being charged. In B the condenser has been disconnected and its plates connected by a wire, whereupon it loses its charge. The arrows indicate the direction of electron flow in the wire.

denser is connected to a source of direct current, such as a battery, electrons are transferred from the negative terminal of the battery to the plate which joins it. At the same time, an equal number of electrons passes from the opposite plate to the positive terminal of the battery. This is indicated in Figure 43A. *No electrons pass from one plate to the other across the space between them,* unless there is a breakdown of the insulator due to application of excessively high voltage. When the condenser is fully charged, it has a difference of potential (voltage) across its plates equal and opposite in direction to that of the current which charged it; the current now ceases to flow in the wires.

If, then, the condenser is disconnected from the battery, it retains its electrical charge until the plates are connected by a conductor as in Figure 43B. Then the condenser discharges and once more becomes neutral. The direction of the discharging current is opposite that of the original charging current, and ceases to flow as soon as the condenser is completely discharged.

How much electricity can a condenser store? The quantity of electricity stored per volt applied to the condenser is called the *capacitance* of the condenser and the unit of capacitance is the *farad.* The larger the area of a condenser plate, and the smaller the space between the plates, the greater the capacitance or electrical storing ability. The insulator, or *dielectric* as it is more often called, which separates the plates also determines the capacitance of a given condenser; if the *dielectric constant* (insulating ability) of air is taken as 1, then wax paper has a dielectric constant of 2, and glass a constant of about 7. These materials will increase the capacitance of a given condenser 2 times and 7 times, respectively, as compared with an air dielectric. In practice, a condenser usually is made up of multiple parallel plates which greatly increase the capacitance.

The Work and Power of an Electric Current

Electrical energy, just as any other form of energy is capable of performing work. How much work can an electric current perform? According to the Law of Conservation of Energy, one must conclude that a given amount of electrical energy can do a definite amount of work. On the basis of experimental and mathematical data, one finds that there is a simple relationship between the voltage and amperage in a circuit, and the rate at which the current can do work. Thus the power of a steady direct current, which is the amount of work the current can do per second, may be determined by,

$$P = IV$$
Power = amperage × voltage
in watts

This relationship is called the *power rule*. The unit of power is called the *watt*. 746 watts are equal to 1 horsepower.

It is a well-known fact that when an electric current flows along a conductor, heat is developed in all parts of the circuit. The amount of power (work per second) consumed in this heating effect is related to the current and resistance by the following simple equation:

$$\text{Power Consumed} = I^2R$$
in watts

where I is the current in amperes and R is the resistance in ohms. (It should be noted that this equation can readily be converted to the power rule equation above by simple algebra and Ohm's Law.) Thus, if the current carried by a given circuit is doubled, the power lost as heat is multiplied by 2^2 or 4 times. The practical application of this principle will be discussed later.

QUESTIONS AND PROBLEMS

1. How does an electric current flow along a wire? In a salt solution?
2. What are the two main sources of electric current?
3. Define electromotive force. What is its unit of measurement? What is the difference between difference of potential, electromotive force, and voltage?
4. What is meant by electrical resistance, and on what does it depend?
5. Define electric current and state its unit of measurement.
6. What is meant by "conventional direction of flow of an electric current"?
7. State Ohm's Law.

8. An electric circuit has, in series, appliances with these resistances: 3 ohms, 20 ohms, 6 ohms, 40 ohms. How much current will flow when the applied electromotive force is 110 volts?

9. How many volts are required to push a current of 30 amperes through a circuit having a resistance of 5 ohms?

10. What type of electric circuit is used in ordinary house wiring? Why?

11. A circuit has the following resistances connected *in parallel*: 3 ohms, 6 ohms, 18 ohms. What is the total resistance of the circuit?

12. What is the power formula? What is the unit of power?

13. A circuit has a current of 20 amperes flowing under an impressed electromotive force of 110 volts. What is the power of the circuit?

14. What is an electric condenser? Describe its mode of operation, with the aid of a diagram.

CHAPTER 7 MAGNETISM

Definition

The ability of certain metallic ores, such as lodestone, to attract pieces of iron, is called *magnetism*. This phenomenon was familiar to the ancient Greeks. However, we know now that there are other situations in which the property of magnetism exists, so that our present concept is a much broader one.

Classification of Magnets

There are three main types of magnets: natural magnets, artificial permanent magnets, and electromagnets.

1. *Natural Magnets* include first, the *earth* itself. This is a gigantic magnet which can deflect the needle of a compass. The other type of natural magnet is the ore, *lodestone,* consisting of iron oxide. This material is believed to have become magnetized by lying in the earth's magnetic field from time immemorial. In some parts of the world there are actually magnetic mountains which consist of such magnetic ores.

2. *Artificial Permanent Magnets.* These usually consist of a piece of *hard steel* in the shape of a horseshoe or bar, which has been artificially magnetized; that is, it has been rendered magnetic so that it will attract iron. An example is the *magnetic compass* which is a small permanent magnetic needle swinging freely on a pivot at its center. This device is used to detect the presence of magnetic materials and to locate the earth's magnetic poles. A recently developed alloy called "Alnico" is an extremely powerful permanent magnet that has many times the lifting ability of a steel magnet.

3. *Electromagnets* are produced by means of an electric current, as will be described later, and are almost always temporary.

Properties of Magnets

These are best discussed by first stating the three fundamental laws of magnetism.

1. Every magnet has two poles located at its ends, one of which is called *north pole,* and the other *south pole,* as shown in Figure 44.

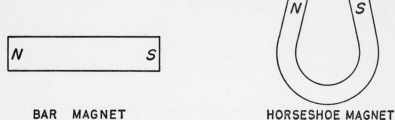

BAR   MAGNET   HORSESHOE MAGNET

Figure 44. Permanent magnets.

2. Like magnetic poles repel each other. Unlike poles attract. Thus, if two bar magnets are brought close together so that the south poles face each other as in Figure 45A there is a force which tends to keep the magnets apart. If, on the other hand, the magnets are brought together so that opposite poles face each other, there is a force which pulls the magnets together as in Figure 45B.

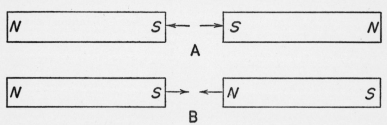

Figure 45. (A) like poles repel. (B) unlike poles attract.

3. The force of attraction (or repulsion) between two magnetic poles varies directly as the strength of the poles, and inversely as the square of the distance between them. This requires some explanation. If the strength of one pole is doubled, then the force between the poles is doubled. If the strength is tripled, then the force is tripled. If the distance between two poles is doubled, then the force between them is reduced to $(\frac{1}{2})^2$ or $\frac{1}{4}$. If the distance is tripled, the force is reduced to $(\frac{1}{3})^3$ or $\frac{1}{9}$.

Magnetic Classification of Materials

All matter can be classified on the basis of whether it is, or is not, attracted by a magnet.

1. *Magnetic Materials.* These are attracted by a magnet. Common examples are iron, steel, and nickel. These substances are also capable of being artificially magnetized. In recent years, an alloy of aluminum, nickel, and cobalt has been developed, capable of lifting many times its weight of iron. This alloy is called *alnico*. It is employed in a very simple method of removing magnetic foreign bodies such as nails, bobbie pins, or steel fragments from the stomach under fluoroscopic control.

2. *Non-magnetic Materials.* These are not attracted by a magnet and cannot be magnetized. Examples are aluminum, wood, glass, and plastic.

Nature of Magnetism

The logical question now presents itself: why are some substances magnetic and others not? The theory that is most widely accepted today is that of Weber, first proposed in the early part of the nineteenth century. It is based on certain observations, such as the following:

1. If a magnet is broken, each fragment becomes a *whole magnet* with its own north and south poles, as in Figure 46.

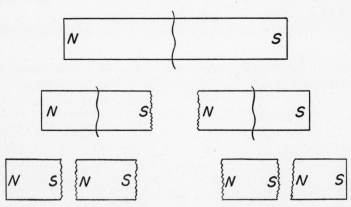

Figure 46. When a magnet is broken, each part becomes a whole magnet with a north and a south pole.

2. If a piece of steel is heated or hammered while it lies near a magnet, the steel becomes magnetized; that is, it becomes a magnet.

3. If a test-tube of iron filings is placed near a magnet and jarred, it becomes a magnet. If the test-tube is now shaken vigorously, it loses its magnetism.

These observations indicate that a magnetic material consists of a multitude of minute magnets, called *magnetic dipoles,* probably molecular or atomic in size. If these tiny magnets are all arranged in an orderly direction, then the body will act as a magnet. If they are disorderly, then the material will not act as a magnet. This is illustrated in Figure 47.

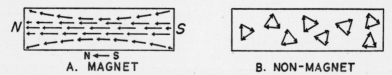

A. MAGNET   B. NON-MAGNET

Figure 47. In A the magnetic dipoles are lined up in orderly fashion and the bar acts as a magnet. In B the dipoles are disarranged and the bar does not have the property of magnetism.

Magnetic Induction

If a piece of soft iron is held near one pole of a magnet, the part of the iron nearest the magnet will have induced in it the opposite pole. The iron becomes magnetized and acts as a magnet as long as it is near the magnet. The reason for this is apparent from the theory of the nature of magnetism. In Figure 48A, the magnetic dipoles in the soft iron become arranged in orderly fashion under the influence of the permanent magnet. When the soft iron is removed, the tiny magnet dipoles lose their orderly arrangement and the magnetism is lost.

Permeability and Retentivity of Magnets

Some materials can be more readily magnetized than others; that is, their minute magnets can be easily lined up under the influence of a nearby magnet. The ease with which a piece of matter can be magnetized is called its *magnetic permeability*.

Some metals resist demagnetization more than others, after they have become magnetized; that is, once their minute magnets have been lined up, they may resist being jumbled. The ability of a magnet to resist demagnetization is called its *retentivity* (ability to retain).

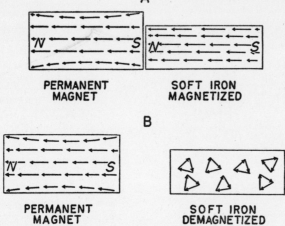

Figure 48. Magnetic induction. In A, the dipoles in the soft iron are orderly and the iron acts as a magnet. When it is removed from the vicinity of the magnet, as in B, the soft iron loses its magnetism because the dipoles have become disarranged.

Examples of the above are:

1. Soft iron: high permeability, low retentivity.
2. Hard steel: low permeability, high retentivity.

Thus, a metal which is easily magnetized, is easily demagnetized (soft iron). A metal which is hard to magnetize, is also hard to demagnetize (hard steel).

Magnetic Fields

What exists around a magnet that is able to bring about the magnetization of certain materials that are brought near it? This zone of influence about a magnet is called its *magnetic field*. This can be demonstrated by placing a piece of cardboard over a magnet. If iron filings are sprinkled on the cardboard, and the latter is tapped gently, the filings will arrange themselves into a pattern, shown in Figure 49. The lines along which the filings arrange themselves are called *lines of force*. In other words, the magnetic field is made up of lines of force. The more concentrated these lines are, the stronger the field is. Another way of saying this is that the more lines of force there are per square centimeter of the field, the stronger is the magnetic field.

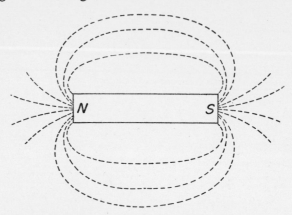

Figure 49. The dotted lines represent the magnetic field surrounding a magnet.

Characteristics of Lines of Force

Certain facts are known or assumed about lines of force.

1. They are assumed to leave the north pole, travel through space in a curved path, and enter the magnet at its south pole.

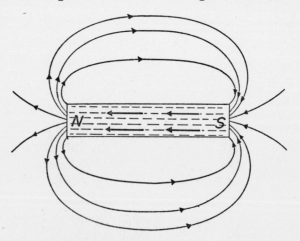

Figure 50. The magnetic lines of force about and in a magnet are assumed to pass in the direction of the arrows.

2. Lines of force repel each other when they travel in the same direction, and attract each other when they travel in opposite directions (see Figure 51).

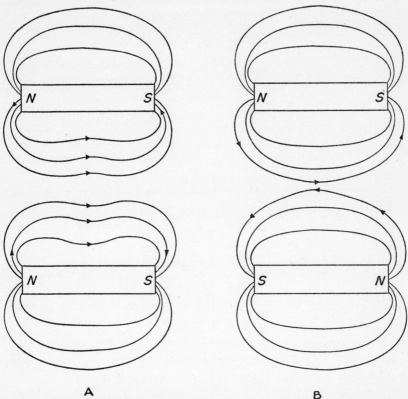

A   B

Figure 51. Magnetic lines of force act upon one another, depending on their relative directions. In A the lines of force are in the same direction and the resultant force tends to separate the magnets. In B the lines of force are in opposite directions and the magnets attract each other.

3. The field is distorted by magnetic materials, and is not affected by non-magnetic materials (see Figure 52).

Detection of Magnetism

The simplest available method of detecting magnetism involves the use of a magnetic compass. This consists of a horizontal magnetic needle which swings about a vertical axis at its center. The needle is deflected when brought into the vicinity of a magnetic object, according to the laws of magnetism. The south pole of the compass will turn towards a magnetic north pole, while the north pole of the compass will turn towards a south pole.

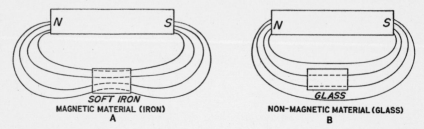

Figure 52. The effect of magnetic and non-magnetic materials on a magnetic field. In A the soft iron concentrates the lines of force because of its great magnetic permeability. In B the glass has no effect on the magnetic lines of force.

QUESTIONS

1. Define magnetism in your own terms.
2. Name and discuss briefly the three main types of magnets.
3. What is believed to be the intimate structure of a magnet? Show by diagram. State three facts which support this theory.
4. State the laws of magnetism.
5. Explain magnetic induction.
6. Compare soft iron and hard steel with regard to their magnetization and demagnetization.
7. What is meant by "magnetic field"? Of what does it consist?
8. What happens to a magnetic field when a piece of soft iron is placed in it?
9. In what direction do the magnetic lines of force travel in space? Within the magnet?

CHAPTER 8 ELECTROMAGNETISM

Definition

Every electric current is accompanied by magnetic effects. These *magnetic phenomena which are associated with electric currents are termed electromagnetism.*

Electromagnetic Phenomena

In 1820 Oersted, a Danish scientist, discovered that a magnetic compass needle is deflected when placed in the vicinity of a wire carrying an electric current. Since this indicated the presence of a magnetic field, Oersted concluded that *a magnetic field is always present around a wire which is carrying an electric current.*

What is the direction of this magnetic field? It can be demonstrated by the so-called *thumb rule,* which is stated as follows: *If the wire is grasped in the right hand so that the thumb points in the conventional direction of the electric current, the fingers which encircle the wire will then point in the direction of the magnetic lines* (see Figure 53).

The existence of these lines of force can be shown in another way, by Davy's Experiment. If a wire conducting a current is made to pierce a sheet of cardboard and iron filings are powdered on the cardboard, then gentle tapping of the cardboard results in the arrangement of the iron particles in concentric circles around the wire. This is illustrated in Figure 54. The concentric circles represent the magnetic lines of force surrounding the electric current in the wire.

It must be emphasized, and thoroughly understood, that the magnetic field exists around the wire *only while the current is flowing.* When the circuit is opened, the magnetism around the wire disappears.

The Electromagnet

If a wire is fashioned into a coil in the form of a *helix* (which resembles a bedspring), as in Figure 55 and an electric current is passed through it, the coil acts in a very interesting manner. One end of the coil behaves as though it were the north pole and the opposite end the south pole of a magnet. If the thumb rule is applied to each turn of the wire in the coil, the direction of the magnetic field inside the coil can be readily determined, and one

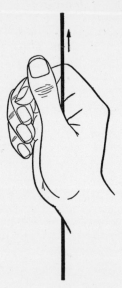

Figure 53. Right hand thumb rule. The thumb points in the conventional direction of the electric current. The fingers designate the direction of the magnetic field around the conductor.

can then predict which end of the coil will be the north pole. Such a coiled helix carrying an electric current is known as a *solenoid*.

It has been pointed out in an earlier chapter that certain materials are able to conduct magnetic lines better than others. Thus, soft iron has a high degree of magnetic permeability and can conduct and concentrate magnetic lines within itself. If a rod of soft iron is placed inside a solenoid, the strength of the magnetic poles at each end is markedly increased. *Such a solenoid with a soft iron*

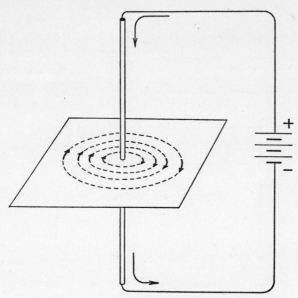

Figure 54. Demonstration of the lines of force around a conductor carrying an electric current. The dotted lines show the magnetic lines of force. The current in the conductor is shown in the conventional direction.

core is called an electromagnet. Figure 56 shows the main features of a simple electromagnet.

The electromagnet has many practical applications, the best known uses being the electric bell and the telegraph system. In

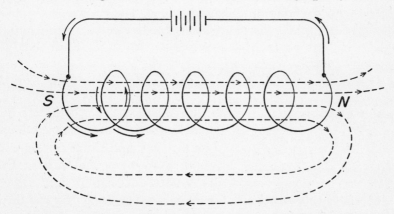

Figure 55. A helix carrying an electric current is called a *solenoid*. This shows the magnetic field associated with a solenoid.

x-ray equipment, electromagnets are very important in remote control switches and relays of various kinds. These will be discussed later under the appropriate sections.

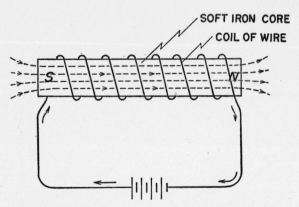

Figure 56. Electromagnet. Note that it is a solenoid into which has been inserted a soft iron core to concentrate the magnetic lines of force. If the current were reversed in the illustration, the magnetic poles would be reversed. If the current were interrupted, the electromagnet would lose its magnetism because of the low retentivity of the soft iron core.

Electromagnetic Induction

We have seen that electrons moving in a conductor are associated with a surrounding magnetic field. The reverse is also true; moving magnetic fields are associated with electric currents under proper conditions. In other words, magnetic energy and electrical energy can be converted from one to the other. *Whenever a conductor forming a closed circuit cuts through a magnetic field, an electric current is induced or set up in the conductor.* Michael Faraday first demonstrated this in 1831, by passing a wire between the poles of a horseshoe magnet.

The magnitude of the induced electromotive force (voltage) depends on four factors:

1. The *speed* with which a wire cuts the magnetic lines of force, or the number of magnetic lines traversed per second. *The more rapidly the lines of force are cut, the higher the induced voltage.*

2. The *strength* of the magnetic field, or the degree of crowding of the magnetic lines of force. *The stronger the magnetic field the higher the induced voltage.* A moment's thought will reveal that this is essentially the same as statement (1). The closer the spacing of the magnetic lines, the more lines are cut per second.

3. The *angle* between the conductor and the direction of the lines of force. As this angle approaches 90°, more lines of force are cut per second, and therefore, a greater voltage is induced. This is illustrated in Figure 57.

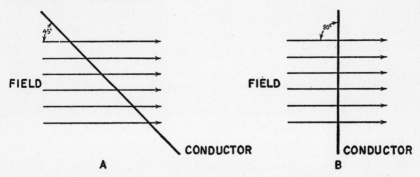

Figure 57. In A, where the conductor cuts the magnetic field at a 45-degree angle (down through this page) the induced voltage is less than in B where the wire cuts the field at 90 degrees.

4. The *length* of the conductor, or the *number of "turns"* in the wire if it is wound into a coil. *The more turns there are in the wire, the greater the induced voltage.*

It must be borne in mind that an electric current is induced in the wire *only when the wire is moving across the field.* If the motion of the wire is interrupted, the induced voltage drops to zero. But the motion of the wire need only be relative; thus, *if the wire is stationary and the magnetic field passes across it, a current will be induced in it* just as well, and the above four principles apply. Finally, *if the wire is stationary and the magnetic field varies in strength a current will be induced in the wire.*

In summary, we may state that there are three ways in which an electromotive force can be induced in a wire by electromagnetic induction:

1. The wire may move across a stationary magnetic field, or

2. The magnetic field may move across a stationary wire, or

3. The magnetic field may vary in strength while a stationary wire lies in it.

We may conclude that *whenever a conductor and a magnetic field move with relation to one another, an electric current is set up in the wire, and the magnitude of the induced electromotive force is directly proportional to the number of lines of force that cross the wire per second.*

Direction of Induced Electric Current

The induced electric current moves in a definite direction depending on the relationship between the motion of the wire and the magnetic field. This is stated in the *right hand rule* or *dynamo rule:* hold the thumb and first two fingers of the right hand so that

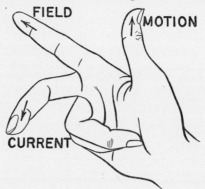

Figure 58. Right hand dynamo rule. This is based on the conventional direction of current flow.

each is at right angles to the others, as in Figure 58. Let the index finger point in the direction of the magnetic lines of force, and the thumb point in the direction the wire is moving. Then, the middle finger will point in the conventional direction of the induced current.

The relationship between the wire, the magnetic field, and the direction of the induced current can be shown most simply by the diagrams in Figure 59. These principles form the basis of the *electric generator* which will be discussed more fully in the next chapter.

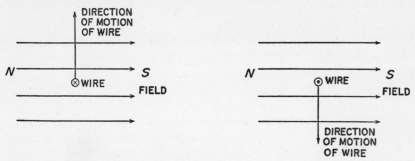

Figure 59. The direction of the current induced in a wire. The wire is shown in cross section. ⊗ indicates that the current is moving into this page. ⊙ indicates that it is moving out of this page, towards the reader.

Self-Induction

When a wire is connected to a primary source of electricity through a switch, at the moment the switch is closed a magnetic field is set up about the wire, and this field builds up rapidly to a maximum where it remains while the primary current continues to flow. If the switch is then opened, the flow of current stops and the surrounding magnetic field collapses almost instantaneously.

During the short interval in which the magnetic field "grows up" around the wire, immediately after the switch is closed, the magnetic field is really expanding, and it therefore *cuts the wire itself*. By the rules of electromagnetism, it induces a current in the wire, and the direction of this induced current is *opposite* to the primary current already flowing. This phenomenon is known as *self-induction*. Thus, when the switch is closed, the self-induced current tends to oppose the flow of the primary current in the wire.

When the switch is opened, there is a very rapid shrinkage of the magnetic field, so that its lines move across the wire in a reverse direction from that occurring when the switch is closed. Consequently, the self-induced current reverses and tends to maintain the current in the wire momentarily after the primary current is interrupted. These phenomena are illustrated in Figure 60. Thus, when the switch is closed, there is a momentarily induced voltage which tends to oppose the flow of the applied current, and when the switch is opened, the self-induced current is reversed and tends to keep the current flowing momentarily.

If the wire is fashioned into a helix, the amount of self-induction

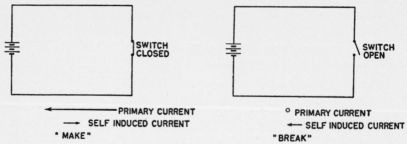

Figure 60. Self-induction. On the "make" (instant of switch closure) there is a momentary self-induced current bucking or opposing the primary battery current. On the "break" (instant of switch opening), the self-induced current is reversed momentarily while the battery current is zero.

is increased, depending on the number of turns in the wire. And if a soft iron core is placed inside the helix, there is a much greater increase in the amount of self-induced current which opposes or "bucks" the applied current. This principle is utilized in the *choke coil* which is described later.

Mutual Induction

If the current in a conductor increases, decreases, or changes its direction it will cause respectively, an expanding, contracting, or changing magnetic field associated with it. If a second wire is placed near the first one so that it is crossed by the changing magnetic field, a current will be induced in the second wire. This is known as *mutual induction*. Note that the magnetic field must be changing in strength or direction in order for mutual induction to occur. If one of the wires has a steady direct current flowing in it the associated magnetic field is constant and consequently no current is induced in the second wire.

If the two wires are in the form of coils, the mutually induced current is increased, and if soft iron cores are introduced into the coils, there is a pronounced increase in the induced current. This principle underlies the construction of a transformer, to be discussed in Chapter 10.

QUESTIONS

1. Define electromagnetism in your own words. How can you determine its presence in a very simple manner?
2. What is the "thumb rule"? How is it applied?

3. Describe an electromagnet. In what two ways can you determine its polarity?
4. What is electromagnetic induction?
5. What are the four factors that determine the magnitude of the induced electromotive force?
6. In the following diagram, what is the direction of the electromagnetically induced current?

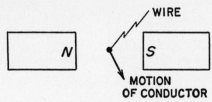

Figure 61.

7. What is self-induction? Mutual induction? What is the practical importance of these phenomena?
8. Two coils of wire are lying parallel to each other. If one is connected to the terminals of a battery, what will happen in the second coil?
9. What is the difference between a helix, a solenoid, and an electromagnet?

CHAPTER **9** *ELECTRIC GENERATORS AND MOTORS*

ELECTRIC GENERATOR OR DYNAMO

Definition

An electric generator, dynamo, or turbine is a device that converts mechanical energy to electrical energy.

Essential Features

Electric generators use the principles of electromagnetism, and depend on the induction of a current in a coil of wire as it cuts a magnetic field. These principles have been discussed in the preceding chapter.

In actual practice, how can a wire be made to cut a magnetic field? Two things are required:

1. *A powerful electromagnet* to set up the necessary magnetic field.

2. *An armature,* which is a coil of wire that is rotated mechanically in the magnetic field. The mechanical energy needed to turn the armature can be obtained from a waterfall as in Figure 62. Sometimes, other forms of energy are used to rotate the armature. For example, steam may be forced against the vanes of the turbine causing it to turn. Or, a windmill may produce the same effect. However, the best source of mechanical energy for generation of electricity at the present time is a waterfall.

Simple Electric Generator

The *elementary form* of electric generator consists of a single loop of wire rotated between the poles of a magnet as shown in Figure 63. What will be the magnitude and direction of the current coming from such a generator? This can be found by studying the relation of the armature to the magnetic field as the armature rotates. The *armature* is represented in the diagram by wire *AB,* the ends of which are *separately connected* to the metal *slip rings*

E and *F*. The rings rotate with the armature. Touching each ring is a *metal brush*, which allows its corresponding ring to turn and at the same time maintains contact with it. The brushes are connected with the external circuit through *R*. The magnetic field passes from the *N* pole to the *S* pole.

When the armature is rotating clockwise, as in Figure 63A, with *A* passing up through the magnetic field, a current is induced in it

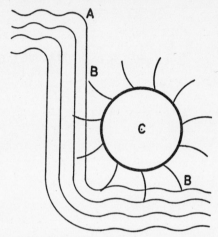

Figure 62. The waterfall at A, dropping on the blades B of the turbine, rotates it counterclockwise about the axis C. If an armature is connected to axis C, it will rotate with the turbine.

in the direction indicated by the arrow (according to the right hand rule). At the same time, *B* is passing down through the field, so that its current is in the direction of the arrow near *B*. The net effect is that the current leaves *B* through slip ring *F*, passes through the external circuit *R*, and enters slip ring *E*.

As the armature coil rotates, *A* moves over to position *B*, and *B* moves to *A* as shown in Figure 63B. Now *A* is moving down through the field and *B* is moving up, and the current *leaves slip ring E* and *enters slip ring F*. Note that the current is now *reversed in the external circuit*. This reversal in current takes place repeatedly as the armature continues to rotate. Such a current which repeatedly reverses its direction is called an *alternating current*, usually abbreviated *a.c.*

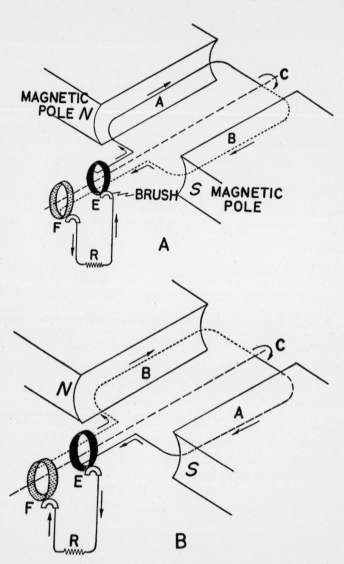

Figure 63. Simple alternating current generator. Armature *AB* rotates clockwise in the magnetic field. In the upper diagram wire *A* moves up through the field while wire *B* moves down. The arrows show the direction of the induced current which leaves the generator through slip ring *F*, passes through external circuit *R*, and completes the circuit through slip ring *E*. As the armature continues to rotate, wires *A* and *B* reverse their positions as shown in the lower diagram, and the current is now reversed in the external circuit *R*.

Let us consider now the magnitude of the induced voltage from moment to moment as the coil turns in the field. This can easily be demonstrated by a diagram. In Figure 64, the generator is seen end-on, A and B representing the cross-section of the wire armature, rotating in the direction of the arrows around the axis C. In position (1) the armature is moving parallel to the magnetic field and is therefore not cutting the magnetic lines. There is no induced electromotive force at this instant, so that the graph in the diagram shows the voltage in the armature to be zero. As the

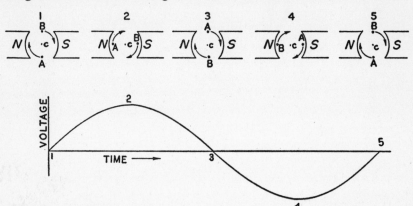

Figure 64. The relationships of the various positions of the rotating coil (armature) of an alternating current generator to the alternating current curve. A and B represent the wire of the coil in cross section. The voltage depends on the angle at which the wire cuts the magnetic field at that particular instant. C is the axis of rotation of the coil armature.

armature moves towards position (2), it cuts progressively more and more lines of force until at position (2), it is moving at right angles (90°) to the magnetic lines and therefore the maximum voltage is induced in the armature. This is represented by the peak of the curve. At (3), the armature is again moving parallel to the field and the induced voltage is zero. At (4), the armature again cuts the field at right angles but in an opposite direction so that the induced current is reversed, and the peak of the curve is below the horizontal axis of the graph. Finally, the cycle is completed when the armature returns to its original zero position.

There are some important characteristics of an alternating current that are neatly summarized in the curve of an alternating current. Such a curve has been used in Figure 64 to show its relationship to the successive positions of the generator armature as it rotates between the magnetic poles. This curve is called a *sine curve,* because its form depends on the angle which the armature wire makes with the magnetic lines of force at any instant.

The alternating current curve is shown again in its usual form in Figure 65. The YY′ axis (vertical) may represent either the current or the induced voltage. The X axis (horizontal) represents

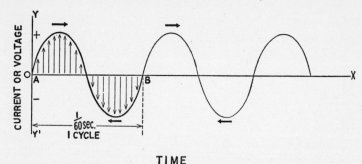

TIME

Figure 65. Sine curve representing a 60-cycle alternating current. The thick horizontal arrows show the direction of the *current* during different phases of the a.c. cycle. Note that the current reverses its direction every $\frac{1}{120}$ sec. The thin vertical arrows indicate the variation in voltage or amperage from instant to instant.

time. The distance between two successive *corresponding points* on the curve, for example AB, represents *one cycle* of the alternating current, and indicates that the armature has made one complete revolution. The most commonly used alternating current is a 60-cycle current, which means that it consists of 60 complete cycles such as AB occurring in each second, or that the armature has made 60 revolutions per second. *The number of cycles per second is called the frequency of an alternating current.* Note that *each cycle consists of two alternations;* that is, the voltage starts at zero, rises gradually to a maximum in one direction (shown above the X axis), then gradually returns to zero, after which it increases to a maximum in the opposite direction (shown below the X axis), and finally returns to zero again. Thus, there are 120 alternations per second with a 60-cycle current, which means that the *current flows back and forth in the conductor 120 times in each second.*

The single sine curve which has just been described is known as the curve of a *single phase* alternating current.

The fact that an alternating current varies from moment to moment in the strength of its voltage and amperage suggests that the units of measurement are not exactly the same as they are in the case of a direct current which flows steadily in one direction. Figure 66 shows the curve of such a steady direct current. Is it possible to assign a simple value of voltage or amperage to an alternating current which varies from one instant to the next? The answer is found in the concept of *effective current*. This may be defined as follows: *The effective value of an alternating current*

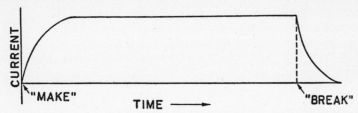

Figure 66. Curve representing a steady direct current from a battery. The circuit is closed at "make." It rises rapidly to a maximum and maintains that value at a constant level until the circuit is opened at "break," when it rapidly drops to zero.

is equal to that direct current which has the same heating effect in a wire as the alternating current in question. For example, if a steady direct current of 1 ampere produces the same heating effect in a wire whose resistance is 1 ohm as does a given alternating current, then the alternating current may be said to be 1 ampere in strength. If we have a pure sine wave alternating current as in Figure 65, then the following relationships hold true between the peak of the curve and the effective value of the current:

$$\text{maximum current} = 1.41 \times \text{effective current}$$

or

$$\text{effective current} = 0.707 \times \text{maximum current}$$

The effective voltage has the same relationship to the maximum voltage:

$$\text{maximum voltage} = 1.41 \times \text{effective voltage}$$

or

$$\text{effective voltage} = 0.707 \times \text{maximum voltage}$$

Properties of Alternating Current Circuits

In an earlier chapter, it was shown that a circuit carrying a *steady direct current* has a property called resistance, which tends to oppose the flow of current. If a coil of wire is introduced into the circuit, the flow of current is further hindered at the time the switch is closed, by the back electromotive force resulting from the self-induction of the coil (see section on self-induction). However, the direct current rapidly reaches its maximum, steady voltage, at which time there is no longer any back electromotive force because the magnetic field around the coil is now unvarying, but there still remains the true electrical resistance of the coil wire. If a condenser is introduced into a direct current circuit, the current flows only until the condenser is fully charged, and then ceases.

In an *alternating current circuit,* on the other hand, the rapid change in magnitude and direction of the current causes an alternating expansion and collapse of the magnetic field about any portion of the circuit which has *inductance,* defined as that property of an electric circuit which opposes or cushions any change in the amount of current flowing. For example, a coil of wire imparts a large inductance to the alternating current circuit in which it is connected. The persistently changing magnetic field around the coil under these conditions sets up a counter-electromotive force which always "bucks" the alternating current, first in one direction and then in the other. This bucking tendency of inductance is called *inductive reactance,* and is measured in ohms.

If a condenser is added to an alternating current circuit, it alternately charges and discharges as the current reverses. This offers a certain amount of hindrance to the flow of current and is known as *capacitive reactance.* The apparent resistance of an alternating current circuit is called its *impedance,* and this depends on the inductive reactance, capacitive reactance, and true electrical resistance. The determination of the impedance from these three factors is *not* that of simple addition, and is too complex for our purposes.

It is interesting to note that Ohm's Law applies to alternating currents if the above discussed properties are taken into consideration,

$$\text{effective current} = \frac{\text{effective voltage}}{\text{impedance}}$$

$$I = \frac{V}{Z}$$

where I is the effective current measured in amperes, V is the effective voltage measured in volts, and Z is the impedance measured in ohms.

Direct Current Generator

The same principle as described under alternating current generator is employed in the direct current generator. The sole difference lies in the use of a *commutator* instead of slip rings to introduce the generated current into the external circuit. This is shown in Figure 67. It can readily be seen that in the extreme positions of the armature, when A moves to position B, and B moves to A, the corresponding half of the commutator always introduces the current to the external circuit in the same direction. The commutator actually consists of a metal ring split in two, with the halves separated by an insulator. Each half is permanently fixed to its corresponding wire.

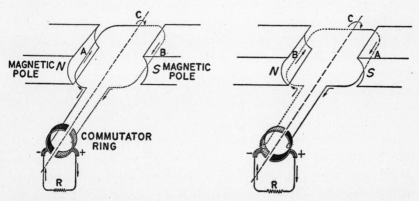

Figure 67. Simple direct current generator. Note that a commutator ring is used, with the result that the current is always supplied to the external circuit in the same direction. (Compare with Figure 63 which illustrates the a.c. generator.)

The type of current obtained from such a generator is represented in Figure 68. Note that the part of the sine wave which is present below the horizontal line in an alternating current, is turned upwards in this case so that it lies above the line. Such a direct current is called a *pulsating direct current*. In actual practice, the direct current generator consists of numerous coils and a commutator which is divided into correspondingly numerous segments. Since the coils are so arranged that some of them are

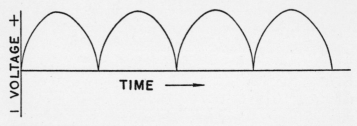

Figure 68. Wave form of a direct current curve obtained from a simple d.c. generator such as is shown in Figure 67. Note that the curve here differs from a sine curve in that the portions of the curve that lie below the horizontal axis are turned up to lie above the axis. This is a *pulsating direct current*, in contrast to the steady direct current supplied by a battery.

always cutting the magnetic field during rotation of the armature, electromotive force is always being induced. There are no instants when the voltage falls to zero, as with the simple one-coil direct current generator illustrated above. Consequently, the resulting voltage is steadier, and does not show as wide pulsations as when a single-coil armature is used. This type of curve is shown in Figure 69.

Advantages of Alternating Current

In common practice, alternating current is employed much more frequently than direct current. There are two outstanding reasons for this preference.

First, an alternating current is necessary for the operation of transformers which are essential to many phases of industry, and particularly to radiology.

In the second place, the transmission of an electric current from the power plant often involves great distances. It has been shown earlier that the power loss (in the form of heat) in an electric line is related to the current and resistance as follows:

$$P = I^2R$$

where P = loss of power in the form of heat, measured in watts
I = current in amperes
R = resistance in ohms

It is seen from this equation that the power loss is proportional to the *square of the amperage*. It is obvious, therefore, that if a current is transmitted at a very low amperage there will be a much

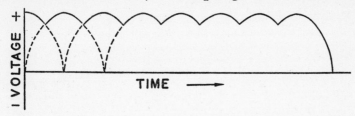

Figure 69. Direct current wave form produced by a multiple-coil generator. The solid line curve represents the voltage variation from instant to instant. This fluctuation is much less than that produced by any one of the coils alone (shown by the broken line).

smaller loss of electric power than if transmitted at high amperage. An example will emphasize this point.

Suppose we wish to transmit 50,000 watts of electric power over a distance of 10 miles (a total of 20 miles of wire), the wire having a resistance of 0.25 ohm per mile. The total R is 0.25 × 20 = 5 ohms. If we use *direct current* with a voltage of 500 and an amperage of 100, (500 × 100 = 50,000 watts), the loss of power is obtained by the equation:

$$Power\ loss = I^2R$$
$$= 100 \times 100 \times 5$$
$$= 50,000\ watts$$

Thus, all the power in the transmission lines is lost as a result of the heating effect in the transmission wires!

If, instead, we used alternating current at 5000 volts and 10 amperes (again 50,000 watts), the power loss would be much less.

The above equation for power consumption cannot be applied accurately to alternating current without a correction factor, but it does give a rough approximation. Neglecting the correction factor,

$$Power\ loss = I^2\ R$$
$$= 10 \times 10 \times 5$$
$$= 500\ watts$$

as compared with a power loss of 50,000 watts with direct current transmitted at lower voltage and higher amperage. The high voltage alternating current (commonly referred to as "high tension"), when it reaches its destination, must have its voltage reduced to useful values, ordinarily 110 volts for lighting and 110 or 220 volts for most x-ray equipment. This is accomplished by means of a *transformer*, an electromagnetic device which will be described in detail in the next chapter. A direct current, on the other hand, cannot be transmitted at high voltage and changed to a lower voltage at its destination because a *transformer will not operate on direct current*.

ELECTRIC MOTOR

Definition

An electric motor is a device that converts electrical energy to mechanical energy.

Principle

The operation of an electric motor is exactly the reverse of an electric generator.

Whenever a wire carrying an electric current is placed in a magnetic field, there is a side-thrust on the wire tending to push it out of the field. It should be emphasized that two conditions must obtain: *The wire must carry a current, and it must be located in a magnetic field.*

The manner in which the magnetic field acts on the current-carrying wire is shown in Figure 70. The wire is seen in cross section, and carries a current towards the reader. By the thumb rule, it has a magnetic field around it in the direction of the curved arrows. The upper curved arrow is in a direction opposite the field between the poles of the magnet, and the field is weakened on that side because lines of force traveling in opposite directions attract each other. The lower curved arrow is in the same direction as the main magnetic field, and the field is stronger on that side because lines of force in the same direction repel each other. The net effect is for the wire to be thrust upwards by the interaction of the two magnetic fields, as shown by the vertical arrow.

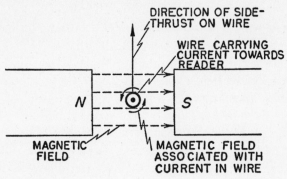

Figure 70. Principle of the electric motor. The wire carrying an electric current, when placed in a magnetic field, experiences a side-thrust due to the interaction of the magnetic field associated with the current (curved arrows) and the magnetic field of the pole magnet (broken lines).

This principle is embodied in the *left hand or motor rule* which is applied in a similar manner as the right hand rule. *The left hand or motor rule states that if the thumb and first two fingers of the left hand are held at right angles to each other, and if the index finger points in the direction of the magnetic field, and the middle finger in the direction of the current in the wire, then the thumb will point in the direction that the wire will move.* Applying this rule to Figure 70, one can see that the same result is obtained as in the above discussion: the wire moves upwards.

The Simple Electric Motor

The diagrams shown in the section on the electric generator apply also to the electric motor, except that current is *introduced* at the brushes instead of being withdrawn. If an alternating current supplies the motor, then *slip rings* must be used. If a direct current supplies the motor a *commutator ring* must be used.

In its elementary form, an electric motor may be represented as in Figure 71, which is a cross section of a single coil armature carrying an electric current in a magnetic field. Applying the *left hand rule*, one notes that wire A is thrust upwards, and B is thrust downwards. The net result is that the armature turns in a clockwise direction about axis C.

It is interesting, at this point, to mention the *back electromotive force* of a motor. When the coil of a motor rotates in the magnetic field, an electromotive force is induced in the coil according to the principles of electromagnetic induction. This induced current is

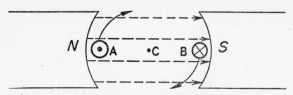

Figure 71. Cross section of an elementary motor. A and B are the coil wire. C is the axis of rotation. The curved arrows show the direction in which the coil armature rotates when the proper current is fed to the armature.

in a direction *opposite* to the direction of the current already supplying the coil. Thus, an electric motor acts at the same time as a generator and sends some current back to the main lines. This is one of the reasons why a motor consumes relatively less current than a heating device.

Types of Electric Motors

There are two main types.

1. *Direct Current Motors*. This is the reverse of a direct current generator.

2. *Alternating Current Motors*. There are two kinds of alternating current motors, *synchronous and induction*.

The *synchronous motor*, in order to function, must be supplied by an alternating current and its construction is similar to that of a single-phase alternating current generator. Thus, it consists of an armature which rotates in a magnetic field when a current is fed to the coils of the armature. Certain conditions are necessary for the operation of a synchronous motor. The armature of such a motor must rotate at the same speed (revolutions per minute) as the armature of the alternating current generator supplying the current, or at some fixed multiple of that speed. In other words, the speed of this type of motor *must be synchronous with the speed of the generator.* Special devices are required to bring the speed of the motor armature up to the required number of revolutions per minute. This type of motor is used in electric clocks, and was employed in mechanical rectification of old-style x-ray machines, as will be described later. The main *disadvantage* of the synchronous motor lies in the limited speed with which it will operate, that is, its speed must be in step with the generator. At the same time, this fixed speed may be of *advantage* in certain types of equipment, such as x-ray exposure timers and electric clocks.

The *induction motor* is the other chief type of alternating current motor. Its construction is very interesting. It consists of a *stator* which is made up of an even number of electromagnets distributed around the sides of the motor. In the center is an armature, which is called a *rotor*, consisting of bars of copper arranged around a cylindrical soft iron core. The arrangement of the copper bars resembles a squirrel cage. There are no slip rings, commutators, or brushes because this type of motor works on a different principle from other types of motors and generators. The stator is supplied by a multiphase current, which means that opposite pairs of coils receive an alternating current that is out of phase (out of step) with the current entering successive pairs of coils. Thus, as successive pairs of coils set up magnetic fields, these magnetic fields actually move round and round, and "drag" the rotor, making it rotate. The reason for this drag on the rotor lies in the fact that currents are induced in its copper bars by the moving magnetic field. Each copper bar, now carrying an induced current and lying in a magnetic field experiences a side-thrust according to the principles discussed earlier, and this side-thrust manifests itself by rotation of the motor. Figure 72 illustrates the principle of the induction motor. It is seen that the stator in this case consists of two pairs of electromagnets to provide the magnetic fields. The rotor is shown in cross section at the center. The stator is supplied

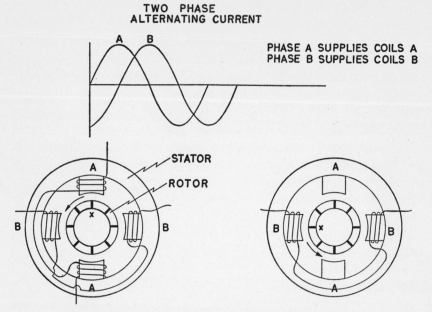

Figure 72. Principle of the two-phase *induction* motor.

by a two-phase alternating current as shown by the two sine curves in the diagram, and this is essentially two alternating currents which are out of step by ¼ cycle.

As the current in the coils supplied by *A* reaches a peak, its magnetic field thrusts the rotor sidewards, and the rotor moves in the direction of the curved arrow. Bar *X* moves towards coils *B*. At this moment, the current in coils *B* is reaching a maximum so the rotor is pushed another ¼ turn and bar *X* is now near the lower *A* coil. At this instant, *A* is reaching a maximum again, but the field is now reversed so that bar *X* continues to move in the same direction. The rotor continues to be moved counter-clockwise in this manner until the cycle is completed and as long as the coils are supplied with the proper current. Thus, we can see from this diagram that the magnetic field rotates counter-clockwise as it is successively set up between the electromagnetic pairs *A* and *B*, and this rotating field pulls the rotor with it.

The induction motor is important in the x-ray field because it is used in the rotating anode tube which will be described later.

Current-Measuring Devices

An interesting and important application of the motor principle is utilized in the construction of instruments for the measurement of current and voltage. The basic device making use of this principle is the *d'Arsonval galvanometer*. It consists essentially of a coil of wire suspended between the poles of a horseshoe magnet. One end of the coil is fixed and the other is attached to a spring helix. If a *direct current* is passed through the coil, we have a coil of wire carrying an electric current and lying in a magnetic field; thus, all the conditions are present to cause the coil to move in the field (the motor principle). In this case, the construction of the instrument, as shown in Figure 73, is such that the coil must rotate through an arc which is a portion of a circle, usually less than one-half circle (180°). The rotation takes place against the spring, and when the current is interrupted, the coil returns to the zero position. The degree of rotation is proportional to the current strength, and if the coil is fixed to a pointer which it deflects over a *calibrated* scale, as shown in Figure 73B, the current strength is thereby indicated.

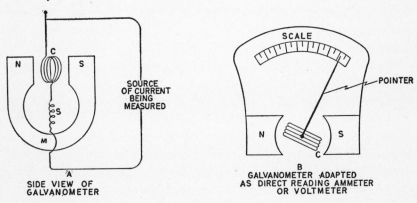

Figure 73. A. D'Arsonval galvanometer. The coil C is suspended between the poles of a horseshoe magnet M. One end of the coil is attached to the spring S. When a current is passed through the coil it rotates, twisting the spring. When the current ceases, the spring returns the coil to the initial position.

B. A direct current meter provided with a pointer and a scale. This must first be calibrated as an ammeter or voltmeter, then it may be used to measure current or voltage.

If the galvanometer, protected by a low resistance in parallel with it, is connected in series in the circuit being measured, it indicates *amperage* and constitutes an *ammeter*. If a galvanometer, protected by a high resistance in series with it, is connected in parallel with the circuit being measured, it determines *voltage* and constitutes a *voltmeter*. Thus, modifications of the same basic instrument—the d'Arsonval galvanometer—allow determination of voltage or amperage in a direct current circuit, provided the instrument has been previously calibrated against known values of voltage or amperage.

Further modification is necessary to measure the voltage and amperage of an *alternating current*, because the coil would "freeze" due to the rapid alternation of the current in the coil. (Recall that a 60 cycle alternating coil sustains 120 reversals in direction per second.) Instead of using a horseshoe magnet, one must provide a magnetic field which reverses its direction at the same rate as the current entering the coil. This is accomplished by using the same alternating current to activate the electromagnetic field between which the coil is suspended. Since the current alternates simultaneously in the rotating coil and in the field coils, the rotation of the coil and hence the deflection of the pointer are unaffected by the alternations of the current. This device, called an *electrodynamometer*, can be calibrated to read the voltage or amperage of an alternating current, that is, an a.c. voltmeter or an a.c. ammeter. The same type of instrument can be calibrated to measure electric power in a circuit, reading the values directly in watts.

QUESTIONS

1. What is the function of an electric generator?
2. What are some of the commonly used sources of energy in a generator?
3. Describe, with the aid of a diagram, a simple electric generator. Show how it produces an alternating current.
4. How does an a.c. generator differ from a d.c. generator?
5. Why is alternating current more universally preferred to direct current?
6. Define an electric motor.

7. What is the "left hand" or "motor" rule?
8. Under what condition will a wire, placed in a magnetic field, tend to move up through the field?
9. What are the two main types of motors?
10. What is a synchronous motor? How does it differ from an induction motor?
11. What is the importance of the synchronous motor and the induction motor in radiographic equipment?
12. What is the underlying principle of the galvanometer of d'Arsonval type? Show with the aid of a simple diagram the construction of a d.c. voltmeter.

TRANSFORMER

For most ordinary purposes, electricity is brought to the consumer at 110 or 220 volts. However, this is inadequate for the direct operation of an x-ray tube, since many thousands of volts are required to impart sufficient speed to the electrons in the x-ray tube in order to generate x-rays of satisfactory quality. By the use of a device known as a *transformer,* such high voltages can be readily obtained, and this device is one of the major components of an x-ray unit. The high voltage transformer is often called the *x-ray generator.*

Principle

A transformer is an electrical device which changes an *alternating current* from low voltage to high voltage, or from high voltage to low voltage, without loss of an appreciable amount of energy. The transformer transfers electrical energy from one circuit to another *without any electrical contact between the two circuits,* employing the principles of electromagnetic mutual induction.

The transformer, in its simplest form consists of two coils of wire, completely insulated from each other, and lying parallel to each other. One of these coils is supplied by an alternating current, and is called the *primary coil.* The other coil develops alternating current by mutual induction and is called the *secondary coil.* This is shown in Figure 74. The primary coil is also called the *input side* of the transformer because the alternating current is introduced to the transformer through the primary coil. The secondary coil is called the *output side* because the current leaves the transformer through the secondary coil and can be used for a desired purpose, such as the operation of an x-ray tube.

How does the transformer work? When an alternating current is made to flow in the primary coil, a magnetic field surrounds the coil. This is not a constant magnetic field, but rather an alternately expanding and contracting field, because the alternating current producing it varies rapidly in magnitude and direction (sine curve). The moving magnetic field sweeps past the secondary coil —a magnetic field crossing a wire—and an alternating current is induced in the secondary coil. This is an application of the principle of *mutual induction* which has already been discussed.

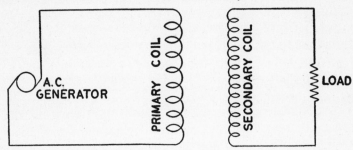

Figure 74. Simplest type of transformer. An electromotive force is set up in the secondary coil by mutual induction.

It will be recalled that one of the rules of magnetic induction is that the *magnitude of the induced voltage or electromotive force is directly proportional to the number of turns in the wire that cuts, or is cut by, a magnetic field.* This same rule applies to a transformer. Thus, if the primary coil has one turn and the secondary coil has one turn, the electromotive force induced in the secondary coil will be equal to that applied to the primary coil. If, instead, the secondary coil has two turns, the electromotive force induced in it will be twice as great as the electromotive force in the primary coil. If the secondary coil has three turns, it will have an induced electromotive force three times as great as the primary, etc. This principle is embodied in the *transformer law: The voltage induced in the secondary coil is to the voltage in the primary coil, as the number of turns in the secondary coil is to the number of turns in the primary coil.* This is expressed simply in equation form as follows:

$$\frac{V_s}{V_p} = \frac{N_s}{N_p},$$

where V_s = voltage in secondary coil
             V_p = voltage in primary coil
             N_s = no. of turns in the secondary coil
             N_p = no. of turns in the primary coil.

Stated even more simply, this means that if the number of turns of wire in the secondary coil is twice the number in the primary coil, then the voltage in the secondary will be twice the voltage in the primary coil. If the number of turns in the secondary coil is three times that in the primary coil, then the voltage induced in the secondary coil will be three times as great as in the primary coil, etc. Such a transformer, having more turns in the secondary coil than in the primary, puts out a higher voltage than is applied to it and is therefore known as a *step-up transformer*, since it increases the voltage.

If the secondary coil has fewer turns than the primary coil, the output voltage will be less than the input, and such a transformer is called a *step-down transformer*, since it decreases the voltage.

What happens to the value of the *current* in a transformer? By the Law of Conservation of Energy, there can be no more energy coming out of the transformer than is put in, and similarly, the power output can be no greater than the power input. Since the power in an electric circuit equals voltage multiplied by amperage, then

$$\mathbf{I_s V_s = I_p V_p}$$

where I_s = current in amperes in the secondary coil
             I_p = current in the primary coil
             V_s = voltage in the secondary coil
             V_p = voltage in the primary coil.

Rearranging this equation, we get the proportion:

$$\frac{\mathbf{I_s}}{\mathbf{I_p}} = \frac{\mathbf{V_p}}{\mathbf{V_s}}$$

In other words, if the voltage is increased, as in a step-up transformer, the amperage is decreased; and if the voltage is decreased, as in a step-down transformer, then the amperage is increased. Thus, a step-up transformer increases the voltage, but decreases the amperage in an inverse ratio; if the voltage is doubled, the amperage is halved, and so on.

In roentgen diagnostic equipment the step-up transformer takes 110 or 220 volts and multiplies this voltage up to 30,000 to 90,000 volts (30 to 90 kilovolts) or more, to provide the high voltage necessary to drive the electrons through an x-ray tube. At the same time it decreases the current to thousandths of an ampere (milliamperes).

Construction of Transformers

There are three main types of transformers, which will be considered separately.

1. *Open Core Transformer.* It is known that if a coil of wire carrying an electric current has inserted within it a soft iron core,

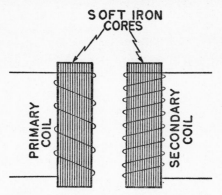

Figure 75. Open core transformer. There is some waste of energy because the magnetic field strength is partly dissipated at the ends of the soft iron cores.

there will be a marked intensification of the magnetic field developed by the coil. Similarly, a transformer becomes more efficient when a soft iron core is introduced into its coils. In the open core transformer, each *insulated* coil has a separate iron core, as in Figure 75. This type of transformer is more efficient than the simplest transformer without a core, but there is still a waste of considerable power due to the loss of magnetic field strength in the air at the ends of the two cores.

2. *Closed-Core Transformer.* In this type, the heavily insulated coils are wound around a *square metal "doughnut"* as in Figure

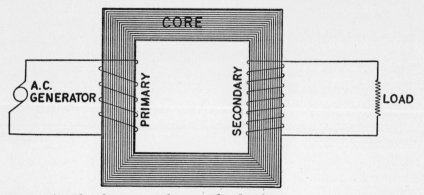

Figure 76. Closed core transformer. The doughnut type core concentrates the magnetic lines of force and also provides a continuous path for the magnetic lines of force.

76. With this type of transformer, the magnetic field is concentrated in the core which provides a continuous path for the magnetic field, so that only a negligible amount of the magnetic energy is lost to the air by leakage. The core is *laminated*, that is, it is made of layers of metal plates. In a solid core, there are eddy currents set up in the core metal by electromagnetic induction, when the transformer is in operation. These eddy currents take energy from the current flowing in the transformer coils, causing a waste of power known as *transformer loss*. The laminated core breaks up these eddy currents and thereby increases the efficiency of the transformer; in other words, there is less power wasted. Silicon steel is often used in the manufacture of laminated cores because it has a high electrical resistance and further reduces eddy current power loss. The doughnut type of closed core transformer is much more efficient than the open core type, and is the one most commonly used in x-ray generating equipment. The entire transformer is submerged in a case containing a special type of oil for maximum insulation and cooling.

3. *Shell-Type Transformer.* This is the most advanced type of transformer we have today, and is used as a commercial or power transformer. The core is laminated, being made up of sheets of silicon steel placed on top of one another, each having two rectangular holes cut in it. This core is illustrated in Figure 77. The coils are wound around the central section of the core, as in

Figure 78. It is important to remember that the *primary and secondary coils are wound together around the same part of the core.* This is possible because in any type of transformer, *the coils must be highly insulated from each other,* and when the coils are placed close together, as in the shell-type transformer, the efficiency is increased. Insulation is accomplished by coating the wires of both coils with a special insulating material, and also by immersing the transformer in a container which has been filled with an insulating oil. The oil also helps keep the transformer cool during its operation.

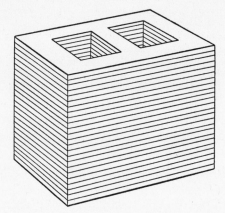

Figure 77. Core of shell type transformer.

Thus, it is evident that the simple principle of construction of a transformer—a core and two coils—is also employed in the most advanced type of transformer. But certain modifications have been introduced to increase its efficiency, namely, a laminated core and heavily insulated coils that are wound close together.

Transformer Losses

It may be of interest to point out the various types of losses of energy in a transformer and the methods of minimizing them.

1. *Copper Losses.* These include mainly the loss of electrical energy due to the resistance of the wires which make up the coils. This type of loss can be reduced by using copper wire of sufficiently large size. In a step-up transformer, the secondary coil

carries a current of low amperage so its wire can be smaller in diameter than the wire in the primary coil which carries a high amperage. Recall that a thicker wire has less electrical resistance and can therefore carry more current with relatively less waste of electrical energy than can a thin wire.

2. *Eddy Current Losses.* These are due to induced currents in the core of the transformer and result in heating the core. This removes electrical energy from the current in the coils of the transformer, diminishing its efficiency. The use of *laminated silicon*

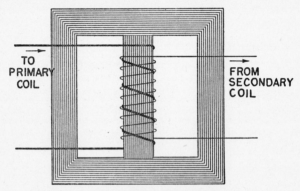

Figure 78. Shell type transformer shown in cross section, top view. Note that the primary and secondary coils are wound around the same part of the core. Very heavy insulation is required.

steel decreases eddy currents and thereby reduces waste of electrical energy.

3. *Hysteresis Losses.* Since the transformer operates on an alternating current (and also puts out an alternating current) the tiny magnetic dipoles of the core are constantly rearranging themselves as the core is magnetized first in one direction and then in another. The rearrangement of molecules causes heat to be produced in the core, and this energy must come from the transformer, thereby wasting electrical energy. Such a loss of energy is called a *hysteresis loss;* it can be reduced by using special types of metal such as silicon steel.

VOLTAGE CONTROL

It is essential to the operation of x-ray equipment that there be some means of controlling the voltage and amperage so that the output of the x-ray tube may be varied at will. This allows the technician to obtain roentgen rays of proper penetrating power and intensity for the particular purpose at hand. Without adequate flexible voltage control, modern radiographic procedures would be well nigh impossible. There are three main devices for obtaining voltage control: (1) the autotransformer; (2) the rheostat; and (3) the choke coil. These will be considered in turn.

Autotransformer

From the description of the step-up transformer it should be clear that there is a *fixed* ratio of voltage output to voltage input. If one desires to vary the output of the transformer so as to have various kilovoltages available for the operation of the x-ray tube and thereby obtain x-rays of various penetrating abilities, he can most readily accomplish this by varying the voltage *input*. Thus, if the ratio of the step-up transformer is 500 to 1, and if the input to the primary coil is 110 volts, then the secondary coil will put out 500×110, or 55,000 volts. This is more simply stated as 55 Kv. If the input is 180 volts, then the output will be $500 \times 180 =$ 90,000 volts (90 Kv). How can the input voltage be varied? This can be accomplished by means of a device known as an *autotransformer*, which is connected between the source of alternating current and the primary side of the transformer.

Principle. The autotransformer is an application of the principle of *self-induction. One coil acts as both the primary and the secondary coil.*

Construction. The autotransformer consists essentially of a coil of *insulated* wire wound around a soft iron core in order to increase the amount of self-induction. At regular intervals along the coil, taps are drawn off to metal buttons, as in Figure 79. A movable contactor, C, varies the number of taps included in the secondary circuit of the autotransformer. As ordinarily used, the autotransformer steps down the voltage.

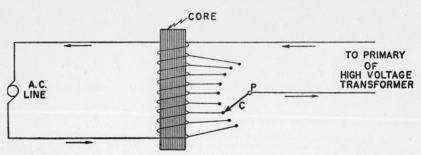

Figure 79. Simplified diagram of an autotransformer. A single coil acts as both the primary and secondary coil. The voltage on the secondary side of the autotransformer depends on the ratio of the number of turns of the coil tapped by contactor C, to the total number of turns in the coil. The transformer law applies just as though two separate coils were used.

How the Autotransformer Works. The primary current is introduced to the coil as in Figure 79. This induces a back electromotive force in the coil by self-induction. The metal contactor C can be turned about pivot P so that it touches various metal buttons which are connected to successive turns in the coil, so that various numbers of turns are included between the wires which lead away the current. The ratio of the voltage in the secondary autotransformer circuit to the voltage in the primary autotransformer circuit follows the same law as the ordinary two-coil transformer. Thus,

$$\frac{\text{Voltage in Secondary}}{\text{Voltage in Primary}} = \frac{\text{Number of Tapped Turns}}{\text{Total Number of Turns}}$$

For example, if the voltage in the primary is 220, and there are 10 turns in all, and if 5 turns are tapped off by the contactor, then from the above equation:

$$\frac{\text{Voltage in Secondary}}{220} = \frac{5}{10}$$

Therefore, Voltage in Secondary $= \dfrac{5 \times 220}{10} = 110$

The wires carrying the secondary voltage of the autotransformer lead to the primary side of the main step-up transformer.

It should be pointed out that the autotransformer can only be used where there is not too great a difference between the secondary and primary voltage. Whenever there is a great difference between these two voltages, separate insulated coils must be used as in an ordinary transformer.

Rheostat

It is possible to regulate the voltage reaching the primary coil of the transformer by another device. This is the variable resistance, called simply a *rheostat*.

Principle. In the discussion of Ohm's Law, it was pointed out that there is a fall in potential, or a voltage drop, across a resistance in the circuit. The voltage drop varies with the amount of the resistance, and may be expressed:

$$V \quad = \quad I \quad \times \quad R$$

Voltage	Current	Resistance
Drop	in	in
	Amps	Ohms

The rheostat consists of a series of resistance coils and a sliding tap which can be moved so as to increase or decrease the amount of resistance in the circuit, thereby varying the voltage which gets through the circuit to reach the transformer. This can be readily seen from a study of Figure 80.

It must be emphasized that the rheostat controls voltage by converting more or less electrical energy into heat. This is a wasteful procedure and reduces the efficiency of the equipment.

Another point that must be considered is that the voltage drop in a circuit controlled by variable resistance depends also on the amperage, as will be seen by referring to the equation, $V = IR$. If more current is drawn from the primary circuit by the transformer as occasion demands, this will result in a fall in the primary voltage and necessarily also in the kilovoltage developed in the secondary of the transformer. Thus, voltage regulation of x-ray equipment is not as stable with a rheostat as with other methods, such as the autotransformer. For this reason, the rheostat has been abandoned as the chief method of voltage control in modern x-ray equipment, and has been superseded by the autotransformer type of control.

In many x-ray installations operating above 100 Kv, the tube must be warmed prior to application of the full voltage in order

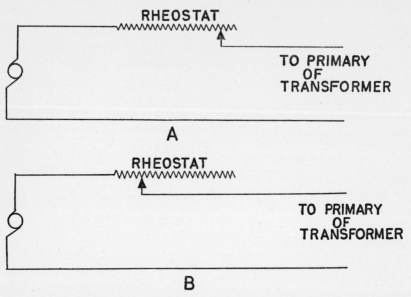

Figure 80. Principle of the rheostat, or variable resistance. In A most of the rheostat is included in the circuit so that there is a large drop in voltage and only a small voltage reaches the transformer. In B only a small segment of the rheostat is included in the primary circuit so that there is only a small drop in voltage and therefore a greater voltage reaches the transformer.

to protect it against puncture. The rheostat is used for this purpose since it can be varied while the tube is in operation. (An autotransformer cannot be used while the x-ray switch is on because sparking may occur between the metal contacts and cause them to char.) Thus, when the main switch is closed, all of the resistance of the rheostat is in the circuit causing a maximum drop in voltage and therefore a low kilovoltage in the secondary of the transformer. As the resistance is turned out of the circuit (by hand or by some automatic device) there is less and less voltage drop in the primary, and consequently, higher and higher kilovoltage generated in the secondary, so that the tube gradually receives the maximum desired kilovoltage. Therefore, the rheostat is still used in *intermediate and high voltage therapy equipment*, but an autotransformer is also included for kilovoltage control.

Comparison of Autotransformer and Rheostat. Either or both can be used to control the voltage input to the x-ray transformer, and therefore, ultimately, the kilovoltage output of the transformer. However, it is instructive to compare the advantages and disadvantages of these two devices, as revealed in Table III.

TABLE III

COMPARISON OF AUTOTRANSFORMER AND RHEOSTAT AS METHODS
OF VOLTAGE CONTROL

Autotransformer	*Rheostat*
Advantages 1. Reduces voltage with only a small loss in energy.	*Disadvantages* 1. Reduces voltage with large loss of energy because it converts electrical energy to heat.
2. Momentary change in current consumption causes relatively little change in voltage—good voltage stabilization.	2. Momentary change in current consumption causes relatively large change in voltage—poor voltage stabilization.
Disadvantage 1. If accidental sparkover occurs, the current continues to flow with relatively little drop in voltage. This is especially dangerous with non-shock-proof equipment.	*Advantage* 1. If sparkover occurs, there is a large drop in voltage because of increased current consumption. Therefore, this is safer for the person intercepting the spark.

Choke Coil

In Chapter 8, it was shown that a coil of wire carrying an electric current has a magnetic field associated with it, so that one end of the coil is a north pole and the opposite end a south pole. If this field varies in direction and strength, as when it is generated by an alternating current flowing in the coil, the magnetic lines cut the coil and induce a voltage which *opposes* the voltage already flowing in the coil. This is the *back electromotive force of self-induction*.

If, now, a soft iron core is introduced into the coil, the magnetic field is intensified, and consequently the back electromotive force is increased, thereby reducing the voltage flowing in the coil. If the core is inserted only part way into the coil, there is less back electromotive force and therefore a greater voltage flowing in the coil. Thus, by varying the proportion of the soft iron core introduced into the coil, we can vary the voltage. This type of device consisting of a coil of wire with a movable core is called a *choke coil.* Its operation will be made clearer by referring to Figure 81. This device is employed to vary the current reaching the filament of an x-ray tube in order to change the temperature and consequent electron emission of the filament.

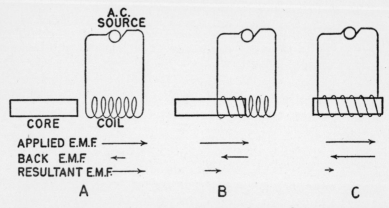

Figure 81. Operation of a choke coil. Note that an alternating current source is required. The length of the arrows represents the amount of voltage in that particular direction. In A, with the core completely withdrawn, there is a small back voltage so that the applied voltage is reduced by only a small amount. In B, with the core partly inserted, there is a greater reduction in the applied voltage. In C, with the core completely inserted into the coil, there is a maximum back voltage of self-induction with a great decrease in the applied voltage. The position of the core can be regulated by a suitable mechanism so that the resultant voltage can be varied at will.

QUESTIONS

1. Why is high voltage needed in x-ray equipment?
2. What device is used to change low voltage to high voltage?
3. What is the transformer law? A transformer is so constructed that there are 100 turns in the primary coil and 100,000 turns in the secondary. If the input is 110 volts, what is the output voltage?
4. Show by diagram a doughnut transformer, first as a step-up transformer, second as a step-down transformer.
5. How are eddy currents reduced in a transformer? Why should they be kept to a minimum?
6. Why is a core used in a transformer?

7. What two types of insulation are used in a transformer and why?
8. What is the function of an autotransformer? How does it operate?
9. What is a rheostat? In what type of x-ray equipment is it most widely used today?
10. Compare the advantages and disadvantages of the autotransformer and rheostat.
11. Describe the principle of the choke coil. Where is it often used in x-ray equipment?

CHAPTER *11* RECTIFICATION

Definition

It will be recalled that an alternating current is one which rapidly reverses its direction from moment to moment. There are various devices which can be used to change such a current into one that flows always in the same direction, that is, *direct current*. The high voltage alternating current taken from the secondary side of the x-ray transformer must be changed to direct current for maximum efficiency of operation of modern x-ray equipment. *Rectification is defined as the process of changing an alternating current to a direct current*. This can be brought about in two ways: (1) by suppressing the portion of the alternating current cycle that lies below the line (negative phase); and (2) by changing the negative phase of the curve to a positive phase so that it lies above the line. The resulting current curves are illustrated in Figure 82.

Why is it desirable to rectify the high tension alternating current coming from the x-ray transformer? This current is to be applied to the terminals of an x-ray tube, and the tube operates with greater efficiency when this current is rectified. The theory and construction of x-ray tubes will be considered in detail in the following chapters, but a brief description is necessary at this point to aid in the understanding of rectification. A modern x-ray tube consists of a glass bulb having a high vacuum, in which are sealed two terminals: the negative terminal or cathode, and the positive terminal or anode. The cathode is provided with a metal filament, and when a special, low voltage current is applied to this filament it becomes hot just as does the filament in an electric light bulb. As a result, electrons "boil off" the filament, and when the high tension current from the transformer is applied between the cathode and anode, these electrons are driven over to the anode at a terrific speed. X-rays are given off when the electrons strike the anode. Under ordinary conditions of operation, the high

122

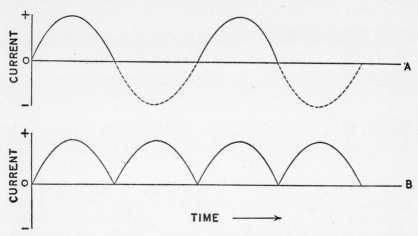

Figure 82. Two fundamental types of rectified circuits. In A, the negative phase lying below the line is *suppressed*. In B the negative phase of the alternating current is *inverted* so that it lies above the line and becomes a positive phase. With either method, one obtains a pulsating direct current.

voltage current can pass through the tube in only one direction, from cathode to anode. If the applied high voltage alternating current is rectified before reaching the tube, so that its direction is always from cathode to anode in the tube, the tube will operate more efficiently than if the current is not rectified.

Methods of Rectifying an Alternating Current

There are three main systems of rectification: (1) Self-rectification; (2) Mechanical rectification; and (3) Valve tube rectification. *All rectifying systems are located between the secondary coil of the transformer and the x-ray tube.*

1. *Self-Rectification.* In this, the simplest type of rectification, the high voltage is applied *directly* to the terminals of the x-ray tube. We have seen that under ordinary conditions, an x-ray tube allows passage of electrons only from the cathode to the anode. This occurs only during the positive phase of the alternating current curve, when the anode is positively charged. During the negative phase, the anode is negatively charged and the current will not pass from the cathode to the anode. The latter phase is known as *inverse current*. The *anode* must be kept *cool* so that

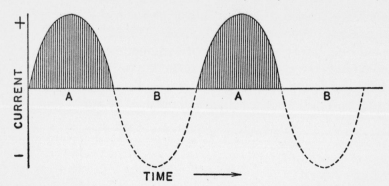

Figure 83. Curve of tube current in a self-rectified circuit. During the first half of the cycle, A, the current passes through the tube; this is *effectual voltage*. During the second half, B, no current flows from anode to cathode; this is called *inverse voltage*. Note that the inverse voltage is greater than the effectual voltage.

during the negative phase, the inverse is suppressed. However, if the tube is overloaded and the anode becomes hot it will emit electrons and they will pass to the cathode under the pressure of the inverse voltage, damaging the filament or cracking the glass envelope. Furthermore, the danger of tube damage is increased by the fact that the inverse voltage is higher than the useful or effectual voltage. A self-rectified circuit, in which the x-ray tube itself acts as rectifier, does not have as high a capacity as when some subsidiary means of rectification is employed. Figure 83 explains the features of the current through the tube in a self-rectified circuit. This type of rectification is known as *self-half-wave rectification*. Self-rectification is employed especially in portable x-ray apparatus, and not infrequently in other types of x-ray equipment.

2. *Mechanical Rectification.* In older x-ray equipment, the current was rectified by a mechanical device which changed the negative phase of the alternating current cycle to a positive phase, resulting in *full-wave rectification*. One such type of rectifier consists of a rotating circular disc of insulating material, such as fiber or mica, with four metal studs mounted on the edge equally distant from each other. These studs are connected in pairs by wires. Such a disc is illustrated in Figure 84. The brushes, B are *fixed* in position, so that as the disc rotates on the shaft of a synchronous motor,

the studs pass successively beneath each brush and contact it momentarily. Whenever such contact is made, current is conducted from the brush B through the contacting stud S to wire W, then through the next stud to its contacting brush and the external circuit. The flow of current is indicated by the arrows in the figure. During the intervals when studs and brushes are not in contact, no

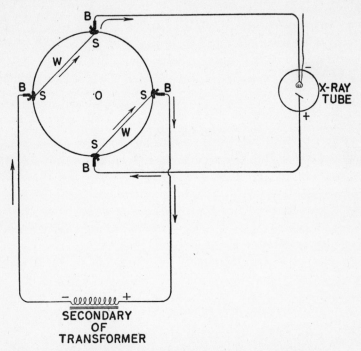

Figure 84. Rectifying disc, used in mechanical rectification.
    B—metal brush to make temporary contact with stud.
    S—metal stud mounted permanently on insulated disc.
    W—wire connecting studs.
    O—shaft on which disc rotates.

current flows. Such contact occurs only for very brief instants during rotation of the disc, and is made to coincide with the peaks of the alternating current.

How does such a rotating disc rectify an alternating current? The disc is mounted on the shaft of a synchronous motor, and rotates at a speed which is synchronous with the alternations of the high tension alternating current arriving at the disc from the secondary of the transformer. The relationship of successive positions of the rotating disc to the direction of flow of the alternating current at that instant is such that the current is admitted to the x-ray tube *always in the same direction.* The exact relationship is revealed in Figure 85, and is explained in the legend. The current is rectified *before* it reaches the x-ray tube. It arrives at the disc as a high tension alternating current and leaves the disc as a pulsating direct current.

The type of wave obtained by mechanical rectification is interesting in that only the peaks of the waves are utilized, because

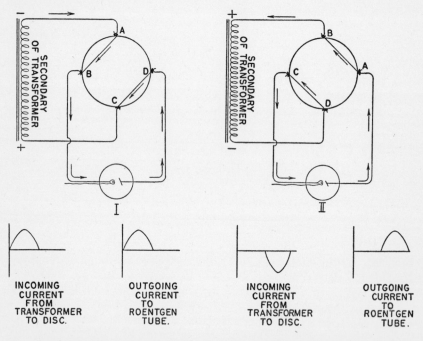

Figure 85. Mechanical rectification. In I the current (electron flow) leaves the negative end of the transformer, passes through the brush to stud A, thence in the direction of the arrows to B, filament, anode, D, C, and finally to the positive end of the transformer. This represents the positive phase of the a.c. cycle. In II the disc has rotated clockwise ¼ turn, while the current has reversed to its negative phase as shown by reversal in polarity of the transformer. The current again leaves the negative end of the transformer and passes in the direction of the arrows to the tube filament. Thus, it still reaches the tube in the same direction. In the next ¼ turn of the disc the situation returns to I.

current flows in the system only at those instants when the brushes are in contact with the metal studs on the disc. The shaded areas in Figure 86 show the type of wave obtained. Since only the peaks of voltage are used, the resulting x-rays are *more penetrating and more uniform in quality* than if the lower voltages were also utilized.

It is of interest to point out that it is just as possible for the disc to be so related to the alternating current direction that the current is always brought to the x-ray tube in the wrong direction. This is determined on mechanically rectified units by the use of a *polarity indicator*. If this indicator shows the rectified current to

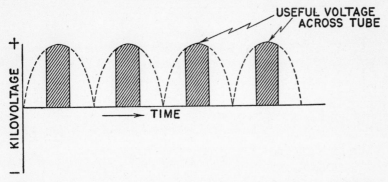

Figure 86. Full-wave rectified circuit obtained by mechanical rectification. Note that only the values of kilovoltage near the peak kilovoltage leave the rectifier and reach the x-ray tube.

be in the wrong direction, the control switch is opened and closed until the polarity indicator shows the correct direction. With a given closure of the control switch, there is a 50:50 chance that the current will be in the correct direction.

3. *Valve Tube Rectification.* A valve tube is a thermionic tube and resembles, in general, a roentgen ray tube, allowing passage of current *in one direction only;* that is, *from cathode to anode.* The details of construction will be considered in a later chapter. Valve tubes can be introduced into the high tension x-ray circuit in such a way as to produce either *half-wave* or *full-wave rectification.*

In a half-wave rectified circuit, one or two valve tubes can be used. A single valve tube can be hooked up as shown in Figure 87. During the positive phase of the alternating current cycle, the direction of the current is from cathode to anode and the current flows through both the valve tube and the x-ray tube as indicated by the arrows in the diagram. During the negative phase, the direction of the current is reversed and it now passes to the anode of the valve tube *first*. This blocks the current and prevents its reaching the anode of the x-ray tube; that is, the *valve tube sup-*

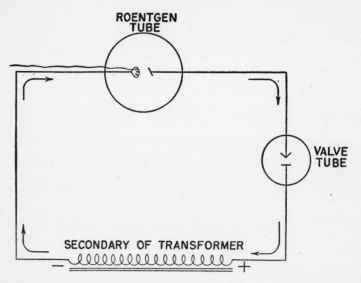

Figure 87. Half-wave rectification with a single valve tube. The inverse voltage is suppressed at the anode of the valve tube, thereby protecting the x-ray tube.

presses the inverse voltage. This diminishes the possibility of heating the anode of the x-ray tube and so eliminates the danger of reverse flow of electrons in the tube which might ruin the filament. The current is rectified *before* it reaches the x-ray tube. Therefore, such a system allows a greater load to be placed on the tube than when self-rectification is employed, although half-wave rectification results in either case (see Figure 83).

If *two valve tubes are used,* as in Figure 88, the high voltage during the negative phase of the cycle is divided between the two valve tubes, increasing the efficiency of the system and improving the capacity of the x-ray tube. The wave form of the rectified current is similar to that in self-rectification (see Figure 83), but it should be noted again that the current is rectified before reaching the x-ray tube.

If *four valve tubes are used,* they can be connected so that the negative phase of the a.c. cycle is reversed, just as with mechanical rectification; in other words, this provides full-wave rectification.

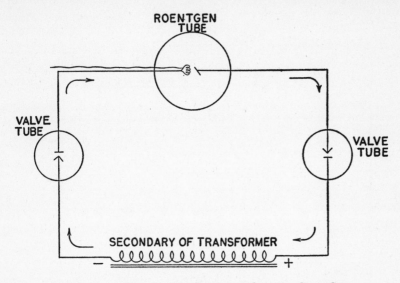

Figure 88. Half-wave rectification with two valve tubes.

Figure 89 indicates the proper connection of a four-valve-tube rectifier. In A, the current passes from the negative pole of the transformer through the successively numbered portions of the circuit to the cathode of the x-ray tube, and finally back to the positive end of the transformer. (Remember that each valve tube permits the current to flow in only one direction, from its cathode to its anode.) In B, the polarity of the transformer is reversed due to alternation of the current. The current again passes through the successively numbered portions of the circuit to the cathode of the x-ray tube and finally reaches the positive end of the transformer. Note that as the current is traced through the circuit, there are occasions when it reaches the junction of two valve tubes at their cathode ends, as at point S in A; the current passes through the

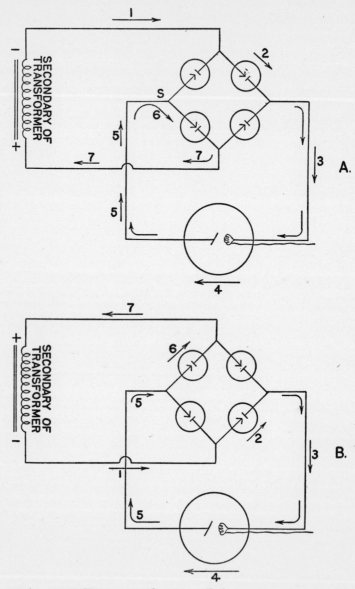

Figure 89. Full-wave rectification with four valve tubes. By following the numbered portions of the circuits in A and B, one notes that regardless of the polarity of the transformer during the different phases of the a.c. cycle, the current always reaches the x-ray tube in the same direction; that is, the entire alternating current is fully utilized.

lower of the two valve tubes because passage through the upper valve tube would lead it back to a point of higher potential and this is electrically impossible.

It may, at first sight, be confusing to the student to memorize the proper connection of the valve tubes. However, if certain simple rules are learned, the connections are easily remembered. These rules are as follows:

(1) First connect four valve tubes without indicating anode or cathode.

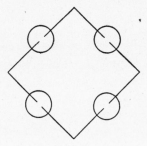

Figure 90.

(2) Then insert two filaments so that they are connected together.

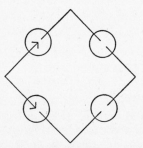

Figure 91.

(3) Now connect these *cathodes* to the *anode* of the x-ray tube.

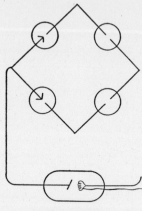

Figure 92.

(4) Insert two *anodes* in the opposite valve tubes, and join them to the *cathode* of the x-ray tube.

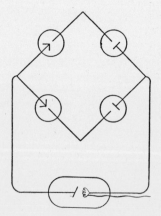

Figure 93.

(5) Now designate the remaining electrodes in the valve tubes.

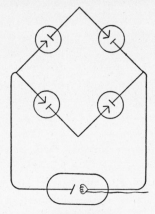

Figure 94.

(6) Finally, connect the remaining valve tube ends to the terminals of the transformer.

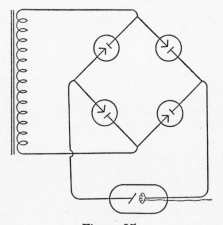

Figure 95.

The above rules are necessary because the connections of the valve tubes to each other and to the x-ray tube and transformer must be made in a definite manner. If this relationship is altered in any way, the system will fail to rectify.

In modern diagnostic roentgen units, the four-valve-tube system of rectification has replaced mechanical rectification. The reasons for this are that four-valve-tube rectification has the following advantages:

1. Operation is noiseless.
2. There are no moving parts.
3. There is no sparking to interfere with radio reception.
4. Valve tubes have a long life, and should rarely need replacement.
5. There is no possibility of wrong polarity if the valve tubes are properly installed.

There is one disadvantage with this type of rectification, and that is the utilization of the entire alternating current wave, resulting in production of a high percentage of soft x-rays at the lower kilovoltage levels (see Figure 96). However, these can be

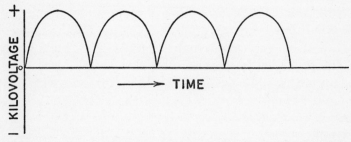

Figure 96. Wave form of a current rectified by four valve tubes. Note that all the values of kilovoltage are represented from zero to the peak value.

minimized by use of appropriate filters; or the low points in the alternating current wave can be boosted to high voltage levels by the use of condensers for deep therapy equipment, as in the so-called *constant-potential circuit*. By way of contrast, it may be recalled that with mechanical rectification only the peaks of the alternating current cycle are utilized so that the resulting x-ray beam tends to be more homogeneous than in the case of valve tube rectification without condensers.

The use of full-wave rectification increases considerably the tube rating, which means that a greater load can be placed on the tube without danger of ruining it. Table IV shows the comparative

TABLE IV

Comparative tube ratings of stationary anode tube with 2.2 mm focal spot operating on 60 cycles. Maximum permissible exposure time without danger of damaging the tube is indicated for the selected values of Kv and Ma.

Type of Rectification	Kv	Ma	Maximum Safe Exposure Time
Full-wave	80	40	20 sec
Half-wave	80	40	10 sec
Self-rectified	80	40	2 sec

values of kilovoltage, milliamperage, and exposure time that may safely be used on a tube with different types of rectification. It is readily seen that with the same factors of kilovoltage and milliamperage, in this particular example, the maximum safe exposure time is increased five times with half-wave rectification, and ten times with full-wave rectification, as compared with self-rectification. It must be emphasized that this table applies to a particular tube; the rating for any given tube must be obtained from the manufacturer, as will be pointed out later. However, with any type of equipment, full-wave rectification increases the tube rating, and this has made possible the development of modern high speed radiography.

QUESTIONS

1. Define rectification.
2. Why is it desirable to rectify the current for x-ray generation?
3. Name the three main types of rectification.
4. Show with the aid of a diagram how a mechanical rectifier operates. What type of current wave does it produce?
5. Show with the aid of a diagram: (a) single-valve-tube rectification, and (b) four-valve-tube rectification. Draw the shapes of the current waves produced by each.
6. What is meant by a "constant potential" unit? Under what conditions, and why, is it desirable?
7. Compare mechanical and full-wave valve-tube rectification, as to their advantages and disadvantages.

How X-rays Were Discovered

In 1895, Wilhelm Conrad Roentgen was conducting experiments with a vacuum tube through which a high voltage discharge could be passed. This was known as a Crooke's tube. One day, while operating the tube in a darkened room, Roentgen noticed that a piece of barium platinocyanide, placed several feet from the tube, glowed even though the tube was wrapped in black paper, a phenomenon known as *fluorescence*. Roentgen knew very well that ordinary forms of radiation such as light would not pass through the black paper and so he began his intensive research into the nature of this new radiation which was capable of passing through black paper. He soon found that many materials, such as wood, glass, and human tissues were penetrated by these rays. He was amazed to discover that he could see the bones in his hands outlined by the rays on a piece of cardboard coated with fluorescent material such as barium platinocyanide or calcium sulfide. He called this new type of radiation *x-rays*, because so little was known about it, and the letter *x* is often used in mathematics to denote an unknown quantity. This discovery has become one of the most outstanding in modern times, not only in medicine, but in science and industry as well.

Roentgen's discovery gave rise to a new branch of science. His name has in recent years been used more and more frequently in connection with x-rays, and in scientific literature they are often called *roentgen rays. Roentgenology is that branch of medicine which deals with diagnosis and treatment by means of roentgen rays. Radiology* is more inclusive, and deals also with the application of radium and radioactive isotopes.

Roentgenography or radiography deals with the art and science of recording roentgen ray images on photographic film.

Roentgenoscopy or fluoroscopy is the observation of roentgen ray images on a screen coated with fluorescent material.

What Are Roentgen or X-rays?

According to present concepts, an x-ray beam is made up of a group of rays which are fundamentally of the same nature as white light, ultra-violet, infra-red, and other similar types of radiant energy. On the basis of Maxwell's theories, they are all *electromagnetic waves*. What are electromagnetic waves? They are believed to be wavelike disturbances which arise in association with vibrating electric charges. It is generally known that any type of wave must be carried by something; for example, we have all seen waves on the surface of water. In this case, water is the transmitting material. When a stringed instrument is plucked, waves are set up in the string, and here the string is the transmitting material. But what transmits electromagnetic waves? Strangely enough, no one knows exactly what carries them, and so the scientists at one time assumed that empty space really consisted of a non-material medium called *the ether*, but this concept has been abandoned.

Roentgen rays are one type of electromagnetic wave, traveling with the same speed as light, 186,000 miles per second in air. This speed remains *constant* at all times. The waves are believed to have a form such as represented in Figure 97. All electromagnetic waves, (including radio, heat, light, ultraviolet, and x-rays) have this type of form and travel with the same speed, but differ in the length of the wave, or as we say, the *wavelength*. The distance between two successive crests in the wave, A to B in Figure 97, is called the *wavelength*. The number of such crests occurring per second is called the *frequency*. It is obvious from comparison of the upper and lower waves in Figure 97, that if the wavelength is decreased, the frequency must increase correspondingly. This can also be shown in another way. The speed with which the wave travels is equal to the frequency of vibration multiplied by the wavelength:

$$c = \nu\lambda$$

where c = speed

ν = frequency (= Greek letter "nu")

λ = wavelength (= Greek letter "lambda")

Since c, the speed of all electromagnetic waves is constant in a given material, an increase in frequency (ν) must always be accompanied by a decrease in wavelength (λ), and conversely, a decrease in frequency by an increase in wavelength.

The wavelength of x-rays is extremely short; for instance, in *ordinary radiography*, the useful range of x-ray wavelengths is about 0.1 to 0.5 Å (recall that 1Å = one one-hundred-millionth of a cm!). In view of the extremely short wavelengths of x-rays the frequencies of these rays are tremendous.

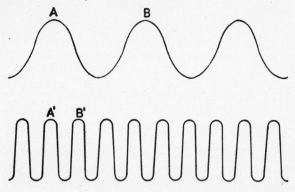

Figure 97. Electromagnetic waves. The upper and lower waves differ in wavelength, that is, the distance between two crests such as A to B and A' to B'. The lower wave thus has a shorter wavelength, and it is evident that it therefore has more crests in a given period of time than does the upper wave. Thus, the wave with the shorter wavelength vibrates faster, i.e., it has greater frequency.

The various types of electromagnetic waves, ranging from radio waves with wavelengths measured in several thousand meters, down to gamma rays with wavelengths in thousandths of an Å are shown with their wavelengths in Figure 98.

Source of Roentgen or X-rays

For use in roentgenography and therapy, roentgen rays are usually produced by man-made machines. *These rays arise whenever a stream of fast-moving electrons suddenly undergoes a reduction in speed.* Gamma rays, which are physically identical with x-rays, occur in nature, being emitted by certain radioactive elements. In general, the wavelength of gamma rays is shorter than roentgen rays, but there is considerable overlapping, as is evident from Figure 98.

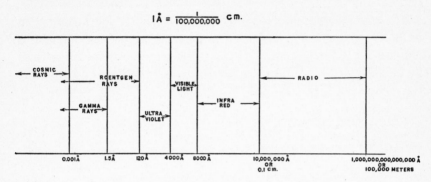

Figure 98. The electromagnetic spectrum.

The X-ray Tube

A man-made device in which x-rays or roentgen rays are produced is called the *x-ray or roentgen ray tube.* The details of construction will be discussed later, but the principles of construction must be considered now in order to appreciate how roentgen rays are produced.

It may be mentioned briefly, out of historic interest, that the old-fashioned x-ray tube was called a *gas tube.* It consisted of a glass bulb in which a partial vacuum had been produced, leaving a small amount of gas. In it were sealed two electrodes, one negative (cathode) and the other positive (anode). *The cathode terminal was not heated.* When a high voltage was applied across the electric terminals in the tube, *ionization* of the gas in the tube occurred, and there resulted a sufficient number of electrons to provide a stream which could strike the positive terminal (anode). When this electron stream struck the target, x-rays were produced. The gas tube is now outmoded because of its inefficient operation and the difficulty of controlling the quality and quantity of the emerging x-ray beam. There is no particular value in studying further the details of the cold cathode gas tube.

In 1913, Dr. Coolidge, at the General Electric Company laboratories, invented the modern roentgen ray tube and revolutionized roentgenology. The principles of construction are surprisingly simple, and a clear understanding of them is a *must* for anyone dealing with x-rays. The Coolidge tube consists of the following (see Figure 99):

1. A *glass envelope* (tube) which has a high vacuum.

2. A *hot filament cathode*. This is obtained by supplying the cathode, or negative terminal, with a *separate* low voltage heating circuit.

3. An *anode*, the positive electrode.

4. A *high voltage* applied across the electrodes. It must be emphasized that in this type of tube, *there are two entirely distinct electric circuits, one low-voltage passing through the cathode to*

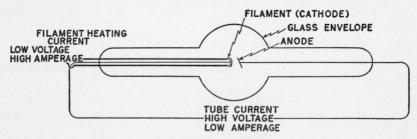

Figure 99. Hot cathode (Coolidge) x-ray tube.

heat it, and the other a high voltage circuit passing across from cathode to anode (see Figure 99).

Conditions Necessary for the Production of X-rays

There are four essential principles in the generation of x-rays in the Coolidge tube. These will be considered in turn:

1. *Separation of Electrons.* Just as in the case of all other atoms, the atoms of the filament wire cathode have electrons in orbits around a central nucleus. These electrons must be freed in some manner. The heating current applied to the filament causes the filament to become extremely hot or incandescent, and this tends to separate the outer electrons from the atoms of the filament metal. We sometimes speak of these electrons as "boiling off" the filament. They form a small "cloud" which surrounds the filament. This process of separation of electrons by the use of a heating current is designated as *thermionic emission.*

2. *Production of High Speed Electrons.* If, now, high potential difference is developed between the filament cathode and the target anode by applying a high voltage across them, the electrons that have been separated by the preliminary heating of the filament are made to move at a high speed. The reason for this is as follows: Since the filament cathode is given a very high negative charge by the applied kilovoltage, it pushes the electrons towards the anode, and the latter with its high positive charge attracts the electrons. The net result is that the *electrons move at an extremely high speed through the tube from cathode to anode;* this stream of electrons constituting the cathode rays or tube current. *The speed of these electrons approaches one-half the speed* of light, and with ultra modern equipment may develop a speed greater than one-half the speed of light.

3. *Concentration of Electrons.* The electron beam in the tube is made to concentrate on a small spot on the face of the anode target—the *focal spot.* This is accomplished by surrounding the filament with a small molybdenum collar which is given a negative charge in order to prevent the electron beam from spreading, thereby keeping it within the confines of a narrow stream; the narrower the electron stream, the smaller the focal spot.

4. *Sudden Stopping of the Electron Stream.* When the electron stream in the tube strikes the target anode, it is stopped abruptly and the kinetic energy of the electrons must be converted to some other form of energy (Law of Conservation of Energy). With equipment ordinarily used in clinical work, about 99.8% of this energy is changed to heat, while only 0.2% is converted to roentgen rays. As a matter of fact, only about one part in a thousand of the kinetic energy of the electrons eventually results in x-rays that are useful in roentgenography!

One must always keep clearly in mind the distinction between the electrons flowing within the tube, and the roentgen rays which emerge from the tube. Imagine a boy throwing stones at the side of a barn. The stones are analogous to the electron beam in the x-ray tube. When the stones hit the barn, sound waves emerge. These sound waves are analogous to the roentgen rays that come from the target when electrons strike it.

Further Consideration of Production of Roentgen Rays

One can now look a little deeper into the detailed production of roentgen rays. When the electron beam strikes the target, some of the electrons are stopped abruptly or markedly slowed down; their energy is converted to heat and roentgen rays. The roentgen rays resulting from the deceleration of electrons are called *primary roentgen rays*.

Some of the electrons are not stopped, but *penetrate into the atoms* of the target material. By collision, they displace another electron from an inner orbit of an atom to one of the outer orbits, or they may knock an electron from an inner orbit completely out of the atom. Such an ejected electron is called a *photoelectron* (see Figure 100). The displaced electron, in being removed from an inner orbit outwards, is really moved to a *higher energy level*, since energy is required to move such an electron away from the positively charged nucleus. The atom is now unstable, and is said to be in an *excited state*. Almost immediately the space vacated by the displaced electron is filled by some other electron falling into it from any of the outer orbits. Since, in the first place, energy was put into the atom to free the electron and remove it from the atom, when an electron falls back into the vacated space a like amount of energy must be emitted (Law of Conservation of Energy). The emitted energy is in the form of a roentgen ray, and the emerging ray is called *characteristic radiation*, because its wavelength is characteristic of the metal of which the target is composed (see Figure 100).

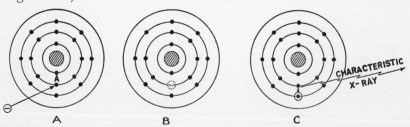

Figure 100. Production of characteristic radiation. In A, the incoming electron collides with one of the orbital electrons. In B, the atom is in an "excited state," electron A now being lost from its orbit. In C, an electron jumps from an outer orbit to replace electron A; characteristic radiation accompanies this, and the atom has returned to its normal state.

This can be summarized briefly as follows: *The primary x-ray beam* which leaves the target consists of two kinds of x-rays:

1. *Primary rays* resulting from the stoppage of electrons by the target.

2. *Characteristic rays* emitted from the atoms of the target metal itself.

Target Material

It is important to note that the target metal must be selected with two aims in mind. First, it must have a very *high melting point* to withstand the extremely high temperature to which it is subjected. In the second place, it must have a *high atomic number,* because the characteristic radiation has a shorter wavelength and is therefore more useful, when material with a high atomic number is the source of characteristic rays. Tungsten is a metal which has both these properties. It has a melting point of 3400 C and atomic number 74, and is now generally employed as the target material in tubes used for clinical work. In order to facilitate the dissipation of heat from the target, the anode in a Coolidge tube is constructed of a tungsten target in the form of a small button imbedded in a block of copper which is a better conductor of heat. The electron beam in the tube is directed so as to focus on a small spot on this tungsten target.

Properties of Roentgen Rays

It may be of interest to list some of the properties of roentgen rays that are of importance in the field of roentgenology.

1. They are invisible rays, belonging to the general category of electromagnetic waves.

2. They are electrically neutral and cannot be deflected by electrical or magnetic fields.

3. They occur in a wide range of wavelengths, from about 0.04 Å to more than 1000 Å. The useful range in roentgenography is about 0.1 Å to 0.5 Å.

4. Most beams of roentgen rays are heterogeneous, that is, they consist of rays having many different wavelengths.

5. Roentgen rays emerge from the tube in straight lines. This is essential to their use in roentgenography.

6. They travel only at the same speed as light, 186,000 miles per second.

7. They are capable of ionizing gases because of their ability to remove orbital electrons from atoms.

8. They cause fluorescence of certain crystals. This is essential to their use in fluoroscopy, and in intensifying screens for roentgenography.

9. They cannot be focused by a lens.

10. They affect photographic film, producing a latent image which can be developed chemically.

11. They produce chemical and biologic changes. This is essential to their use in treatment. Fundamentally, most of these changes depend on ionization.

12. They produce secondary radiation. This is discussed in greater detail in a later section.

Quality of Roentgen Radiation

The quality of a roentgen ray may be defined as its penetrating ability; that is, its relative ability to pass through matter. On what does the penetrating power depend? It is determined primarily by the energy content of that particular ray, which, in turn, varies inversely as the wavelength of the ray. This means, simply, that *rays of short wavelength have more energy than rays of long wavelength.* We have seen earlier in this chapter that the wavelength times the frequency of an electromagnetic wave equals the speed of light, which is constant, and that, consequently, short wavelength is associated with high frequency. Therefore, it may be concluded that *rays of high frequency have more energy than rays of low frequency.* One may sum up these facts by stating that *x-rays of great penetrating power have short wavelength and high frequency; and conversely, x-rays of poor penetrating power have long wavelength and low frequency.*

How can we vary the energy content of x-rays? The energy of a given roentgen ray depends on the energy of that particular electron in the x-ray tube which was responsible for the production of that roentgen ray. The energy of the electron depends on its speed, which, in turn, depends on the kilovoltage applied to the tube. *The higher the kilovoltage the greater the speed of the electrons in the tube, the greater their kinetic energy, and the greater the amount of energy in the roentgen rays produced, and, therefore, the greater the penetrating power of these roentgen rays.* In practice, this is applied directly in that the penetrating ability of x-rays is increased by increasing the kilovoltage applied to the tube, and the penetrating ability is decreased by decreasing the kilovoltage.

It must be emphasized, however, that an ordinary x-ray beam, as it emerges from the tube, consists of innumerable rays which differ in wavelength and penetrating ability. In other words, an x-ray beam is *heterogeneous, consisting of many waves of different wavelengths.* An analogy with white light may clarify this. Ordinary white light consists of various colors blended together. If such light is passed through a glass prism, it may be separated into its component colors which are the colors of the rainbow, or the *spectrum* as it is called scientifically. These colors differ in wavelength. For instance, the wavelength of "red" is about 7000 Å, whereas the wavelength of "violet" is about 4000 Å. A light beam of one pure color is called *monochromatic.* In a similar manner, an x-ray beam consists of different x-ray "colors" or wavelengths, although they cannot be detected as such by the human eye. However, x-rays may be refracted through certain crystals and separated into beams of waves having similar wavelengths, that is, *monochromatic x-rays.*

Why is an ordinary x-ray beam heterogeneous in wavelength? One reason has already been mentioned; the beam as it emerges from the tube consists of primary x-rays (produced by stoppage of electrons by the target), and characteristic x-rays (arising from electron transfers in the atoms of the target). The primary and the characteristic x-rays which make up the primary beam have different wavelengths. In the second place, the kilovoltage applied to the tube fluctuates according to the alternating current cycle (see Figure 65), and since changes in kilovoltage are reflected in changes in wavelength of the resulting x-rays, there must of necessity be a range of wavelengths corresponding to the fluctuation in the kilovoltage. A third consideration is that the electrons may strike several atoms of the target before they are completely stopped, and at each collision, x-rays of different wavelengths are produced. And finally, some of the electrons may strike metal parts of the anode other than the target, producing *stem radiation;* this factor has in large part been eliminated by advanced tube design.

It is possible to represent a roentgen beam in the form of a graph showing the relative numbers of waves of different wavelengths in the beam. This is shown in Figure 101. It is noted that

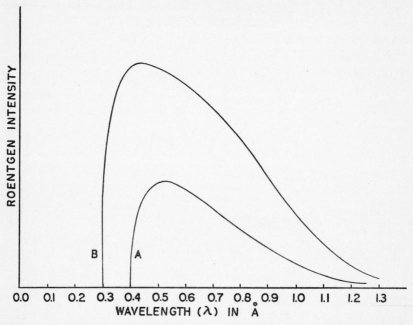

Figure 101. General radiation from a tungsten target, at 30 Kv (curve A) and at 40 Kv (curve B).

the peak of the lower curve occurs at about 0.55 Å, and this means that most of the rays in this particular beam have a wavelength of about 0.55 Å. The curve crosses the horizontal axis at 0.4 Å, which is the minimum wavelength (or highest energy) wave occurring in the beam. This minimum wavelength depends on the peak kilovoltage applied. It is obtained from the equation:

$$\lambda_{min} = \frac{12.40}{KVP}$$

where λ_{min} = minimum wavelength in Å

KVP = peak kilovoltage applied to tube

If KVP = 30, then from the equation

$$\lambda_{\min} = \frac{12.40}{30} = 0.43 \text{ Å}$$

The curve crosses the horizontal again somewhere above 1 Å, which is the limitation imposed by the glass enclosing the x-ray tube. Any wavelengths longer than this are absorbed by the glass.

It is evident from comparison of the two curves, that as the kilovoltage is increased, there is a relative increase in the number of waves of shorter wavelength, but there is also a general increase in the number of waves of all wavelengths shown.

If a sufficiently high kilovoltage is applied to the tube (at least 69.0 Kv), the curves are modified by the appearance of a *sharp*

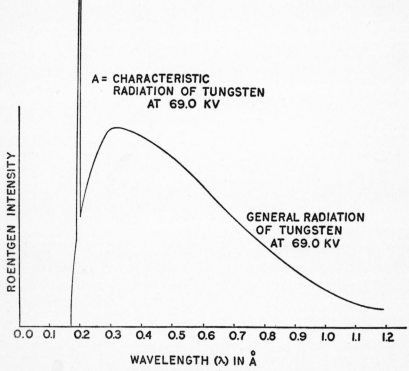

Figure 102. A represents the characteristic radiation of tungsten appearing at 69 Kv. This characteristic peak of radiation actually consists of four closely spaced peaks.

peak at about 0.2 Å, because of the addition of characteristic radiation from the tungsten target (see Figure 102).

In view of the heterogeneous nature of the x-ray beam, the question arises as to how one may specify numerically the quality of a given beam. There are several ways of doing this. The most commonly accepted method is the *half value layer, which is defined as that thickness of a stated metal that reduces the intensity of the beam by one-half.* For example, we have a beam of x-rays whose quality we wish to establish. We determine the quantity of x-rays (by means of an r-meter) remaining in the beam after it has passed through copper filters of various thicknesses and plot these data on a graph. From the graph, we find that thickness of copper which reduced the strength of the x-ray beam 50 per cent. For example, if 1 mm of copper is found to reduce the strength of the beam by one-half, then the half value layer of the beam is stated to be 1 mm of copper. Other metals can be used to define half-value layer; for example, in low voltage x-ray therapy the beam quality is usually described in terms of the half value layer in aluminum.

Other methods, such as the equivalent constant potential and the photographic methods, can be used but their application is limited and will not be considered further.

Hard and Soft X-rays

X-rays may be roughly classified on the basis of their average penetrating power as *hard* or *soft*. This is a simple way of expressing the quality of a beam in non-scientific terms:

1. *Hard X-rays.* These have a relatively high penetrating power, and have relatively little absorption in the skin as compared with the interior of the body. Hard x-rays may be produced by:
   a. Higher kilovoltage.
   b. Introduction of filters such as aluminum or copper which absorb relatively more of the less penetrating rays. The higher the atomic number of the filter and the greater its thickness, the greater is its hardening effect on the roentgen beam.
   c. Use of tube targets of high atomic number.

2. *Soft X-rays.* These have relatively low penetrating power, and are absorbed to a great degree in the skin. They may be produced by:

   a. Lower kilovoltage.
   b. Lighter filtration.
   c. Targets of low atomic number.

Quantity of Roentgen Rays

This may be defined as the total amount of ionizing energy at a particular place in the roentgen beam. It must be differentiated from *roentgen intensity* which is a measure of the quantity of radiation delivered in a given unit of time at a given point in the beam. The *quantity of radiation is equal to the intensity multiplied by the time.* Thus, if the intensity is 50 units per minute and the exposure time is 10 minutes, then the quantity of radiation is $50 \times 10 = 500$ units. (The unit of radiation quantity is discussed below.)

One method of measuring quantity is to study the amount of blackening of a photographic film produced by an unknown beam, as compared with the blackening produced by a beam of known amount. This method is subject to error and is not widely used.

The best method of measuring x-ray dosage or quantity for clinical purposes is to determine the amount of ionization an x-ray beam produces in air, since the degree of ionization depends on the amount of radiation *absorbed* under certain controllable conditions. The international unit of radiation dosage or quantity was established on that basis and is called the *roentgen,* usually abbreviated as *r.* One roentgen is defined as *"that amount of x- or gamma radiation such that the associated corpuscular emission per 0.001293 gram of air, produces in air, ions carrying one electrostatic unit of quantity of electricity of either sign."* It may be simply explained as follows. A roentgen is a definite quantity of radiation. When this amount is passed through a standard quantity of air (chosen as 0.001293 g of air, which is really the weight of 1 cc of air at a temperature of 0 C and a pressure of 760 mm mercury) it produces ionization in this volume of air, with the appearance of a certain number of ions and electrons (called corpuscular emission in the definition). Eventually, all the usable energy of the roentgen quantity of radiation is converted to the production of pairs of oppositely charged ions. If these ions are collected separately and measured, it will be found that exactly one electrostatic unit (esu) of electricity of positive or negative sign will have been carried by the ions, if the amount of the original beam was exactly one roentgen. In other words, 1 r of x- or gamma rays causes ionization in 1 cc of air under standard conditions, such that the ions carry 1 esu of electricity. It should be pointed out again that the term *intensity* is not the same as quantity. Intensity is defined as the quantity of radiation delivered in a given period of time; for example, r per minute, or r per second.

In measuring the quantity of radiation of a roentgen beam, the physicist must be careful that his instrument collects and measures all the produced ions, and that ions are not accidentally lost to the surroundings in greater numbers than the ions that accidentally enter from the surroundings. The measuring instrument is very precise and is called a *standard free air ionization chamber*. For practical purposes, as in calibrating the roentgen output of an x-ray therapy unit, one uses a *thimble type ionization chamber* which has been calibrated initially against the more precise type of instrument. The thimble chamber was developed by H. Fricke and O. Glasser, and is incorporated in the Victoreen meter. This device is sufficiently accurate for clinical work and is very convenient and simple to use, but it must be returned to the manufacturer for calibration at regular intervals. It must be borne in mind that its accuracy holds only for a limited range of kilovoltages, and outside this range certain correction factors must be introduced.

The quantity of radiation as measured in roentgens is not necessarily the same as the total quantity of radiant energy in the beam. The former is of more practical value to the radiologist because the *roentgen* quantity of a beam indicates its ionizing ability which, after all, is responsible for biologic and roentgenographic effects. In clinical radiology we specify the strength or practical intensity of x-rays (or gamma rays) by the term *dose-rate*, usually measured in *r per minute*.

The dose-rate of an x-ray beam may be altered by manipulating four factors: (1) milliamperage, (2) kilovoltage, (3) distance (this affects the quantity of radiation in a given cross sectional area of the beam), and (4) filtration.

1. *Milliamperage.* As the amperage in the tube filament circuit is increased, more electrons are liberated at the filament and therefore more will be available to strike the target, increasing the tube current (milliamperage). This results in an increase in the number of rays in the roentgen beam. The radiation dose-rate is directly proportional to the milliamperage, if the other factors remain constant. It should be emphasized that a change in milliamperage does *not* affect the quality.

2. *Kilovoltage.* Radiation dose-rate is increased when the kilovoltage is increased. This is due to an increase in the speed of electrons passing from the cathode to the anode. The resulting x-ray beam has more energy than one produced at lower kilovoltage. Note that an increase in kilovoltage increases both the dose-rate and penetrating power of an x-ray beam, but that this is not directly proportional.

3. *Distance.* In determining x-ray dose-rate, one must specify the distance from the target to the measuring device. The reason for this is that the x-ray beam leaves the tube target in a spreading beam shaped like a cone. The farther the beam is from the target, the fewer the rays in each square centimeter; in other words, the smaller the quantity of radiation per square centimeter. Since the measuring device (for example, thimble chamber) has a fixed size, it will actually measure the amount of radiation in a constant small area of the beam. The amount of radiation measured in this way, in a given interval of time, follows the inverse square law of radiation, which is discussed in detail in Chapter 18.

4. *Filtration.* The dose-rate of radiation in the x-ray beam may be altered by changing the type or thickness of the filter placed in the beam. The thicker the filter and the higher its atomic number, the greater the reduction in the amount of radiation beyond the filter. At the same time, the beam is hardened due to the relatively greater removal of soft than of hard rays by the filter.

THE INTERACTION OF PENETRATING RADIATION
AND MATTER

When a beam of x-rays enters a body of matter, a part of the energy of the beam is *absorbed* and at the same time, penetrating radiations are *emitted from the body in all directions*. The latter constitute the *scattered* and *secondary* radiations and arise from collision of the x-rays in the primary beam with the atoms of the body in the path of the beam. *Secondary radiation* is defined as the radiation *emitted* by the atoms that have been penetrated by x-rays. *Scattered radiation* refers to those rays that have suffered a change of direction after collision with atoms. It is to be noted that the emission of secondary radiation goes hand in hand with x-ray *absorption*. However, some of the x-rays do not collide with atoms but pass through the body unchanged, because these rays are electrically neutral and therefore may penetrate matter for a considerable distance without encountering an atom. This accounts for the fact that a portion of the beam is not absorbed and passes completely through the body.

The various types of collisions between x-rays and atoms form one of the most fascinating chapters in x-ray physics. In order to simplify the discussion, as well as to make it more accurate scientifically, one must assume that an x-ray beam consists of minute, discrete packets or chunks of energy traveling with the speed of light. Such a tiny unit of energy is called a *photon* or *quantum* (pl. quanta). This may seem to contradict the electromagnetic wave theory of radiation discussed earlier, but actually, the phenomena of radiation absorption and emission can be explained only on the assumption that a given x-ray exists at the same time *both as a wave and as a particle of energy*. We can now explain how characteristic radiation is produced in an x-ray tube when an electron drops from a higher to a lower energy level in the atom of the target metal (see Figure 100). Such a characteristic ray is a quantum or photon of energy, and its energy content and wavelength are characteristic of the target element. Thus, an atom of a given element can emit rays of definite characteristic quanta only, and these are different from those of any other element. The amount of energy in a given quantum represents the difference in the energy levels of the orbits between which the electron has jumped.

On the basis of this concept, known as the *quantum theory,* an x-ray beam consists of showers of photons or bullets of energy traveling with the speed of light and having no electric charge. This is also known as the *corpuscular theory of radiation,* and applies equally to other forms of electromagnetic radiation, for example, light and gamma rays.

What determines the amount of energy in a given quantum? It has been found that the quantum energy is directly proportional to the frequency of vibration of its electromagnetic wave. In other words, the quantum represents the energy content of a particular, individual roentgen ray, and depends on its frequency. Max Planck, a German physicist, established the following equation to represent the energy of a quantum:

$$\textbf{quantum energy} = \textbf{a constant} \times \textbf{frequency}$$
$$\mathbf{E = h\,\nu}$$

In this equation, h is known as Planck's constant because it never varies, and the Greek letter ν (nu) represents the frequency of vibration. From this equation, it is evident that the greater the frequency, the greater the quantum energy. This agrees with the observed fact that the penetrating power of x-rays increases as the frequency increases. And since the speed of x-rays is constant and equals frequency times wavelength, an increase in frequency is accompanied by a decrease in wavelength. Thus, highly penetrating x-ray photons have high frequency and short wavelength, while conversely, soft x-rays have low frequency and long wavelength.

Let us now consider in detail what occurs when x-ray photons penetrate a body of matter. There are three main types of interaction: (1) Unmodified Scattering, (2) Photoelectric Collision with True Absorption, and (3) Compton Collision with Scattering Absorption. Each of these will be described separately. It should be noted again that some of the photons pass completely through the body without striking an atom.

1. *Unmodified Scattering.* If an x-ray photon penetrates an atom of matter placed in its path, and happens to glance off the

nucleus or a strongly bound electron, the photon suffers no loss of energy because the atomic mass is tremendous compared with that of a photon. Since the energy of the photon is unchanged it emerges with the same energy as it had when it entered the atom. In other words, the emerging photon has suffered no change in frequency or wavelength, although its direction has been changed as shown in Figure 103. Thus, unmodified scattering merely changes the direction of the photon, but not its hardness. This type of interaction occurs chiefly with elements of higher atomic

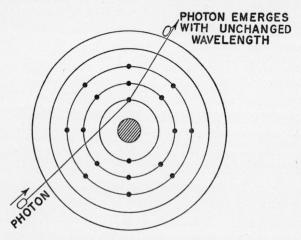

Figure 103. Unmodified scattering. The entering photon has undergone a change of direction only.

number than aluminum. It constitutes but a small fraction of the scattered radiation in clinical radiology.

2. Photoelectric Collision with True Absorption. A high energy photon may enter an atom and collide with an electron in an inner orbit. In so doing, the photon may transfer *all* of its energy to the electron, a part of this energy being used to tear the electron from its orbit, and the remainder to give the electron a high speed and therefore a high kinetic energy. Since all of the photon's energy has been given to the electron, the photon disappears and is said to be absorbed—this constitutes *true absorption* of an x-ray. The electron, on the other hand, now has kinetic energy which it obtained from the photon. This electron emerges from the atom as a part of the secondary radiation and is called a *photoelectron,* this type of photon-electron encounter being called *photoelectric collision.*

Since the atom has absorbed a photon of energy and lost an orbital electron, it is now unstable—excited state—and in order for the atom to become stable again, this vacated space in the orbit must be filled. This is precisely what happens. As soon as the photoelectron is emitted, another electron from a higher energy level, such as one of the outer orbits, jumps into the vacated space in the inner orbit. In so doing, the atom must emit energy since its electron has jumped from a higher to a lower energy level (see Figure 104). In other words, when the atom absorbed energy, it became unstable. To regain its stability it must give off an equal amount of energy. This energy is emitted in the form of a photon and is known as *characteristic radiation* because its quantum energy, and therefore its frequency and wavelength, are typical of a given element. The characteristic photon has less energy than the primary photon (the explanation is too involved to consider here) so that it is softer than the primary ray. In general, a characteristic ray from an atom of a given atomic number will excite characteristic radiation only in atoms of lower atomic number.

Thus, with photoelectric collision, there result two types of secondary radiation: (1) photoelectrons; and (2) characteristic radiation. The photoelectrons, being negatively charged, produce ionization on striking atoms in their path. This is the basic mode of action of penetrating radiations biologically—ionization by secondary or photoelectrons. The characteristic rays are electrically

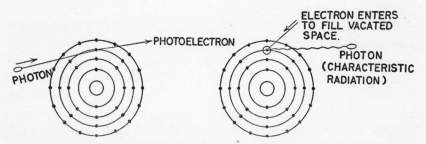

Figure 104. Photoelectric collision with true absorption. All of the energy of the entering photon is used up in dislodging the electron from its orbit and giving it a high speed. The high speed electron is called a photoelectron.

neutral, just as are the primary x-rays, and they therefore produce similar effects; that is, more photoelectrons (now tertiary electrons) and softer characteristic radiation.

3. *Compton Collision with Modified Scattering.* If the entering photon collides with an orbital electron at an angle, it may dislodge the electron and itself continue on in a different direction, as shown in Figure 105. The dislodged electron is called a *Comp-*

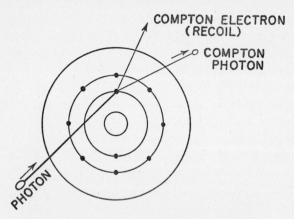

Figure 105. Compton collision with modified scattering. *Part* of the photon's energy has been used up in removing an orbital electron. Therefore, the emerging photon has less energy, and it has also undergone a change in direction.

ton Electron or *Recoil Electron*. It acquires a certain amount of energy which it must subtract from the energy of the entering photon, in accordance with the Law of Conservation of Energy. Consequently, the energy of the primary photon is decreased, and when it emerges from the atom it has a longer wavelength. This phenomenon was discovered in 1922 by Dr. A. H. Compton, a renowned physicist, and is therefore called the *Compton Effect*. The emerging photon which has a changed direction and softer quality is called a *Compton Photon*. These reactions may be simplified as follows:

| energy of primary photon | − | energy given to recoil electron | = | energy of Compton photon |

or

$$h\nu_{\text{primary}} - E_{\text{energy given}} = h\nu_{\text{Compton}}$$

photon   to recoil   photon

electron

From this equation, the frequency of vibration of the Compton photon is seen to be less than that of the primary photon, which accounts for the fact that the Compton photon is softer. These rays, in turn, behave in a similar manner as do other x-rays on colliding with atoms. The recoil electrons cause ionization of atoms just as do photoelectrons. The Compton Effect becomes more pronounced as the tube kilovoltage and the frequency of the primary x-rays are increased. Also, the higher the kilovoltage, the greater the percentage of the Compton photons that are scattered in a forward direction, that is, in a direction approximating that of the incident primary x-ray beam.

In general, one may summarize the foregoing discussion as follows:

Secondary and Scattered Radiation Consists of

1. Electrons dislodged from atomic orbits by collision
   a. Photoelectrons
   b. Compton or recoil electrons
2. Secondary and scattered x-rays
   a. Unmodified scattered
   b. Characteristic
   c. Modified scattered (Compton photons)

The secondary x-rays are softer than the primary, except for the relatively small factor of unmodified scattering. The production of secondary radiation accounts for the absorption of x-radiation by matter, since this removes energy from the primary beam. Photoelectric emission is responsible for true absorption because the incoming photon is completely absorbed. When a filter is used to harden a beam of x-rays, it does so because secondary radiation is set up in the filter and relatively more of the softer rays than the harder rays are used up in the process. In other words, the filter does not act as a sieve, but rather it absorbs a greater proportion of soft rays than of hard rays, so that the emerging beam retains a relatively greater percentage of hard rays. If a copper filter is used, it emits a certain amount of soft characteristic radiation of its own. This is absorbed by placing a secondary filter made of aluminum in the path of the beam. The aluminum also emits characteristic rays, but these are so soft that they are absorbed by a few centimeters of air.

Detection of X-rays

There is a number of ways in which the presence of roentgen rays may be detected, though not necessarily measured.

1. *Photographic Effect*—the ability of x-rays to affect a photographic emulsion so that it can be developed chemically.

2. *Fluorescent Effect*—the ability of x-rays to cause certain materials to glow in the dark. Such materials include calcium sulfide, barium platinocyanide, calcium tungstate, and barium lead sulfate.

3. *Ionizing Effect*—the ability of x-rays to ionize gases and discharge certain electrical instruments such as the electroscope.

4. *Physiologic Effect*—the ability of x-rays to redden the skin, destroy tissues, and sterilize reproductive organs.

5. *Chemical Effect*—the ability of x-rays to change the color of certain dyes.

ROENTGEN RAY DOSAGE

The tissue effect of penetrating radiations is believed to be due to the ionization produced in the tissues by the primary and secondary rays. The greater the amount of energy absorbed, the greater the tissue effect. The changes in the tissues depend on the number and distribution of the ions produced. In general, the degree of ionization depends on the quantity of radiation reaching a given point in the tissues. It is recognized that more hard than soft radiation is needed for a given effect on the tissues, such as the development of skin reddening (erythema). The reason for this is uncertain, but it is believed to be due to the differences in distribution of the ions produced by secondary radiation from x-rays of different degrees of hardness.

To specify radiation dosage, we make use of the unit described above—the roentgen (r). This indicates the *quantity* of radiation being delivered to the particular area. In addition, we must state the *quality* of the beam. This is usually done by indicating the treatment factors, including the kilovoltage applied to the x-ray tube, the filtration, and the half value layer. The milliamperage, time, and distance are also usually included, but these have no bearing on the quality of the roentgen beam. The total duration of a therapy course in terms of days or weeks has a distinct bearing on the effect of treatment, since a given number of roentgens administered at one sitting has a much more pronounced tissue effect than does the same dosage fractionated over a period of days or weeks. Thus, we may state that specification of roentgen therapy on the basis of the number of roentgens administered, the quality of the beam, and the fractionation of the treatments gives us an idea as to the biologic effects we may anticipate.

It may be of interest to point out that the radiation varies in quantity from point to point as it passes from the skin into the deeper tissues. The amount is usually maximal on or near the skin, the skin dose being the sum of the quantity of the primary beam *at this point,* plus the quantity of the secondary radiation scattered back from the underlying tissues (backscatter). As the primary beam passes into the depths, it becomes progressively weaker because of absorption and increasing distance from the x-ray source. The *tissue dose* is defined as the quantity of radiation, in r, at a given point in the tissues. The tumor dose is the radiation quantity, in r, at the level of the tumor being treated. The *depth dose percentage* is the ratio of the roentgen exposure at a stated distance below the skin, to the exposure on the skin, multiplied by 100.

$$\text{depth dose \% at x cm} = \frac{\text{r at point x cm below skin} \times 100}{\text{r on the skin}}$$

If the roentgen output of the therapy machine with a given set of treatment factors has first been determined by measurement with an ionization chamber, this can be converted to skin dosage by referring to appropriate tables. The depth dose percentage under the stated conditions at the desired depth below the skin is also found in tables. The tissue or *tumor dose in roentgens* is then obtained by simply multiplying the skin dose by the appropriate depth dose percentage and dividing by 100. In general, the depth dosage *increases* with an *increase* in Kv, distance, filtration, and area of treatment field.

QUESTIONS

1. What are roentgen rays? What are the two apparently contradictory theories as to their nature?
2. What is the relationship of wavelength and frequency of roentgen rays?
3. How do soft rays differ from hard rays?
4. What are the four essential components of a modern x-ray tube?
5. State and discuss briefly the fundamental principles in the production of roentgen rays in an x-ray tube.
6. What is characteristic radiation and how does it arise?
7. Of what does the primary beam consist?
8. Name ten properties of roentgen rays.
9. What is meant by the quality of roentgen radiation? What determines it? How can it be measured?
10. Explain fully why a beam of roentgen rays emerging from the target is heterogeneous.
11. What are monochromatic x-rays?
12. Define and explain briefly half-value layer.
13. How is the quantity of roentgen radiation measured?
14. What are the factors influencing the dose-rate of radiation in a roentgen beam?
15. Discuss the three types of interactions of x-rays and matter, showing how the corpuscular theory of radiation applies.
16. Of what do scattered and secondary radiations consist?
17. How does a filter work?

13 *MODERN X-RAY TUBES*
RADIOGRAPHIC TUBES
THERAPY TUBES
VALVE TUBES

General

It should be recalled from the preceding chapter that roentgen rays are produced when a stream of fast-moving electrons undergoes a sudden deceleration or loss of speed. This is accomplished by the use of *thermionic vacuum tubes,* more commonly called hot filament or Coolidge tubes. Before considering the construction details of such tubes, one must have clearly in mind the principles underlying their operation. The main features of hot filament tubes are as follows:

1. *A hot filament cathode* which is the source of thermionic emission of electrons when heated by the separate filament current. The amount of emission increases with the temperature of the filament, which depends on the filament current. The heating current in the filament constitutes the *filament current* measured in amperes.

2. *If no kilovoltage is applied,* the emitted electrons remain in the vicinity of the filament, forming an electron cloud.

3. *If a kilovoltage is applied* between the cathode and anode, the electrons are driven over to the anode by the large potential difference. The average speed of the electrons increases as the kilovoltage is increased. The flow of electrons across the gap between the cathode and anode constitutes the *tube current* measured in milliamperes.

4. *If the electron speed is great enough,* x-rays are produced when the electrons strike the anode, their energy being converted to heat (99.8 per cent) and x-rays (0.2 per cent).

All modern x-ray tubes consist basically of a *hot filament cathode,* an *anode* made of high atomic weight metal, *two circuits* to provide for heating of the filament and for driving electrons to the anode, and a *glass envelope* which contains a high vacuum. These are fundamentally *thermionic tubes*. There are, however, certain characteristic features of tubes which adapt them to special purposes. We shall consider separately the structural features of roentgen diagnostic tubes, therapy tubes, and valve tubes.

ROENTGENOGRAPHIC TUBES

These tubes are designed for the express purpose of making x-ray examinations of various parts of the body. The essential components of modern diagnostic x-ray tubes will be considered in turn.

Glass Envelope

The working parts of the tube are surrounded by a glass container or *envelope* in which a high vacuum has been produced. In modern tubes, this envelope is usually cylindrical in shape. The entire tube is immersed in insulating oil within a metal casing. This makes it possible to manufacture smaller tubes than would be possible without the use of such insulating oil, because the oil prevents spark-over of the high voltage between the terminals.

Cathode

This consists of the *filament* and the surrounding metal which supports and houses it. Loosely speaking, the terms "cathode" and "filament" are used interchangeably. The filament is made in the form of a small coil of tungsten wire, the same metal which is used in the manufacture of electric light bulb filaments. The filament in most diagnostic tubes measures about 0.2 cm in diameter and 1 cm or less in length. It is mounted on two stout wires which support it and also carry electric current to it. These wires lead through one end of the glass envelope so that they can be connected to the proper electrical source (see Figure 106). A low voltage current is applied through the wires to provide the *filament current* which heats the filament, and one of the wires is *also* connected to one end of the high tension transformer to provide high voltage for propelling the electrons towards the anode at great speed. The filament is backed by a negatively charged concave molybdenum cup which tends to confine the electrons to a narrow beam so that they are focused on a tiny spot when they strike the anode.

The filament current, used to heat the filament and provide a source of electrons within the tube, usually operates at about 10 volts and about 3 to 5 amperes. This current is supplied to the filament by its supporting wires. If the filament current is increased, the temperature of the filament is raised and consequently more electrons are released from it.

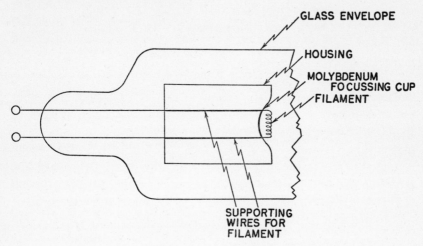

Figure 106. Details of the cathode of an x-ray tube.

With prolonged use, the filament gradually becomes thinner because of *evaporation of its metal,* especially during short, intense exposures. As the filament decreases in diameter, its electrical resistance increases and it becomes hotter at a given value of filament current. This results in a greater release of electrons and a higher milliamperage through the tube than would be anticipated for a given filament amperage. To avoid this error, the amperage settings should be checked from time to time against the resulting milliamperage and any corrections noted. It will be found that *as the tube ages, a progressively lower filament current setting is required for a desired tube milliamperage.*

Some tubes, such as those used in portable equipment, have a single filament. In most modern diagnostic roentgen ray tubes, however, there are *two filaments* which are mounted side by side. One is smaller than the other, and a switch is provided in the control equipment to select one or the other filament as the electron source. These produce focal spots of two different sizes on the anode, giving rise to the designation *double focal spot tube*. Note that *only one filament* is used for any given x-ray exposure. The two filaments are mounted on three supporting wires, one of which is connected in common with both filaments (see Figure 107). In the diagram, if terminals 1 and 3 are connected to the low voltage source, the large filament lights up. If, instead, terminals 2 and 3 are connected to the low voltage source, the small filament lights

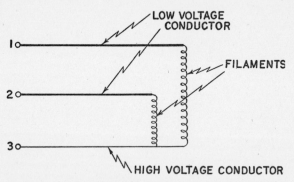

Figure 107. Simplified diagram of the connection of two filaments of an x-ray tube (double focal spot tube) to three wires, one of which is common to both filaments.

up. The high voltage is applied through wire 3 so that it will be common to both filaments and provide either one with a high negative potential.

Anode

There are two types of anodes employed today: (1) stationary, and (2) rotating.

1. *Stationary Anode.* The anode is separated from the cathode by a distance of a few centimeters. The anode is constructed of a block of copper in which is imbedded a small button of tungsten. These metals are selected for definite reasons. First, the tungsten is so placed that the electron beam strikes it in full force, forming the actual target of the x-ray tube. Since more than 99 per cent of the electrons' energy is converted to heat at the target, and since tungsten has a high melting point—about 3400 C—it is the metal

of choice for this purpose. It also has a high atomic number, which favors the production of x-rays of greater penetrating power (short wavelength). In the second place, copper is a better conductor of heat than is tungsten and it therefore conducts heat away more rapidly, thereby protecting the tungsten target from overheating, within certain limits, of course. The heating capacity of the tube can be further increased by circulating water, oil, or air around the anode. This permits heavier exposure than would otherwise be possible.

The area of the target bombarded by the stream of electrons is known as the *focal spot*. As will be shown later, the sharpness of the radiographic image is enhanced by employing the *smallest* practicable focal spot. Consequently, radiographic tubes require extremely fine focal spots, obtained by the use of a fine filament and a molybdenum focusing cup as described above. However, as the focal spot is decreased in size, there is a greater concentration of heat in the focal spot with resultant danger of more easily overloading the tube and melting the target. Tubes are manufactured so that the focal spot is small enough to give satisfactory radiographic detail, and at the same time not so small as to endanger the practical usefulness of the tube.

Stationary anodes are now constructed on the *line-focus principle*. The purpose of this is to obtain a focal spot which is smaller when projected towards the film, than is the actual focal spot on the target. This permits heavier exposure and at the same time provides a relatively fine focal spot effect. This principle can best be explained by a diagram as shown in Figure 108. In the diagram, the actual focal spot area on the target is a rectangle as shown in A. Assume this rectangle to measure about 2 mm × 4 mm. In B, the side view of the tube, it is noted that the target is inclined, making an angle of 17° to 20° with the vertical. Since the film is to be placed at some distance directly below the target, the *effective focal spot* area from the standpoint of the film is only D which is about 2 mm × 2 mm. Perhaps it would become clearer if one were to imagine himself lying down in the position of the film and looking upwards at the target—the focal spot would appear to the eye as a small square rather than as a rectangle. In other words, the focal spot is foreshortened, just as a pencil appears shorter when held at an angle with the eyes, than it is when held parallel to the eyes.

The usual modern stationary anode tube has effective focal areas of 2 mm × 2 mm and 4 mm × 4 mm but other sizes are available.

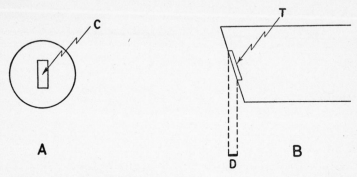

Figure 108. Line-focus principle. In A is shown the anode in face view, with the rectangular focal spot at its center. In B is shown the anode as seen from the side. C is the actual size of the focal spot. D is the projected or effective size of the focal spot relative to the film placed below.

2. *Rotating Anode.* Since 1936, there has been on the market a type of anode of revolutionary design—the *rotating anode.* As the name implies, this anode is attached to the shaft of a small induction motor and *rotates during an x-ray exposure.* This anode consists of a disc of tungsten measuring about 3 inches in diameter and having a beveled edge. It may or may not be backed by a heavy block of copper, but the latter definitely increases the rate of heat dissipation and the heat storage capacity of the tube, allowing for high energy exposures in short exposure times. The cathode is so placed that the electron beam strikes the anode on its beveled edge, as shown in Figure 109. The beveled edge is inclined so that the line-focus principle may be taken advantage of. The stator of the induction motor is outside the tube while the rotor is inside, connected to the anode. Self-lubricating ball bearings coated with *metallic barium or silver* reduce friction in the rotor mechanism, thereby prolonging the life of the tube.

How does such an anode operate? The target rotates during the radiographic exposure when it is bombarded by the electrons com-

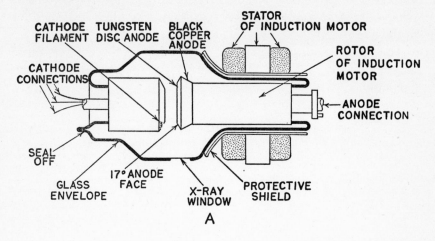

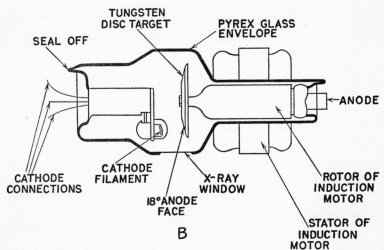

Figure 109. Rotating anode tubes. A is the General Electric tube model *CRT*. B is the Machlett *Dynamax* type tube.

ing from the filament. As it rotates, it is constantly "turning a new face" to the electron beam, so that the energy of the beam is not concentrated at one point, as in the stationary anode, but its heating effect is spread over a considerable area on the face of the anode. However, the effective focal spot remains constant in position relative to the film because of the extremely smooth motion of the anode. As a result of this ingenious device, it is possible to have effective focal spots of 1 mm × 1 mm, the smallest practicable today,* and it is also possible to pass very high milliamperage through the tube. For instance, with a stationary anode, the upper limit of milliamperage for a 4 mm focal spot is 200, whereas with a rotating anode, the upper limit for a 2 mm focal spot is 500 Ma, the maximum exposure time being approximately the same in both cases. The rotating anode tube usually has two filaments to provide 1 and 2 mm focal spots. The smaller spot is used for very fine detail, while the larger spot is usually employed at high milliamperage and extremely short exposure time in order to eliminate motion during radiography.

It is apparent, from the above discussion, that the trend has been constantly in the direction of obtaining smaller and smaller focal spots to improve radiographic sharpness, and at the same time increasing the capacity of the roentgen ray tube for heavy exposures. The acme has been reached in the double focus, rotating anode tube.

Saturation Current

All roentgen ray tubes (with the exception of valve tubes) are said to operate *near the saturation current*. What does this mean? It may be recalled that the filament has a *separate* heating or filament circuit, and that the temperature of the filament depends on the amperage flowing through it. At any given temperature, there is a corresponding rate of emission of electrons from the filament. Suppose that at this given temperature of the filament, a low kilovoltage is applied across the tube. A certain proportion of the emitted electrons will be driven to the target. Now, if the kilovoltage is gradually raised it will be found that the number of electrons per second moving to the anode increases—that is, the tube current or milliamperage increases. Finally, a point is reached where all of the emitted electrons are being driven to the anode as rapidly as they appear, so that further increase in kilovoltage does not increase the number of electrons reaching the target. This

---

* The North American Philips Company, Inc., has recently announced a new rotating anode tube with a 0.3 mm focal spot. Because of the minute size of this focal spot, enlargement radiographs with good detail can be made of any part that can be immobilized. At present, this focal spot cannot withstand short, high energy exposures.

particular milliamperage is known as the *saturation current*. Refer now to Figure 110. At filament current I_1 amperes, an increase in the kilovoltage increases the tube current gradually until the point marked by the arrow is reached. Further increase in kilovoltage does not increase the tube current, which is now represented by the horizontal part of the curve. If the filament current is raised successively to values I_2, I_3, and I_4, similar curves are obtained.

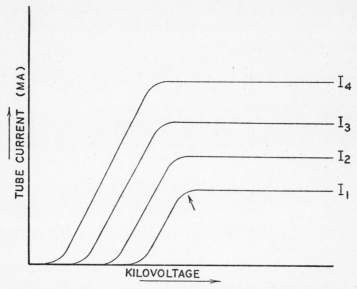

Figure 110. These curves represent the relationship of tube current (milliamperage) to kilovoltage at different values of filament current I_1, I_2, I_3, and I_4. The horizontal portions of the curves represent the saturation current in the tube for the stated value of filament current. Note that under saturation conditions, the milliamperage does not change when the kilovoltage is increased.

The *saturation current may therefore be defined as the maximum tube current obtainable at a given filament current.* The lowest kilovoltage across the tube that will drive this saturation current is the *saturation voltage.* This would allow one to vary the kilovoltage independently of the milliamperage, thereby greatly facilitating roentgenographic technique, because *under saturation conditions,* a change in kilovoltage would not produce a significant corresponding change in milliamperage. The milliamperage could then be increased only by increasing the filament current—that is, the amperage through the filament.

In actual practice, however, an x-ray tube deviates from saturation conditions when milliamperage is greater than 50. The cause of this variation from the ideal, is the occurrence of a phenomenon called *space charge effect*. This can be simply described as follows: the electrons emitted by the heated filament tend to repel or hold back other electrons that are just about to be emitted (like charges repel). At low filament temperatures, this effect is negligible. However, at higher temperatures many more electrons are emitted and these have a definite inhibitory effect on the emission of additional electrons; in other words, there is a sort of electron traffic congestion. The result is that as the kilovoltage across the tube is increased, the milliamperage is also increased because the space charge electrons are pulled away to the anode at a faster rate and the traffic congestion is alleviated. Or, conversely, as the kilovoltage is increased, a lower filament current is required to obtain a desired tube current (milliamperage). The space charge effect is manifested to a greater degree as the filament current is increased and is very pronounced at the amperage required to supply a 500 Ma tube current. In fact, a protective compensator is introduced to correct for the space charge effect, otherwise the tube would be ruined by excessive milliamperage. *The space charge compensator automatically decreases the filament current as the kilovoltage is raised so that the correct tube current is maintained.*

Tube Rating Charts

In the operation of x-ray equipment, the high milliamperages used for diagnostic work place a heavy load on the tube. Most roentgenographic tube failures are due to "burning out" the *filament*. This can result from application of excessive amperage to the filament, which raises its temperature beyond safe limits; or it can result from prolonged heating of the filament at normal amperage, just as an electric light bulb filament burns out after a certain period of normal use. In some modern installations, a special booster circuit is introduced into the filament circuit; this allows the filament to be activated by a low amperage until the x-ray exposure is made. At this instant, the booster circuit automatically raises the filament current to the correct level so that the correct filament temperature is attained. This is of greatest importance in prolonging tube life when high milliamperage technics are employed. It is to be noted that relatively few tube failures are due to damage to the *target* by overloading with excessively high kilovoltage or long exposure times. In general, one should observe the following rule: when one wishes to increase a radiographic exposure, there is less load on the tube by increasing the kilovoltage than by increasing the milliamperage-time factor, provided the safe exposure limits of the tube are not exceeded.

How can one determine the safe limits within which a tube can be operated? This can easily be found by referring to the chart provided by the manufacturer for the particular tube. This chart indicates the maximum safe factors of kilovoltage, time, and milliamperage for a single exposure. Figure 111 illustrates such a *tube-rating chart*. This chart is entirely fictitious and should not be applied to any x-ray tube; it is used here only my way of an example. In this chart, it is noted that there is a series of lines representing various milliampere values of tube current. The vertical axis of

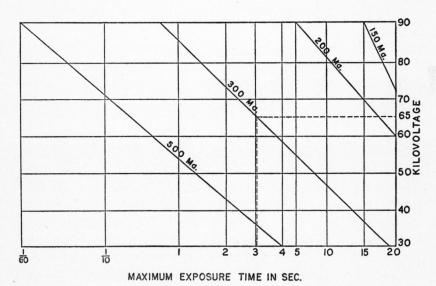

MAXIMUM EXPOSURE TIME IN SEC.

Figure 111. Tube rating chart, arbitrary values. The chart for any particular tube must be obtained from the manufacturer.

the graph represents Kv, and the horizontal represents maximum safe exposure time. The use of this chart is very simple. Assume that it was provided for the particular tube of *given focal spot size,* and with a *given type of rectification.* Suppose we wish to make an exposure using 300 Ma and 65 Kv, and we wish to determine the maximum allowable exposure time. Start at 65 on the vertical axis and follow horizontally from this point to the point where it meets the 300 Ma oblique line. Then start at this point of intersection and follow vertically down to the horizontal line which it crosses at 3 sec. The maximum exposure time with these factors is therefore 3 sec, and if a longer time were to be used, the tube would most probably be damaged.

It must be emphasized here that the chart only applies to a stated type of rectification. With half-wave rectification, the maximum safe exposure time is less than with full-wave rectification. If one has a double focal spot tube, the graph for the particular size focal spot must be used, since a small focal spot has a shorter safe exposure time than a large spot. Finally, the charts are different for a "hot" tube than for a "cold" tube, because once a tube has been heated by a number of exposures, a subsequent exposure will have a lower safe maximum time than if the tube has been allowed to cool.

When numerous exposures are made, especially in a short period of time, consideration must be given to the ability of the anode to store and to dissipate heat. This is measured in *heat units,* which are defined by the following equation:

$$\text{Heat Units (H.U.)} = \text{Kv} \times \text{Ma} \times \text{Sec}$$

The *heat storage capacity* of the anodes of various diagnostic tubes ranges from about 100,000 H.U. to about 250,000 H.U., depending on the size of the anode and the ease with which it transfers heat to its surroundings. The cooling characteristics of a tube are designated as the *heat dissipation rate,* which must be determined from cooling curves supplied by the manufacturer of that particular tube. After the tube has been heated to its full storage capacity by a number of exposures, the safety of further exposures is governed by the heat dissipation rate. Suppose a number of chest radiographs are to be made in rapid succession, requiring on the average an exposure of 70 Kv, 100 Ma, and 0.1 sec. The heat units developed per exposure would be obtained by the above equation as follows:

$$H.U. = 70 \times 100 \times 0.1$$
$$H.U. = 700$$

If the cooling curve of the tube shows that it can discharge heat at the rate of 20,000 H.U. per minute, divide 20,000 by 700 = about 27 exposures per minute as the safe maximum. Obviously, this number is beyond the realm of possibility in ordinary roentgenography, but it assumes major importance in mass chest surveys where frequent and heavy exposures are required. In brief, for ordinary radiography the customary tube-rating chart has the greatest practical value, whereas in photofluorographic mass surveys and in extremely busy x-ray departments the heat storage capacity and the heat dissipation rate must be taken into account.

The equation defining heat unit storage can be applied to demonstrate that an x-ray tube operates more efficiently at higher kilovoltages. For example, a given radiographic technic calls for an exposure of 60 Kv, 100 Ma, and 1 sec. Such an exposure would develop the following number of heat units in the anode:

$$H.U. = 60 \times 100 \times 1$$
$$H.U. = 6000$$

If the kilovoltage is increased by 10 and the time reduced one-half, the exposure would remain practically the same, but now let us see how many heat units would be developed in the anode:

$$H.U. = 70 \times 100 \times \frac{1}{2}$$
$$H.U. = 3500$$

Thus, by using a higher kilovoltage the heat units developed in the anode have been decreased almost one-half, even though the exposure has remained almost constant.

With minor degrees of overloading of the tube, tiny depressions appear in the target, a process known as *pitting*. Excessive pitting may reduce the roentgen output of the tube.

After prolonged use of a roentgen tube, the glass aperture, which lies in the path of the x-ray beam, becomes purple due to a chemical change produced in the glass. This does not affect the output of the tube.

Under ordinary conditions of radiography, accessory means of cooling an x-ray tube are not employed. However, when a heavy load is to be applied as in mass radiography of the chest or in high voltage radiography, tube life can be prolonged and its efficiency improved by means of a small fan built into the tube housing to circulate air around the tube. Some diagnostic tubes are provided with internal oil or water circulating systems to improve heat dissipation. One type of tube called the "superdynamax" has an oversize rotating anode with a 35 per cent greater surface area than in conventional rotating anodes; this results in a considerable increase in the heat storage capacity and heat dissipation rate of the anode.

ROENTGEN THERAPY TUBES

These are x-ray tubes constructed for the purpose of treating various diseases. Such tubes operate at relatively low milliamperage values of tube current, and they are manufactured in various models, depending on the kilovoltage range to be applied.

In roentgen ray therapy there are four main kilovoltage ranges to provide x-rays especially suitable for treatment at different depths in the body.

1. *Low Voltage.* This includes a range of about 50 to 120 Kv and is used to treat lesions in the skin. It is also known as *superficial therapy*.

2. *Intermediate Voltage.* This is about 130 to 160 Kv and is employed mainly in treating lesions a few centimeters below the skin surface.

3. *High Voltage.* The usual range is 200 to 250 Kv. This provides x-rays of relatively high penetrating power and is applied in deep x-ray therapy for treatment of lesions deep within the body.

4. *Supervoltage.* This ranges upwards from 400 Kv and the specially designed tubes for this type of equipment will not be considered here.

The construction of therapy tubes is essentially similar to that of diagnostic tubes, but in the therapy tube the filament is usually larger, the anode is always stationary, and the focal spot is larger because a relatively large beam is desirable. The anode consists of a tungsten mass imbedded in a large block of copper; and its face is usually inclined at an angle of 45 degrees in order to provide a beam of uniform intensity. As in the case of diagnostic tubes, the therapy tubes have a separate filament current to heat the filament and produce an electron cloud; and a high voltage current to drive the electrons to the target at high speed.

Since there may be a tremendous amount of heat developed in the target, especially at higher kilovoltages, special means of cooling the tube must be provided. In superficial therapy tubes, the cooling of the anode may be enhanced by circulating air, water, or oil around the anode. In intermediate therapy tubes, oil or water is circulated. In deep therapy tubes, oil must be pumped around the anode and a separate means of cooling the oil is often provided; this can be accomplished by piping the hot oil into a cooling unit around coils in which cold water circulates so that the water cools the oil which in turn has cooled the anode. Formerly, deep therapy tubes were cooled by circulating air, but modern tubes are oil-cooled.

The oil serves another purpose. It is highly refined and of special composition so that it has superb insulating qualities. The use of such insulating oils reduces the size of the housing in which the tube is mounted, thereby making the unit less bulky and more easily maneuverable. This is of distinct value in deep therapy equipment. In some therapy units, the tube and transformer are mounted in the same casing; this is called a *self-contained* unit.

VALVE TUBES

The use of valve tubes in rectification has already been described. They are vacuum tubes having the same general construction as x-ray tubes, but differing in certain details because of their specific requirements. These peculiar structural features will now be considered.

Cathode

The filament consists of a coil of tungsten wire which is longer and larger in diameter than the filament of a roentgen ray tube. In the General Electric Kenotron type of tube, the filament is placed in the longitudinal axis of the tube. It is supported by a large spiral made of molybdenum, as shown in Figure 112. In the Machlett type valve tube, the filament axis is transverse (see Figure 113). The filament of a valve tube is heated through its own filament circuit, and there is also a connection with the high tension circuit. Thus, the valve tube has two circuits just as does a roentgen ray tube.

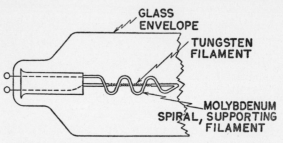

Figure 112. Cathode of a Kenetron type valve tube.

Anode

The valve tube anode has a *large surface,* and may be in the shape of a *cylinder* (resembling a metal can). It surrounds the filament, so that the electrons are drawn to its entire surface when it is in operation. This type of anode is used in the Kenotron tube. The Machlett valve tube employs a large anode facing the filament (see Figure 113).

Principles of Operation

Unlike the x-ray tube, a *valve tube does not normally operate near saturation conditions, but at a point well below saturation.* The large filament, when heated by its filament current, emits a generous cloud of electrons, and when the high voltage is applied to the tube, a large stream of electrons is driven towards the anode. As the kilovoltage is increased, more of the emitted electrons pass to the anode, and as the kilovoltage is decreased, fewer electrons pass to the anode. Because of the superabundance of electrons, the electrical resistance of such a tube is relatively small, and there is normally a very small drop in kilovoltage across the valve tube; for example, with a 500 Ma tube current in the roent-

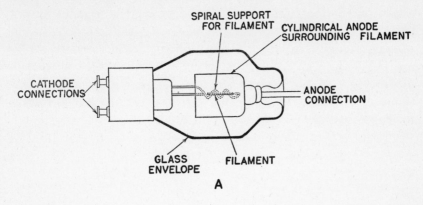

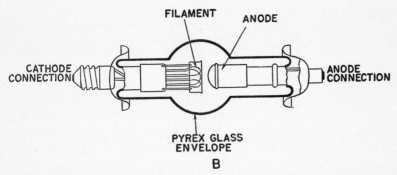

Figure 113. Two leading styles of valve tubes. A is a diagram of a General
Electric Kenetron. B represents a Machlett valve tube.

gen ray tube, there should be a drop of only 3 Kv in the valve
tube. Since the speed of the electrons in the tube varies with the
amount of kilovolt drop across the tube, it is evident that the electrons do not gain considerable speed with a drop of only 3 Kv,
and therefore have insufficient energy to produce roentgen rays.
That is why, under proper conditions of operation, there are no
appreciable roentgen rays emerging from a valve tube. If there
should develop some defect in the valve tube that would increase
its resistance, there might be sufficient drop in kilovoltage across it
to develop high speed electrons which would give rise to roentgen
radiation; and at the same time, a large fall in kilovoltage across
the valve tube would decrease the kilovoltage remaining for the
operation of the roentgen ray tube.

It must be borne in mind that the milliamperage through a valve tube must be equal to that flowing in the x-ray tube because they are connected in series and all parts of a series circuit carry an identical current. We have shown in an earlier chapter that current is defined as the rate of flow of electricity. One may say that an electric current represents the flow of a certain number of electrons per second. During operation, there is the same number of electrons per second passing from cathode to anode in the roentgen ray tube as in the valve tube. But in the valve tube, the electrons move less rapidly and in a larger group, while in an x-ray tube the same number of electrons moves in smaller groups, but at a very high rate of speed. An example may help to clarify this. Suppose that in the valve tube 1 trillion electrons were passing to the anode in one second; each electron moves slowly but at the end of the second, 1 trillion have reached the anode. Now, consider 1 trillion electrons being produced by the filament of an x-ray tube. Under the large kilovoltage drop, each one moves at very high speed, taking only a tiny fraction of a second to reach the anode, but at the end of a second, 1 trillion have reached the anode, the same number as in the valve tube. In this case, however, each electron travels at a much greater speed than the electrons in the valve tube.

The valve tubes are placed within the oil in the transformer casing since this affords protection from roentgen radiation that might be emitted if there should be valve tube failure resulting in a decrease in electron emission and development of saturation conditions in the valve tube. Furthermore, this arrangement decreases the bulkiness of the x-ray apparatus, at the same time making the valve tube assembly shockproof.

One should regularly check the equipment to be sure that all of the valve tubes are operating satisfactorily. It is possible to determine this merely by watching the milliammeter, because the milliamperage will fall below normal for a given filament current if one of the valve tubes is out of order. Under these conditions, there is definite danger of overloading and blowing the x-ray tube because of the following facts. The milliammeter registers only an *average value* of milliamperage, while actually, with full-wave rectification, the *peak* milliamperage is about one and one-half times the milliammeter reading. Now, if one valve tube in a full-wave rectified circuit fails, we have in effect a half-wave rectified circuit. By increasing the filament current, we can obtain the same *average milliamperage* through the tube as we had with full-wave rectification, but now the peak milliamperage will be *much greater* than the average and may even exceed the capacity of the tube. The danger is that the x-ray tube is on half-wave rectification without our being aware of it, and since its capacity is less under this condition, the tube may be overloaded and damaged.

The simplest method of testing for competence of the valve tubes is the so-called *spinning top method*. This is a flat metal top which has a small hole punched near one edge. It is placed on an x-ray film and made to spin, while an x-ray exposure of ⅒ sec is made. If all four valve tubes are functioning properly, the circuit is fully rectified and there will be 120 pulsations per sec and 120 corresponding peaks of x-ray output (on 60 cycle current). Therefore, in ⅒ sec there will be 12 peaks and the image of the spinning top on the x-ray film will show 12 spots, as in Figure 114A. If only six dark spots are present on the image of the top, this indicates that there were only six pulsations in ⅒ sec or 60 pulsations per

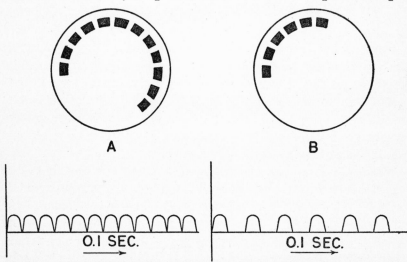

Figure 114. Spinning top test. In A the radiograph of the spinning top shows 12 spots in ⅒ sec, representing 120 pulsations; this is full-wave rectification. In B there are 6 spots in ⅒ sec, representing 60 pulsations; this is half-wave rectification.

sec, which is proof that the circuit is half-wave rectified and one or more valve tubes have failed. The spinning top may be used in a similar way to test the accuracy of the roentgen ray exposure timer.

QUESTIONS

1. Describe the main features of a thermionic tube.
2. Compare the structural details of diagnostic tubes, therapy tubes, and valve tubes.
3. Describe with the aid of a diagram, a double focus, stationary anode tube.
4. What effect does evaporation of the filament have on tube operation? How is it corrected?
5. What are the advantages of a rotating anode tube?
6. Describe the line focus principle, and discuss its importance in roentgenography.
7. What is meant by saturation current? Saturation voltage?
8. How does the "space charge effect" influence the operation of a tube? How does a change in filament current affect the space charge?
9. Using the chart in Figure 111, determine the maximum safe exposure time at 70 Kv and 500 Ma.
10. Discuss the importance of heat storage and heat dissipation rates.
11. Why does a roentgen ray tube have a greater capacity with full-wave rectification than with half-wave rectification?
12. Compare the values of peak milliamperage and milliammeter readings, with full-wave and half-wave rectification.
13. Show by a labeled diagram the construction of a valve tube. Why must it operate below saturation conditions?
14. Compare the current flowing in an x-ray tube and valve tube connected in the same circuit. Compare the kilovolt drop in each.
15. How are deep therapy tubes cooled?
16. Describe the spinning top method, and state two uses for the method.
17. What are the main causes of x-ray tube failure? How can this be minimized?

The major items of an x-ray unit have been considered in some detail, but they have been discussed individually without definite relation to each other. There now remains the task of combining these major pieces of equipment so that they will constitute an x-ray machine. A number of auxiliary devices are necessary for the proper operation of roentgen equipment, and these will be described in order.

Source of Electricity

The electric current is brought to the *pole transformer* outside the building, at high voltage. This transformer, which is mounted atop a pole, is a step-down transformer. It reduces the voltage coming from the power house to 110 or 220 volts, depending on the type of equipment it is to supply. This voltage, entering the radiology department, is designated the *line voltage.*

The current is conducted into the building most often by a *three-wire system.* The two outside wires are "hot" while the middle wire is "grounded" (neutral). The voltage between the two outside wires is 220, while the voltage between either outside wire and the middle one is 110 volts. This is illustrated as a simple diagram in Figure 115. If a 220-volt line is needed in the installation of x-ray equipment, the two hot wires are used to supply the current. On the other hand, if one wishes to obtain current at 110 volts for ordinary lighting purposes, the neutral wire and one hot wire are used as the source of current. The 110-volt source is also used in operating small x-ray units.

It must be emphasized that the incoming supply is *alternating current.* Moreover, the current feeding the primary coil of the x-ray transformer must be alternating, because we have already seen that a transformer will operate only on alternating current. If the source of supply is limited to direct current, it must first be converted to alternating current before it can be used to operate an x-ray unit.

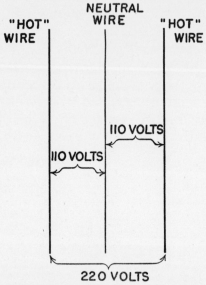

Figure 115. Three-wire system which brings electric power into the building. By connecting the electrical appliance or equipment to the appropriate wires as indicated, one may obtain 110 or 220 volts.

The Main X-ray Circuits

In order to understand more easily the electrical connections of an x-ray unit, one may conveniently divide the circuit at the x-ray transformer. That part of the circuit which is connected to the primary side of the transformer is called the *primary* or *low voltage* circuit, while that part which is connected to the secondary coil is called the *secondary* or *high voltage* circuit. This scheme is perfectly natural, since the two coils of the transformer are electrically insulated from each other, and since the great difference in voltage in the two circuits requires separate consideration. It should be mentioned that some parts of the equipment are connected to both the low and high voltage sides.

1. *Primary Circuit.* This portion of the circuit includes all the equipment that is connected at any point between the electrical

source and the primary coil of the x-ray transformer. Each essential component will be considered in order.

a. *Main Switch.* This is usually a double blade, single throw switch, illustrated in Figure 116.

b. *Fuses.* Each wire leading from the main switch has in series with it a *fuse.* This consists of an insulated cylinder with a metal cap at each end, in the center of which lies a strip of easily-melted metal joining the caps. If the circuit is overloaded and the amperage rises to a high level, the metal strip within the fuse melts due to the heating effect of the high current, and breaks the circuit.

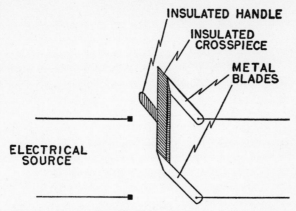

Figure 116. Double-blade single-throw switch. When the switch is closed towards the left the metal blades contact the corresponding wire and the circuit is completed to the x-ray machine.

Figure 117 shows the construction of such a fuse, and also its connection in the circuit. Fuses protect the equipment and also avoid fire hazard. This type of fuse can be replaced easily, since it is held in position by two spring jaws at each end.

c. *Autotransformer.* This has been discussed in detail in Chapter 10. Its function is to vary the voltage fed to the primary of the transformer, so that various kilovoltages can be applied to the x-ray tube.

d. *Pre-reading kilovoltmeter.* This is an alternating current meter having a high resistance, and is used for the purpose of determining difference of potential. It is connected in parallel with the autotransformer. When used as a pre-reading meter, a volt-

meter must first have been calibrated against known peak kilovoltages corresponding to different points on its scale. These
points are then labeled to correspond to these respective kilovoltages. Thus, although the pre-reading voltmeter indicates kilovolt peak values, it does not actually measure them because it is
located entirely in the primary circuit. The meter is calibrated by
the manufacturer, and occasionally must be re-checked by the use
of *spark gap measurements*. This can be described briefly as follows: if two metal spheres or points are connected to the high

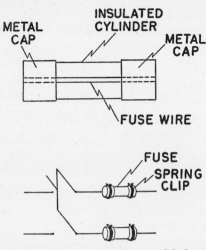

Figure 117. A safety fuse, and below,
its connections in an electric circuit.

voltage side of the transformer and are gradually brought closer
together, at a given distance corresponding to the peak kilovoltage, a spark will jump between them. There is a definite sparking
distance for any peak kilovoltage, depending on the size of the
spheres, the temperature, the atmospheric pressure, and the relative humidity. The correct peak kilovoltage under the given conditions may be found in appropriate tables. In practice, the
readings on the pre-reading kilovoltmeter in the primary circuit
should correspond closely to the actual kilovoltages obtained by
spark gap measurements. The main advantage of the pre-reading
kilovoltmeter is that slow fluctuations in line voltage are easily
compensated for. If, for instance, there should be a drop in line

voltage, the autotransformer controls are adjusted manually until the correct kilovoltage is indicated on the pre-reading kilovolt meter.

Some types of roentgen equipment do not employ a pre-reading voltmeter. Instead of this, there are *labeled settings* of the auto-transformer control corresponding to *previously determined* peak kilovoltages. The calibration of these settings is similar to that of a pre-reading voltmeter, using the spark gap method. However, these fixed settings indicate kilovoltage accurately only if the voltage coming into the main lines (i.e., the line voltage) is at the same value as it was during the actual calibration. Since the line voltage may fluctuate slowly, depending on the amount of other electrical equipment in use, a means of determining such fluctuation must be provided. This is accomplished by a second voltmeter connected in parallel across a portion of the primary side of the autotransformer. This voltmeter carries a scale marked with a line which indicates the correct line voltage and is called the *compensator voltmeter*. If the pointer is above or below this mark on the meter, a *line voltage compensator* is used to adjust the line voltage so that it is correct. This compensator utilizes the primary side of the autotransformer, varying the number of turns on the primary side until the compensator meter needle indicates that the correct line voltage has been established.

e. *Timer and X-ray Exposure Switches.* These switches complete the primary circuit to the primary coil of the transformer, so that the x-ray exposure can be made. The switches themselves are modifications of an ordinary pushbutton, as shown in Figure 118, and can be used either for hand or foot switches. However, these

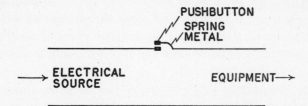

Figure 118. Pushbutton switch. When the button is pressed, it makes contact with the wire beneath it and the circuit is closed.

are not heavy enough to withstand the high amperage which may pass through the primary circuit (as high as 90 amperes with a 200 Ma unit), and there is also the danger of shock. Therefore, these switches are used to operate a remote control switch, which in turn finally closes the primary circuit.

f. *Remote Control Switch.* This is operated by either a hand or foot switch. Its basic design can best be appreciated by studying Figure 119. Actually, there is also a timer in the circuit which is set for a given time of exposure, and when this is completed, the circuit is automatically broken by the timer.

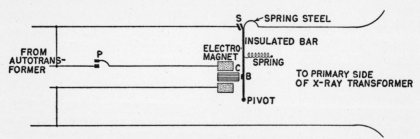

Figure 119. Remote control switch. The pushbutton P, when depressed, completes the circuit through the coil of the remote control switch. This magnetizes the core C which attracts the metal button B on the insulated bar. This closes the primary circuit by bringing together the contacts at S. When the pushbutton is released, the reverse occurs, breaking the circuit.

g. *Timer.* There are three main types in use at present. They include the *synchronous timer,* the *impulse timer,* and the *electronic timer.* The synchronous timer is operated by a small synchronous motor and usually can be set from $\frac{1}{20}$ to about 20 seconds. The impulse timer operates at $\frac{1}{120}$ or $\frac{1}{60}$ second up to $\frac{1}{5}$ second. This type of timer is much more accurate than the synchronous, because it initiates and stops the current close to, or at the zero point of the alternating current cycle. The electronic timer is a new development, and can be used over the entire range from $\frac{1}{30}$ second to 20 seconds.

A recent innovation in radiography has been the development of *photoelectric timing.* This requires the use of a *phototube,* which is a special type of electronic device that passes an electric current when light falls upon its cathode. The phototube is made indirectly sensitive to roentgen rays by the introduction of a small fluorescent screen. This device is placed behind the back of a cassette, the back being made of radiotransparent material. When a predetermined quantity of radiation has reached the phototube, depending on the part being radiographed, the phototube activates a mechanism which automatically terminates the exposure. This device produces radiographs of precisely reproducible density. It is now widely used in photofluorography and in spot film devices. Radiographic phototiming was invented by Drs. Morgan and Hodges at the University of Chicago.

h. *Circuit Breaker.* Additional precaution against overloading the circuit is obtained by the use of a circuit breaker. Its advantage is that it can be reset very easily, while a blown fuse has to be replaced. It is usually connected in series with the hand or foot switch, timer, and remote control switch. Figure 120 illustrates schematically the operation of a magnetic circuit breaker. The circuit breaker is shown in the exposure circuit, 2. When the hand or footswitch (exposure switch) is closed, circuit 2 is completed through the timer, the electromagnet of the remote control switch, and the circuit breaker contacts which are in the closed position. This activates the electromagnet of the remote control switch closing the primary circuit, 1, which goes to the primary side of the x-ray transformer. If there should be a momentary surge in the primary current, this will, through circuit 3, increase the mag-

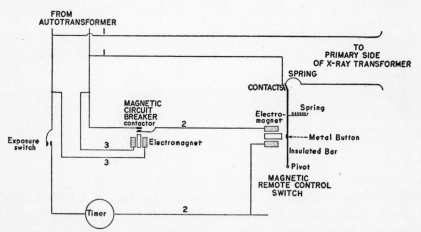

Figure 120. Magnetic circuit breaker together with the magnetic remote control switch, as they are connected in the primary circuit.

netization of the circuit breaker electromagnet to the point where it will open circuit 2, thereby interrupting the current to the remote control switch electromagnet, opening the remote control switch, and breaking the primary circuit, 1. The circuit breaker must then be reset manually before another exposure can be made.

i. *Motor Circuit.* The synchronous motor which is needed with mechanically rectified equipment is operated by a parallel connection with the primary source. This is omitted in self-rectified and in valve tube-rectified units.

j. *Filament Circuit of X-ray Tube.* The primary circuit furnishes the electricity to *heat* the filament of the x-ray tube. The incoming current must be decreased to about 3 to 5 amperes and about 4 to 12 volts. The amperage is reduced by the use of either a *rheostat* (variable resistance) or by a *choke coil.* The latter consists of a coil of heavy wire with a soft iron core. The core is movable within the coil. The greater the depth to which it is introduced into the coil, the greater the reduction in the current, and also the voltage. In series with this is an *oil immersed step-down transformer,* which further reduces the voltage to the required value. This is shown in Figure 121. This transformer is oil immersed for high insulation because its secondary coil is on the high voltage side of the x-ray unit.

There is often included in the filament circuit an x-ray tube *filament stabilizer.* It has been found by experience that a relatively

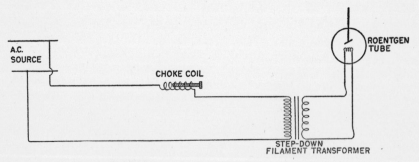

Figure 121. Filament circuit. Sometimes a rheostat is used instead of the choke coil. The choke coil varies the amperage supplying the filament, thereby controlling the filament temperature and the resulting emission of electrons, which in turn controls the milliamperage in the tube. The step-down transformer reduces the incoming voltage to the proper filament voltage.

small change in the filament voltage and current produces a marked change in electron emission and consequent tube current (milliamperage). The filament stabilizer corrects for instantaneous fluctuations in line voltage and current that may be caused by momentary demand elsewhere on the line, such as in the starting of an elevator. It may be so effective that a variation in line voltage of 10 per cent will cause no greater change than ½ per cent in the voltage to the filament. The stabilizer consists of a condenser and a small, modified split transformer which are so arranged that they compensate for a rise or fall in line voltage and provide a more uniform filament voltage, so that the filament current is maintained more nearly constant.

k. *Filament Ammeter.* In order to determine the filament current, and hence the amount of heat developed in the filament, an ammeter is connected in series in the *filament circuit.* By previous calibration, one can establish the readings of this meter that correspond to desired milliamperages in the x-ray tube at a given kilovoltage. In modern advanced design equipment, there is provided automatic control of the tube current for different kilovoltage values, by the use of a space-charge compensator.

l. *Primary coil of x-ray transformer.* This is the last connection of the primary circuit. The primary coil, with the secondary coil, is immersed in special oil to provide adequate insulation.

In general, the wires in the primary circuit must be relatively large, because of the high amperage that is carried. Circuit breakers and fuses should be conveniently located for easy resetting or replacement.

2. *Secondary Circuit.* All the equipment that is connected to the secondary coil of the x-ray transformer constitutes the secondary or high voltage circuit.

a. *Secondary Coil of X-ray Transformer.* As we have indicated earlier, this consists of many turns of electrically insulated thin wire. By the transformer principle, it steps up the primary voltage to provide the high voltage required to operate the x-ray tube.

b. *Milliammeter.* In order to measure the milliamperage flowing through the high voltage circuit and x-ray tube, an ammeter sensitive to milliamperes is introduced in series in the high tension circuit. Such a meter is called a *milliammeter*. In old-fashioned, non-shockproof equipment the milliammeter is placed in the overhead circuit away from the control stand, and has to be read at a distance, because it carries high voltage and is not grounded.

In modern shockproof equipment, the milliammeter is grounded together with the midpoint of the secondary coil of the x-ray transformer. Since it is grounded it is at the same potential as the person manipulating the controls, and the milliammeter can therefore be safely mounted in the control panel.

Attention must be called to the fact that the *tube current is measured in milliamperes by the milliammeter* placed in the high voltage circuit, while *the filament current is measured by an ammeter placed in the low voltage filament circuit*. The milliammeter measures average values and gives no indication of the peak values of tube current.

c. *Ballistic Meter*. In modern equipment operating at high milliamperages of 200 or more, there is added in series with the regular milliammeter a *ballistic milliampere-second meter*. This device has a high degree of inertia, due to the mass of the rotating mechanism, causing the indicating needle to swing relatively slowly so that it registers the product of milliamperes and time, that is, it indicates *milliampere-seconds*. This device is necessary because the ordinary milliammeter does not have time to register the true milliamperage at very short exposure intervals such as $\frac{1}{60}$ of a second. The ballistic meter is therefore of distinct importance in testing the tube current at very short exposure times, and because of its great sensitivity, it must be used in conjunction with an impulse timer. At exposure speeds greater than $\frac{1}{10}$ second, the ordinary milliammeter will register the correct average milliamperage.

d. *Rectifier*. In all but self-rectified units a system of rectification is introduced in order to change the alternating current coming from the transformer, to direct current. As we have already noted, rectification increases the capacity of the x-ray unit as a whole, safely permitting heavier and longer exposures.

e. *Cables*. In modern shockproof equipment, the midpoint of the secondary coil of the transformer is grounded. Thereby, the total kilovoltage across the ends of the transformer secondary remains unchanged, because one-half is below ground potential. For example, if there is 90 Kv across the transformer, and the center is not grounded, the kilovoltage will fluctuate between 90 Kv above ground and 90 KVP below ground according to the alternating current sine wave. If the center of the secondary coil is grounded, the peak kilovoltage will still be 90, but in this case one-half or 45 KVP will be above ground or zero-potential, and one-half will be 45 Kv below. The difference between 45 above zero and 45 below zero is still 90.

By grounding the secondary coil in this way, the kilovoltage applied through the cable ends is unchanged, but the kilovoltage between either cable and ground is one-half the value of the kilovoltage between the cable ends. Thus, if 90 Kv is the maximum that could be applied to the roentgen tube, each cable would have to be insulated for only 45 Kv, and this kilovoltage would not cause breakdown of the cable. If the center of the secondary coil were not grounded, each cable would have to be insulated much more heavily, to withstand the entire 90 Kv.

The cables are so constructed that there is no danger of shock as long as the insulation covering them is intact. Ordinarily, a very bulky and impractical thickness of insulation would be required to prevent the high voltage from sparking over to the patient or other objects coming close to the cable. However, by the use of a grounded woven wire sheath surrounding the cable, the danger of sparkover is eliminated. Figure 122 shows a shockproof cable in cross section. These cables conduct the high voltage current from the secondary of the transformer to the terminals of the roentgen tube. The cable, as illustrated in the figure, has three conductors which make contact with the leads to the two filaments of a double-focal spot tube (see Figure 107). This is called a *cathode cable*. The *anode cable* requires only one conductor, but some manufacturers use the same type of cathode cable interchangeably for both the anode and the cathode. When such a three-conductor cable is connected to the *anode,* only one of the conductors actually carries current.

f. *X-ray tube.* The ultimate goal of the x-ray equipment is the operation of an x-ray tube, and this is the last piece of equipment connected in the high voltage circuit.

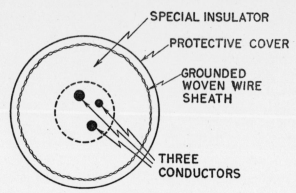

Figure 122. Cross section of a shockproof cable.

Completed Wiring Diagram

In order to visualize clearly the relationship of the various parts of the x-ray unit, one must connect them in their proper positions in the circuit. Figure 123 is a schematic representation of the wiring of a full-wave rectified x-ray unit employing four valve tubes. Most of the auxiliary items, though desirable or even necessary for proper operation, have been purposely omitted to avoid complicating the diagram. The proper hook-up of these accessory devices has been indicated in the preceding sections. This basic diagram can be readily modified; for self rectification, simply omit the rectifier and connect the transformer to the tube terminals. In a mechanically rectified unit, substitute the disc rectifier for the valve tubes.

The X-ray Control Panel

In order for the technician to operate x-ray equipment, he must be able to make adjustments of kilovoltage, milliamperage, and time in a convenient manner, and he must also have readily accessible meters to check the operation of the equipment. The controls and meters are mounted compactly in a separate unit which is connected electrically to the x-ray equipment. This unit, carrying the controls and meters, is called the *control panel*. It is readily apparent that its function is comparable to the dashboard instruments of an automobile.

The x-ray control panels that are available vary greatly in complexity, depending on the design of the individual x-ray machine.

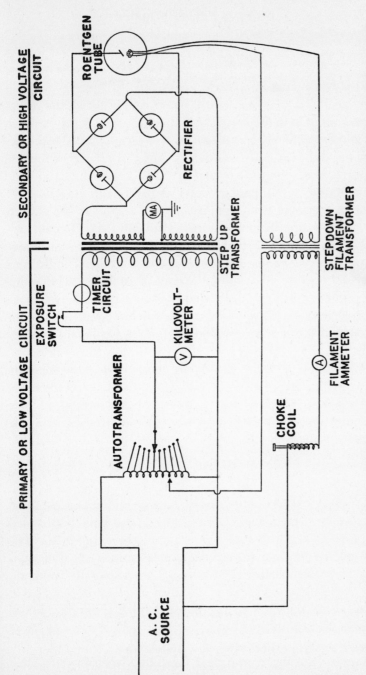

Figure 123. Schematic diagram of a four-valve tube full-wave rectified x-ray unit. Only the essentials have been included. Note that the filament circuits to the valve tubes have been omitted for the sake of simplicity.

If the student will bear in mind that all control panels, regardless of their intricacy, are based on certain basic elements of design, the problem of operating unfamiliar equipment becomes a relatively simple matter. The more complicated units are merely variations of the basic pattern.

In Figure 124 is shown a control panel which has all the essential items, and familiarity with this diagram will make it much easier to understand the operation of the various units manufactured by the different x-ray companies. The three meters shown in the figure include the milliammeter, the filament ammeter, and the kilovoltmeter. The milliammeter registers the current flowing through the x-ray tube from cathode to anode, as has already been explained. The filament ammeter indicates the filament current, which is the current that heats the tube filament, and which ultimately determines the milliamperage in the tube. The filament current can be varied by turning the control knob in the lower left hand corner of the diagram, labeled "filament control." This control really operates the choke coil in the filament circuit by varying the position of the iron core within the coil, as has been described earlier in this chapter.

The kilovoltmeter does not actually measure kilovolts directly, but is connected across the primary circuit and therefore measures volts. However, these readings have been calibrated beforehand against known tube kilovoltages and the meter scale has been marked accordingly in kilovolts. This meter acts at the same time as a compensating voltmeter, because a fall in the line voltage results in a lower kilovoltage reading on the meter, and the technician then adjusts this manually by turning the kilovoltage controls. These are shown in Figure 124 labeled "kilovoltage major" and "kilovoltage minor." These controls are connected to the autotransformer, which, it may be recalled, is the device that varies the voltage input to the primary of the x-ray transformer. The major control varies the kilovoltage in steps of 10, while the minor varies it in steps of 1.

The timer is indicated in the lower right hand corner of the diagram, and serves to time the roentgen exposure. The exposure is initiated by the pushbutton x-ray switch. In addition, there is a main switch; when this is in the "on" position, the primary current enters the autotransformer and registers on the kilovoltmeter which is connected in parallel across the primary circuit. The current also flows through the *filament only* of the x-ray tube and registers on the filament ammeter. Thus, *when the main switch is closed, only the filament ammeter and the kilovoltmeter should normally be activated.* Now, when the x-ray switch is closed, the

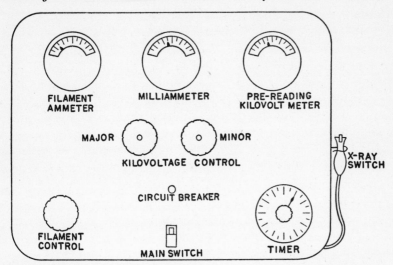

Figure 124. The essential components of an x-ray control panel. The filament control knob regulates the choke coil in the filament circuit, varying the filament current and consequently controlling the tube current (milliamperage). The filament ammeter measures the current in the filament circuit. The kilovoltage control operates the autotransformer in steps 10 Kv (major) and 1 Kv (minor). Actually, the autotransformer varies the primary voltage which is registered on the pre-reading kilovoltmeter in "kilovolts." The milliammeter indicates the tube current.

primary current is allowed to reach the x-ray transformer, the voltage is stepped up by the transformer, and the current finally passes through the x-ray tube. This is indicated on the milliammeter. Thus, the milliammeter does not register until the x-ray switch is closed.

The construction and operation of the circuit breaker have already been discussed.

There are several modifications of this basic plan that should be mentioned because they are used by some manufacturers. In one type of control panel, the kilovoltmeter is omitted and instead, a range of kilovoltages can be selected by turning the kilovoltage control knobs which operate through the autotransformer. These kilovoltage settings have been arrived at by calibration of the machine at the factory. In other words, when the settings read "56," it means that if the kilovoltage were to be determined by the spark gap method, it would be 56 kilovolts. With this arrangement, it is necessary to have a compensator voltmeter and a line voltage compensator control on the panel in order to correct for changes in line voltage. This has been discussed earlier in this chapter.

A second frequent modification is the milliamperage selector. Instead of obtaining the desired milliamperage by adjusting the filament control for a certain predetermined reading of the filament ammeter, we have a series of about six settings of a milliamperage selector knob. At each position of the knob, there is one definite milliamperage that will flow in the tube automatically, because this has been so arranged at the factory. Thus, if the selector is turned to 100 Ma, the milliammeter should register 100 when the x-ray exposure is made.

Finally, modern diagnostic equipment is often provided with a radiographic-fluoroscopic changeover switch, so that the radiologist may do spotfilm work automatically. When the cassette in the spotfilm device is shifted into the radiographic position, the control settings in the control panel switch over to the radiographic position. When the spotfilm is withdrawn from the radiographic position, the settings automatically return to fluoroscopy.

The student will find it to be advantageous to study and correlate the sections on the various items of x-ray equipment with the operation of the basic control panel. In this way, he will have a much clearer concept of the function of the various parts, and his daily work will become all the more fascinating.

QUESTIONS

1. Describe with the aid of a diagram the overload circuit breaker.
2. What is the function of a fuse and how does it work?
3. What is a pre-reading kilovoltmeter? How is it calibrated?

4. Why is a remote control switch necessary? How is it constructed?
5. What are the three main types of exposure timers? What is meant by phototiming?
6. What is the advantage of a circuit breaker over a fuse?
7. Show by diagram the filament circuit and its important components.
8. Why can a milliammeter be safely mounted on the control stand? What is a ballistic milliammeter and under what conditions is it an essential part of the control apparatus?
9. Explain why the center of the transformer secondary coil is grounded.
10. Explain how the kilovoltage control knob varies the kilovoltage. Which device does it operate in the primary x-ray circuit?
11. Which device in the filament circuit is operated when the filament control knob is manipulated? What function does it serve?
12. Describe, with a diagram, a shockproof cable.

I t is impossible to overemphasize the importance of the dark-room in radiography. It has truly been said that radiography begins and ends in the darkroom, where the films are loaded into the proper light-tight holders in preparation for exposure, and where they are returned for processing into a finished radiograph. The purpose of the darkroom, then, is to provide a place where the necessary handling and processing of film can be carried out safely and efficiently, without the hazard of accidental exposure to light or x-rays to which film is so sensitive.

The term "darkroom" is not entirely accurate, since it is well-known that blackout conditions are not necessary. As will be pointed out later, considerable safe illumination can be provided to facilitate darkroom procedures. A better term is "processing room" but it is not widely used and we shall therefore continue to use the term "darkroom," bearing in mind that it is dark only insofar as *it must exclude all outside white light.*

Location of the Darkroom

This is of fundamental importance and can best be determined when the radiology department is originally planned. In any case, the darkroom must be centrally located with regard to the radiographic rooms in order to save time and eliminate unnecessary steps. On the other hand, it should be remote from high voltage therapy equipment and the radium store because of the expense of added protection from these highly penetrating rays. The dark-room should be readily accessible to plumbing, electrical supply, and to a satisfactory means of ventilation.

Building Essentials

The walls of the darkroom adjacent to the x-ray rooms should contain enough lead thickness, or its equivalent in other building materials to protect the films at all times from x-rays. This is doubly important because efficiency demands that the darkroom should be close to the radiographic rooms. Construction costs can be lessened by locating high voltage therapy equipment and radium storage as far away from the darkroom as is possible within the department. Otherwise, additional lead protection is required, thereby increasing these costs.

In a busy department, the smoothness of operation can be improved by having passboxes built into the walls at appropriate locations. These are light-tight and x-ray proof and have two interlocking doors so arranged that both cannot be opened at the same time. The cassettes, after radiographic exposure, are placed in the passbox through the outside door, and the darkroom technician removes them through the inside door. The most suitable location for the passbox is obviously near the film-loading bench.

The darkroom walls should be covered with chemical-resistant materials, particularly near the processing tanks. Such materials include special paint, varnish, or lacquer; or one may use a ceramic tile or plastic wall covering.

The floor should be covered with chemical-resistant and stain-proof material such as asphalt tile. Porcelain or clay tile may be used, but a non-skid abrasive should be incorporated to minimize the danger of slipping. Ordinary linoleum is fairly readily attacked by the processing solutions.

Entrance

This should be so arranged that it is conveniently located with relation to the darkroom equipment. The simplest type of entrance is the single door. It must be absolutely light-tight; this is most readily accomplished by weatherstripping. The single door is suitable for a small office because it saves space, but it should be provided with a lock to prevent opening in the course of film processing.

In larger offices and radiology departments a more elaborate type of entrance is desirable. The best is a passageway called a *labyrinth* or *maze*. It is so constructed that a complete turn must be executed in going through the three doorways, as shown in Figure 125. The walls are painted dull black to absorb all outside light and thereby prevent it from entering the darkroom. If properly designed, the labyrinth does not require doors. Its greatest disadvantage is that it requires a relatively large amount of floor space, but this is compensated for by the convenience of having such a safe and efficient entrance. An emergency entrance may be

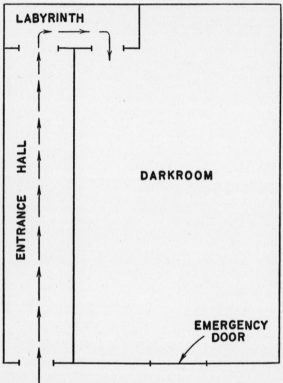

Figure 125. Darkroom floor plan, with labyrinth entrance.

provided to allow moving the darkroom equipment into the darkroom. Other more intricate labyrinths can be designed, but the one shown here is a very simple type.

Another kind of protective entrance is a small hall with two electrically interlocked doors. These should be so designed that one door cannot be opened until the other is completely closed, thus preventing the entrance of light (see Figure 126). With this type of arrangement a separate door is desirable for emergency use and for moving equipment into and out of the darkroom.

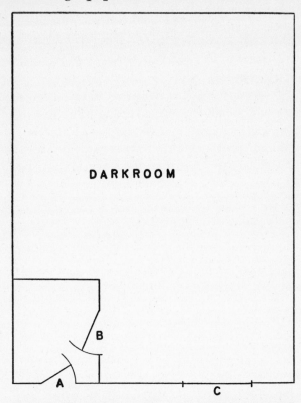

Figure 126. Darkroom floor plan with interlocked doors. If door A is opened, an electrical relay prevents anyone from opening door B, and vice versa. C is an emergency door, which is usually kept closed.

Size

The size of the darkroom will vary, of course, with the size of the department. It must be large enough to house conveniently all the necessary benches for loading and unloading films, a film storage bin, cupboards, processing tanks, refrigerator, and dryer. It is advisable to have the loading bench across the room from the tanks in order to avoid accidental splashing of water and solutions on the films, bench, cassettes, or other equipment that may come in contact with the films. The size of the darkroom should not be too large, otherwise it may be inconvenient and result in waste of time and steps.

Ventilation

This must be adequate to remove odors and stale, humid air, and to supply fresh air. It is essential to efficient work and to the technician's health. The ventilating system must be completely light-proof. It may be led through a duct into the ventilating system of the building, or through the wall to the outside. In the latter case, an intake or exhaust fan should be installed to aid in the circulation of fresh air, but it is advisable to provide a means of filtering out dust at the point of entry of the fresh air. Air conditioning, when available, is an excellent method of ventilating the dark-room.

Lighting

Proper lighting is essential if one is to avoid ruining films by fogging. Two types of illumination are necessary. First, one must provide a source of white light for cleaning, mixing solutions, and carrying out any procedures other than handling unprocessed films. In the second place, one must have a source of light which will not fog films under processing conditions, and still be bright enough to be of value. This is best accomplished by installing safe-light lamps with safelight filters of the proper color. Safelight lamps are made expressly for that purpose. One must be careful to maintain a working distance of at least 3 feet and to use an electric light bulb of the proper wattage. If a brighter bulb is used than is recommended by the manufacturer, too much light may pass through even a correct glass filter and cause film fog. Safe-light lamps are available for either indirect ceiling illumination or for direct lighting.

The only certain method of assuring the safety of darkroom conditions is by actual test exposure. This may be done as follows: cover one-half of an x-ray film with black paper and leave it exposed in the darkroom under conditions simulating as closely as possible those normally existing when a film is loaded and unloaded. Then develop the film for the regular period of time and if the unexposed half remains clear while the exposed half turns dark, it indicates that lighting conditions are unsafe. The test can be made more sensitive by first exposing screen film with intensifying screens to a small quantity of x-rays, just enough to cause slight graying, and then going through the above procedure. It has been found that the sensitivity of screen x-ray film to safelight fogging is greater after an initial exposure to the fluorescent light given off by intensifying screens.

If the darkroom conditions are found to be unsatisfactory, every effort must be made to eliminate the source of light responsible for the fogging. It should be pointed out that it is no longer considered necessary to paint the darkroom walls black. Any color which enhances the safelight illumination is to be desired, as this improves illumination without danger to films.

Apparatus and Equipment

In most departments at the present time, processing chemicals are bought ready mixed as dry powders or as liquid solutions. These are made up to the proper volume by the addition of water, according to the instructions printed on the label. The apparatus needed for this includes an enameled pail (if the processing tanks cannot be reached by a water inlet) to be used for dissolving the powdered mixtures, and two stirring paddles, one for the developing solution and one for the fixer. A thermometer is essential, since it serves a double purpose; it is used to determine the temperature of the developing solution, and also serves to check the temperature of water used to prepare the solutions. It is important to bear in mind that all apparatus coming in contact with the processing solutions be made of material that will not contaminate the solutions. Plastic, hard rubber, enamelware, and stainless steel of the proper composition are the most suitable materials for the purpose.

The *major equipment* includes first of all, the *processing tanks*. The simplest type consists of a three-compartment tank. One end compartment is used for developing and the opposite end for fixing. The middle compartment is used for both rinsing and washing the films and should be supplied with running water. If the water temperature is controlled it will also control the temperature of the processing solutions. The best construction material for processing tanks is stainless steel of the proper alloy composition, because it not only resists corrosion but also permits rapid equalization of the temperature of the processing solutions with that of the water in the middle compartment (stainless steel is a fairly good conductor of heat as compared with rubber or stone). It is advisable to have the outside walls of the tank insulated to prevent condensation of moisture and to help maintain the proper temperature within the compartments. Hard rubber, composition, or stone is suitable for tank construction, but temperature regulation is slower than with stainless steel. Besides, porous material such as unglazed stone absorbs chemicals which may eventually contaminate the developing solution and cause chemical fogging of films.

A more satisfactory type of arrangement, especially in a busy department, is shown in Figure 127. This consists of a large double-compartment master tank which should be insulated. Two insert tanks, preferably of stainless steel, are placed in one of the compartments. The first insert is the developing tank and the second insert is the fixing tank. The water between the inserts in this compartment is used for rinsing and for controlling the temperature of the solutions. The fixing tank should have about twice the volume of the developing tank since the process of fixing films takes approximately twice the time of development. The other main compartment serves as the washing tank and should be about twice the size of the fixing tank, since washing requires about twice as long as fixation.

The tanks which contain the processing solutions should be measured to determine their true volume. The number of gallons

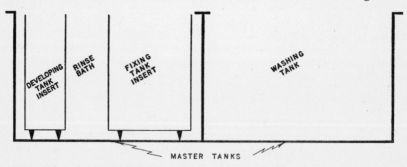

Figure 127. A popular type of processing tank arrangement. The developing and fixing tanks are separate units placed in the master tank on the left. Note the relative sizes of the tanks.

equals the height minus one, times the length, times the breadth all measured in inches, divided by 231.

$$\text{Volume in gallons} = \frac{(\text{height} - 1) \times \text{length} \times \text{breadth}}{231}$$

The height of the wash tank should be such that the wash water passes completely over the tops of the hangers so that they will be maintained as chemically clean as possible.

Running water is essential in the darkroom for high quality processing. There should be a convenient inlet that can be used to wash the tanks and to make up the solutions. Warm and refrigerated water should be available and the temperature of the water should be regulated by a thermostatic control so that it can be circulated around the processing tanks to maintain an optimum temperature level.

Various types of *drying devices* are now available to speed up the drying of films. Most of these consist essentially of a rack to hold the films and a fan to circulate air around them. A source of heat may also be included to speed the drying. Such a dryer can either be built in the form of a wooden cabinet, or can be purchased as an enamel or stainless steel cabinet. The most desirable type is constructed of stainless steel throughout, because wood tends to warp, and enameled metal must be repainted at frequent intervals due to chipping and corrosion. In the last few years an entirely new, chemical type film dryer has been placed on the market. It consists of a metal cabinet in which a fan circulates air. The air is passed through a chamber containing a chemical mixture which is a powerful dehydrating agent; that is, it has the ability to absorb a large amount of water. By turning the switch to the indicated point, the chemicals are *recharged* at night, or when there is a lull in the day's work. It is said that the chemicals last for many years, and that under average conditions, films can be dried in about 10–15 minutes.

A *lightproof storage bin* for unexposed film should be placed under the loading bench. The bin is subdivided by vertical partitions so that film boxes of different sizes can be accommodated. The drawer of the bin should be counterweighted so that when the handle is released, the drawer closes automatically. A warning should be printed across the front of the bin to prevent its being opened when the white light is on.

Film hangers of proper size and in sufficient number should be available to hold the films during processing.

Finally, it is desirable to have a large *scissors* or a mechanical *corner cutter* to trim the corners of the films. Very often, the corners of the films which were placed in the hanger clips are still wet after the remainder of the films is dry, and these wet corners may stick to other films. It is also possible for the rough corners to scratch adjacent films and it is more difficult to handle such films because they cannot be readily slid over each other. Finally, the rough corners are thick and thereby increase the thickness of the films so that filing space is wasted.

QUESTIONS

1. What is the best location for the darkroom?
2. What is meant by a maze? Why is it used?
3. What are interlocking doors?
4. What characteristics are desirable for the material used in construction of processing tanks?
5. Describe a darkroom safelight lamp. What precautions are necessary to assure that the safelight is really safe?
6. What color should be used in painting the walls of the darkroom? of the maze?
7. Make a diagram of a convenient arrangement of the processing tanks, and indicate their comparative sizes.
8. A developing tank measures 8 in. wide x 16 in. long x 19 in. high. How many gallons of developer does it hold when filled to a level one inch below the top?
9. How can you prevent x-rays from entering the darkroom, and why?
10. Describe briefly the various types of film dryers.
11. Why is running water essential in the darkroom?

I n the early days of roentgenography, glass photographic plates coated with an emulsion sensitive to light were used to record the x-ray image. The disadvantages of plates included the danger of breakage, the hazard of cutting one's hands, the difficulty in processing, and the inconvenience in filing these plates for future reference. With the introduction of modern films, these disadvantages were eliminated.

Composition of X-ray Film

There are two essential components: the *base* and the *emulsion*.

1. *The Base*. Modern safety film has a base consisting of a sheet of transparent *cellulose acetate* which is tinted blue by some manufacturers. It is called "safety" because it is non-explosive, being no more inflammable than the same thickness of paper.

2. *The Emulsion*. This consists of one or more *silver salts* (such as silver bromide) suspended in *gelatin*. The emulsion is coated in a layer about $\frac{1}{1000}$ inch thick on both sides of the film base. The chemical composition of the emulsion has been designed experimentally by the film manufacturers so that it is sensitive both to blue fluorescent light and to x-rays. Furthermore, it must be capable of rendering the radiographic image of a great variety of tissues in good density, contrast, and detail. The emulsion must have *speed*, that is, it must be very sensitive; and at the same time, it must have *wide latitude*, which means that it must record a satisfactory image having a long range of densities from white through various shades of gray, to black.

Types of Films

There are two main types of x-ray films in use at the present time in medical radiography.

1. *Screen Film.* This is designed to be sensitive mainly to blue light, which is the light emitted from intensifying screens. However, this type of film is sensitive also to the direct action of x-rays. Screen film is used chiefly in cassettes equipped with intensifying screens, and it is this combination, as will be pointed out later, that has contributed so much to the high speed and high quality of modern radiography.

2. *No-screen or Non-screen Film.* This is designed to be sensitive mainly to the direct action of x-rays. The emulsion is thicker than in the screen type film and differs also in its chemical composition. Screen film used with intensifying screens is faster (requires less exposure) than no-screen film in cardboard holders. This comparison depends on the kilovoltage and temperature, as will be pointed out later in the discussion of screens. Screen film may be used in cardboard holders in radiography of small parts, but it is *one-half as fast as no-screen film,* so that screen film in cardboard holders requires twice the x-ray exposure to produce the same degree of film darkening. Furthermore, no-screen film has wider latitude and greater contrast.

Practical Suggestions in Handling Unexposed Film

1. Films deteriorate with age, so that the expiration date stamped on the box should be observed. The older films should always be used first.

2. Moisture and heat hasten deterioration, so that films should be stored in a cool dry place. This precaution has been minimized by some manufacturers who package their films in special protective foil.

3. Films are sensitive to light and must be protected from it at all times, until processing has been completed.

4. Films are sensitive to x-rays and radium rays and should be protected by distance and by interposition of protective materials such as lead.

5. Films are marred by finger prints, scratches, dirty intensifying screens, and by crink marks due to sharp bending.

6. Rough handling causes static marks due to static electricity. These appear as fine, jagged lines, black spots, and tree-like structures after development.

FILM EXPOSURE HOLDERS AND INTENSIFYING SCREENS

Each x-ray film must be carried to the radiographic room in a suitable container which protects it from light, and at the same time allows it to be exposed to x-rays for radiographic purposes. These film holders are available in various sizes to accommodate the different film sizes. The simplest type of container is the *cardboard film holder* which has a light-proof envelope into which the film is loaded *in the darkroom*. The film *with its paper wrapping* (for additional protection from light) is placed in the folder, the long flap of the envelope is folded over it, and then the two shorter side flaps and end flap are closed over. The holder is closed by means of a small hinged clip at the open end. It is now ready to be taken to the radiographic room for exposure. It should be noted

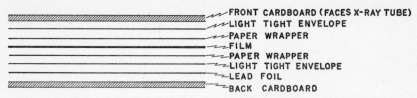

Figure 128. Cross section of a cardboard film holder.

that the front of the holder must face the x-ray tube. The back cardboard is lined with lead foil to prevent fogging of the film by x-rays scattered back from the table. Figure 128 shows a cardboard film holder in cross section.

The *cassette* is the second type of film holder. It is simply a case provided with an aluminum or stainless steel frame, a hinged lid with one or more flat springs, and a bakelite front. The cassette measures about one-half inch in thickness. One of a pair of intensifying screens is mounted on the inside of the bakelite front, and the second screen is mounted on the inside of the lid. The front of the cassette faces the x-ray tube during an exposure. The cassette is loaded by raising the hinged lid *in the darkroom* slipping a film *with its wrapping paper removed* gently into the cassette of the same size, and closing the lid by means of the flat springs. The film is thus sandwiched between two screens. Figure 129 shows a cassette in cross section.

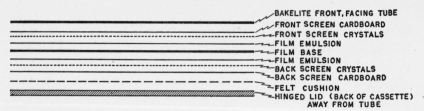

Figure 129. Cross section of a cassette with intensifying screens and film.

Intensifying Screens

We have been discussing the use of screens, and it may be of interest to consider some of the features of this very important roentgenographic device.

1. *Composition.* The intensifying screen consists of fine crystals of a material which fluoresces, that is, emits light, when it is struck by roentgen rays. Such a material is *calcium tungstate* or *barium lead sulfate.* These minute crystals are incorporated in a binding substance and spread on one side of a special cardboard; the crystals constitute the *active layer* of the screen.

2. *Principle.* The crystals that make up the active surface of the screen fluoresce when they are struck by x-rays. Each tiny crystal emits light in all directions, and since there are innumerable crystals closely packed, they would appear to the eye as a uniform area of brightness. The film must be in close contact with the screens during the radiographic exposure, and since the film emulsion is particularly sensitive to the blue light emitted by the screens, it is obvious that there will be a considerable photographic effect on the film. In fact, *more than 90 per cent of the recorded density on the film exposed with intensifying screens is photographic in origin,* that is, due to light emerging from the screens. Less than 10 per cent is due to the x-rays which strike the film directly. The result is that the screens actually intensify many times the effect of the x-rays on the film, which means that less x-ray exposure is required to obtain a given amount of film blackening when screens are used. The development of modern screens has made it feasible to use grid diaphragms, thereby yielding films of superb quality even in the radiography of large anatomic areas such as the abdomen.

To sum this discussion up, one may say that the x-rays pass through the bakelite front of the cassette and impinge on the front intensifying screen. This emits light which affects the film emulsion facing that screen. X-rays also pass on directly to the film, causing a small degree of darkening. Some x-rays also penetrate all the way to the back screen which fluoresces and affects the film emulsion nearest it. Thus, it becomes evident why a film is coated on both sides with sensitive emulsion; one side receives light from the front screen, while the other side receives light from the back screen. This is shown in Figure 130.

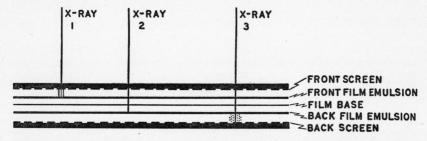

Figure 130. Schematic representation of the principle of the intensifying screen. X-ray 1 strikes the front screen causing it to fluoresce at that point. Another x-ray such as 2 may pass directly to the film and affect it at that point. Or a ray such as x-ray 3 may pass through the front screen and the film, striking a crystal in the back screen and exciting fluorescence in it. Actually the screens and film are in close contact.

3. *Speed of Intensifying Screens.* A screen is said to be fast or to have high speed when a relatively small x-ray exposure is required to give a certain degree of blackening. A screen is said to be slow when a relatively large exposure is required for a given amount of blackening. *The speed factor of a pair of intensifying screens may be defined as the ratio of the exposure required without screens to the exposure required with screens to get the same degree of blackening of x-ray films.* Another name for speed factor is *intensifying factor.*

$$\text{Speed Factor} = \frac{\textbf{Exposure without intensifying screens}}{\textbf{Exposure with intensifying screens}}$$

Since the denominator is always less than the numerator, the speed factor of a pair of screens is always greater than unity, which means simply that the exposure with screens is less than that without screens for the same amount of film blackening. The speed of a screen depends on a number of factors. For instance, as the temperature increases, the speed of most screens decreases; when the temperature rises from 50 F to 100 F, the radiographic exposure must be increased 1½ times to maintain constant film darkening. The speed increases with an increase in kilovoltage; thus, at 40 Kv; the speed factor of a given screen is 20, whereas at 80 Kv it is almost 40. The speed factor increases also with an increase in the quantity of radiation reaching the screen. The most important factor influencing the intensification factor of a screen is its *grain size*.

4. *Grain Size*. The screen coating can be prepared with fluorescent crystals or grains of different sizes. What is the effect of varying grain size? The larger the size of the crystals, the more light is emitted by each crystal and therefore the faster is the screen. However, as the size of the crystals is increased, the light which they emit becomes broader and broader, so that point detail is blurred. In other words, *large grain size increases the speed of the screen, but decreases the detail or sharpness of the radiograph.* Therefore, a happy medium is sought—a screen which has a grain size that is large enough for convenient speed, and at the same time small enough to provide excellent detail. Most screen manufacturers have on the market three types of intensifying screens; slow, medium, and fast. These are respectively high, medium, and

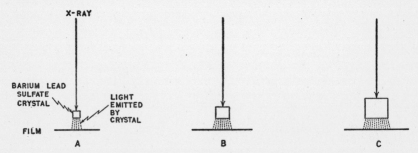

Figure 131. The effect of grain size on screen speed and radiographic detail. A = slow speed screen. B = average speed screen. C = high speed screen. Note that screen speed increases with an increase in grain size, but that the image cast by each grain also becomes larger. This creates a more coarsely granular and poorly defined image. Thus, high speed screens give poorer detail than slow screens.

low definition or detail. Figure 131 shows the effect of grain size on speed and detail.

It should be emphasized that regardless of grain size, radiographic sharpness is limited by the diffusion of light over the surface of the screen. This is caused by the scattering of light emitted from the crystals by neighboring crystals.

5. *Screen Contact.* The film must be sandwiched evenly between the two screens. There must be perfect contact throughout. If there is any appreciable space between the film and screen at any point, the light rays emerging from the screen at that point spread over a wider area producing a blurred image of that particular point (see Figure 132). One can test very easily the evenness of contact of the screens with the film. Place a piece of wire netting with ¼ to ½ in. mesh over the front of the cassette and make a film exposure (about 60 Kv-15 MaS-40-in. distance using a filter of 6 mm aluminum). If screen contact is good, the image of the wire mesh will be recorded in sharp detail over the entire film. In zones of poor contact, the image will be blurred.

There has recently appeared on the market a screen which is so designed that almost perfect contact is assured. This screen has attached to its *back* a sheet of transparent, non-porous material filled with air. When the screen is mounted in the cassette, the air is sandwiched between the screen and the cassette. The air re-

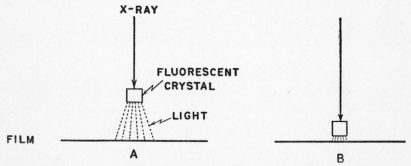

Figure 132. Poor screen contact causes a blurred image. In A, there is an appreciable space between the fluorescent crystal and the film (when screen contact is poor), so that a tiny but spreading bundle of light rays strikes the film, producing a blurred image instead of a fine point. In B, the crystal is in close contact with the film so that the image is about the same size as the crystal. (The crystal is magnified many times in the diagram.)

mains in this reservoir for a remarkably long time, the loss amounting to about 1 cc per year. When the cassette is closed, the air is compressed, and this pressure is transmitted equally in all directions so that the screens are in effect, squeezed very tightly against the film. This makes for extremely intimate contact of the screens and film. These screens are manufactured by the Eastman Kodak Company and by E. I. du Pont de Nemours and Company (Patterson). A word of caution should be given here; some cassettes are not deep enough to accommodate this type of air-cushioned screen, resulting in strain on the hinges, poor closure of the cassette, light leaks, and impairment of screen contact. Therefore, the size of the cassettes should be checked by the dealer before such screens are purchased.

6. *Care of Screens.* Intensifying screens should be mounted with rubber cement or special adhesive tape. Water-soluble paste should never be used. The screens customarily come in pairs, one screen being thicker than the other. The thin screen is mounted in the front of the cassette, whereas the thicker screen is mounted on the lid.

Screens should be kept scrupulously clean, since dust and other foreign material absorb light from the screen and cast a white shadow on the film. If the screens are of washable type, they can be washed with cotton and bland soap, rinsed with cotton moistened with water, and then dried with cotton. Excessive amounts of water should be avoided. The screens are further dried by standing the half-opened cassette on its side for about one-half hour in a dust-free room. The screens of one manufacturer can also be cleaned with *pure* grain alcohol and cotton, but care must be used not to spread the alcohol over the printed letters near the edge of the screen, since these may "run" and stain the screen.

Care must be exercised not to nick, scratch, or chip the screens. This can occur accidentally by carelessly digging the film out of the cassette with the fingernail, or by scratching the screen with a corner of the film. In loading the cassette, the film should be carefully slipped into the cassette with the lid elevated about 2 inches. The lower leaf of the folded paper which covers the film is allowed to hang down over the edge of the cassette, and after the film is in place, the paper is slipped away. This manipulation should be done gently to avoid static marks. To remove the film after exposure, one must carefully raise a corner of the film, being certain that the fingernails do not slip across the surface of the screen.

The cassette must be kept closed at all times, except when it is being loaded or unloaded. This prevents accidental damage to the screen surface and minimizes the amount of dust falling on the screens, either of which will interfere with light from the screen reaching the film at that point, leaving a white spot on the finished radiograph.

Fluoroscopic Screen

It should be mentioned here that a fluoroscopic screen is similar in principle to the intensifying screen, but there are certain differences. The best fluoroscopic screen usually has *cadmium zinc sulfide* as the fluorescent material. The screen is backed by lead glass to protect the fluoroscopist.

This type of screen has the property of fluorescing, that is, emitting light while it is being activated by x-rays. But it also has the property of *phosphorescence,* which is the emission of light for an interval of time after the x-rays have been turned off. Phosphorescence of a screen is known as *screen lag.* Most intensifying screens have only a slight degree of phosphorescence or lag, whereas fluoroscopic screens have a comparatively greater degree of lag.

QUESTIONS

1. Show by a cross-section diagram the structure of x-ray film.
2. What is meant by "safety film"?
3. What are two differences between screen and no-screen film?
4. Describe the structure of an intensifying screen. How does it differ from a fluoroscopic screen?
5. How is the speed of an intensifying screen determined? How does temperature affect screen speed? How does kilovoltage affect screen speed?
6. What is the difference in the composition of a slow screen and a fast screen? How do they differ in their effect on the detail of the resulting radiographs?

7. How does an intensifying screen intensify the roentgen image? Approximately what proportion of the film density results from light emitted by the screens?

8. Why is an x-ray film duplitized (coated on both sides with sensitive emulsion)?

9. Why is the folded paper left on the film when placed in a cardboard holder? Why must the paper be removed when placed in a cassette?

10. What is meant by "screen lag"? What is the difference between fluorescence and phosphorescence?

11. How does grain size affect detail? Explain.

12. Why should one avoid scratching or otherwise marring a screen surface?

13. What is the effect of poor screen contact on radiographic sharpness? Why?

17 CHEMISTRY OF
RADIOGRAPHY AND
FILM PROCESSING

Theoretical Concepts

Fundamental to an understanding of the production of an image on an x-ray film, is the concept of the *latent image*. The silver bromide is present in the film emulsion in the form of minute crystals which are practically invisible to the naked eye. When radiant energy such as light or x-rays strikes these crystals, they undergo an electrochemical change which makes them more susceptible to the action of certain chemicals, than are the neighboring unexposed crystals. A group of silver bromide crystals that has been so exposed to radiant energy that it has been rendered easily susceptible to chemical development is known as the *latent image*. *The latent image may be defined as that invisible image, produced in the film emulsion by light or x-rays, which is converted to a visible or manifest image upon development.*

Chemistry of the Roentgenogram

What is meant by development? Certain chemicals known as *reducing agents* or *developers* have the unique ability of penetrating those crystals of silver bromide that have been altered by preliminary exposure to light or x-rays. The developer produces an additional change in these crystals, removing the bromide portion and leaving metallic silver, a change known as *development* or *reduction*. This is illustrated in Figure 133. These particles of metallic silver appear black because they are very minute and closely spaced. Thus, *the black areas on an x-ray film consist of metallic silver in a very fine state of subdivision.*

What happens to the portions of the film emulsion that are not struck by light or x-rays? Since the silver salts in these areas have not been altered, they are relatively unaffected by the developer. However, they must be removed in order to allow the unexposed film areas to become transparent, and also to prevent fogging by subsequent exposure to daylight. The removal of the unexposed and undeveloped silver bromide is accomplished by the use of a *fixing agent,* sodium thiosulfate ("hypo"), and the process is called *fixation.* As a result of this procedure, the areas from which the silver salts have been dissolved appear clear, while the areas that have black silver deposits remain black since metallic silver is not dissolved by the fixing agent in the ordinary course of processing. However, prolonged immersion in the fixing solution will cause bleaching of the image; this may be appreciable even in 24 hours. The effect is more rapid with solutions prepared from liquid chemicals than from powdered chemicals.

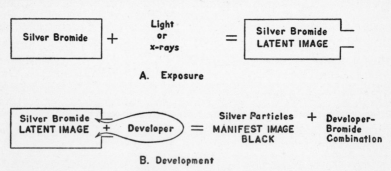

Figure 133. Scheme of the basic theory of photographic chemistry. In A radiant energy in the form of light or x-rays converts a silver bromide crystal into a latent image. In B the developer enters this altered crystal and reduces it to metallic silver, which constitutes the manifest image.

In a finished radiograph, there are areas of various degrees of blackening, corresponding to the amount of x-ray energy reaching the film either directly or by exciting fluorescence in screens, after penetrating the varying thicknesses and densities of tissues which have been placed between the source of the x-rays and the film. For example, a radiograph of a hand shows lighter areas representing the bones—these absorb x-rays to a great extent and therefore the silver bromide crystals in the film emulsion just beneath the bones do not receive a large amount of x-ray energy. As a result, these crystals are not affected to a great degree and the reducing action of the developer produces a small degree of darkening. The soft tissues, on the contrary, offer very little hindrance to the passage of x-rays and therefore the areas of the film emulsion beneath the soft tissues receive a relatively large amount of x-ray energy. As a result, the silver bromide in these regions is affected to a greater extent and the developer causes considerably greater blackening. It should be noted that the finished radiograph is really a *negative* (corresponding to a negative in ordinary photography), and represents the shadows cast by tissues of different densities depending on their relative penetration by x-rays.

FILM PROCESSING

It is now necessary to discuss the practical aspects of rendering the latent image visible. The conversion of the latent image to a visible or manifest image and the preservation of that image are brought about by *film processing*. This includes development, rinsing, fixing, washing, and drying. Each of these important steps will be considered in order. It must be strongly emphasized at the outset that cleanliness is of paramount importance. The hands should be rinsed frequently and thoroughly, and dried on a clean towel. The tanks and mixing utensils must also be kept scrupulously clean.

Development

The function of this step is to convert the latent image to a visible image. This requires the use of a *developing solution* which has four essential ingredients.

Developing Solution. Composition:

1. *Organic Reducing Agents.* These usually include a mixture of *hydroquinone* and *metol* (or *elon* which is a synonym for metol). By using two such reducing agents together, we secure greater density and contrast than with either developing agent alone.

2. *Preservative—Sodium Sulfite.* This protects the organic reducing agents—hydroquinone and metol—from being oxidized by the air. It therefore prolongs the effective life of the developer.

3. *Accelerator—Sodium Carbonate or Sodium Hydroxide.* This compound swells the gelatin emulsion slightly so that it is more readily penetrated by the developing agent. Furthermore, this swelling of the emulsion allows the reaction products to diffuse

out of the emulsion layer more rapidly. As a result of these two factors, the developing process is speeded up.

4. *Restrainer—Potassium Bromide.* This preferentially holds back any action of the developer on the unexposed silver bromide grains without preventing the action of the developer on the exposed grains. Thus, it inhibits fogging of the lighter areas without interfering with the development of the radiographic image.

Practical Factors in Development. The two most important factors in development are (1) the temperature of the developing solution and (2) the total time during which development is carried out. If a film is correctly exposed, it will be completely and properly developed at a certain temperature and time. If a film is incorrectly exposed, it is almost impossible to correct the error by manipulating the temperature and the time of development. A simple analogy presents itself. One may mix an excellent batter, but if the temperature of the oven is not correct, and the baking time is incorrect, the cake will be ruined. On the other hand, if a poor batter is mixed, a poor cake will result no matter how long or at what temperature it is baked.

With modern fast x-ray developers, the optimum temperature is 68 to 70 F. If the developer is too cold, that is, below 60 F, the action of the reducing agent is impaired and the resulting film lacks detail and density. However, even at 60 F the quality is not impaired if the developing time is sufficiently long. If the developer is too warm, that is, above 75 F, there is danger of softening the emulsion and producing heat fog. At a given, suitable temperature, there is a definite developing time which yields correct development, this being best determined from the data furnished by the manufacturer of the particular films and chemical solutions in use. However, there is no great difference in the developing time recommended by various manufacturers and for practical purposes one may use the graph shown in Figure 134. This graph is a composite of the data supplied by the three leading film companies (Eastman, du Pont, and Ansco), for *screen film* and *rapid developer*. From this graph, one may readily determine the correct developing time at various temperatures, based on a normal time of 3 minutes in a solution at a temperature of 68 F. At 60 F the

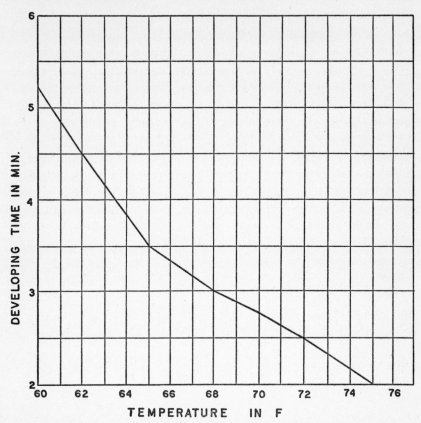

Figure 134. Time-temperature development chart. This is a composite based on the data furnished by the three leading American manufacturers.

developing time is 5¼ minutes and at 75 F it is 2 minutes. With no-screen film, the developing time is increased about 2 or 3 minutes because of the greater thickness of the emulsion and the difference in its chemical structure. It is to be noted that as the temperature of the solution increases, the developing time decreases. Processing of films on the above basis is called *time-temperature development.*

Some manufacturers (Eastman and du Pont) state that the radiographic exposure technic may be so established that development in rapid developer is complete in 5 *minutes at 68 F.* This method yields radiographs of superior contrast, with about 5 Kv less exposure than is required for 3-minute development. However, this method requires great care in processing, and the developer must be maintained as fresh as possible because of the greater susceptibility of films to chemical fogging with prolonged development.

In modern darkroom work, it should be emphasized that the time-temperature method is the only correct method of controlling development. One must never attempt to control the process by inspecting the film during development because it is extremely inaccurate and produces inconstant results. Furthermore, repeated removal of the film from the developer during "inspection development" may result in slight fogging of the film by the oxygen in the air.

The aging of the developer and the reaction of the chemicals with the film emulsion will gradually weaken it, so that as more and more films are processed, the solution must be fortified or the developing time must be increased in order to assure full development. There are two methods by which the weakening of the developer can be corrected:

1. *Exhaustion Method.* This involves counting the number of films of different sizes that have been processed, and gradually increasing the developing time according to the chart furnished for that purpose by the manufacturer. With the exhaustion method, *it is essential that each film be drained carefully* for 15 or 20 seconds as it is removed from the developer; the drainage is allowed to drop into the developing tank. Based on the work of Crabtree and Henn, the operation of the exhaustion method with their materials may be indicated roughly as follows: with 5 gallons of fresh developer, the first 53 films size 14 x 17 are developed at 68 F for 3 minutes. The next 59 films are developed at the same temperature for 3½ minutes, and the last 53 films for 4½ minutes. Then the developer is discarded. In general, about 165 films size 14 x 17 or the equivalent in smaller sizes can be developed in 5 gallons of solution before it is exhausted. The level of the developer in the tank is maintained by frequent addition of fresh developing *solution* and never by addition of water. It is a good policy to discard the developer at the end of one month and prepare a new solution, regardless of how few films have been

processed, if satisfactory results are to be anticipated. Exhausted or aged developer may not only stain the film, but also yields films of poor contrast and impaired density.

2. *Replenisher Method.* This is the second method of compensating for a weakened solution, and the one preferred by the author. With this method, *the films are removed from the developer rapidly without allowing them to drain.* This tends to carry away the relatively exhausted solution which clings to the films. The level of the developer in the tank is maintained by adding special *replenisher solution,* which at the same time fortifies the developing solution. With this system, the developing time does not change with the number of films processed because the strength of the developer is maintained relatively constant by removal of the weaker solution and addition of replenisher. The solution can be used until it has been replaced by three to four times its volume of replenisher, but in any case, the solution should be discarded at the end of one month.

When films are immersed in the developer, either method requires that they should be *agitated gently* at first, and then about once every minute during the development process. This will insure even development and prevent streakiness of the radiographic image. During development, bromides are freed from the emulsion and if these are not removed by agitation, they tend to inhibit development wherever they cling to the film. This is most frequently manifested by light streaks below the letters of the identifying label on the film. Agitation of the film removes these waste products of development and allows fresh developing solution always to be in contact with the film emulsion, so that streakiness is prevented.

Rinsing

After development, the film must be rinsed by immersion in running water to remove most of the chemicals carried over from the developer, thereby diminishing contamination of the next solution, the fixer. Films should be rinsed about 30 seconds in running water. Rinsing can be made more efficient by using a dilute solution of acetic acid (about 1 per cent), which neutralizes the alkali carried on the film when it is removed from the developing solution. Otherwise, this alkali neutralizes the acid in the fixing solution and decreases its effectiveness as well as its useful life. If rinsing is not thorough, the fixer then does not act evenly and streakiness results.

Fixation

The purpose of this step is to remove the unexposed and undeveloped silver salts, to preserve the film image, and to harden the emulsion so that it will not be easily damaged.

Fixing Solution. This consists of four essential ingredients.

1. *Fixing Agent—Hypo* (Sodium thiosulfate.) This dissolves out the silver salts in the unexposed and undeveloped areas, leaving only the metallic silver deposits in the exposed and developed areas of the film.

2. *Preservative—Sodium Sulfite.* This protects the sodium thiosulfate from decomposition and delays discoloration of the fixing solution by the developer that is carried in by the films.

3. *Hardener—Chrome Alum or Potassium Alum.* This "tans" or hardens the emulsion, thereby protecting it against scratches.

4. *Acid—Sulfuric Acid or Acetic Acid.* This serves two purposes: it neutralizes the alkali still remaining on the film, and provides an optimum medium for the fixer and hardener.

The time of fixation depends, of course, on the age of the fixer and the number of films that has been carried through. A satisfactory fixing solution requires about 1 to 4 minutes to clear a film —that is, remove all of the unexposed silver salts—but it requires about two or three times this period for adequate hardening of the emulsion. No-screen film, because of its thicker emulsion, requires longer fixation. The solution should be discarded when the clearing time becomes unduly prolonged because of exhaustion of the solution. When the films are immersed in the fixing bath, they should be moved up and down several times so that the chemicals may act evenly on the emulsion, thereby avoiding streakiness. The films should not be allowed to touch each other. White light should not be admitted until the films have been fixed for at least 2 minutes in order to avoid fogging. Prolonged immersion in the fixing bath should be avoided because of the danger of bleaching the image. The temperature of the fixing bath should be maintained at 68 F to 70 F for optimum action; at low temperatures the action of the chemicals is retarded, while at high temperatures the film emulsion may be softened and rendered more susceptible to damage.

Washing

This is a very important step in film processing. Before the films reach the final wash, they have been subjected to the action of a multitude of chemicals. These must be completely removed, otherwise they will eventually discolor the film and impair its value as a permanent record. The washing process is most satisfactorily accomplished in running water in which the water content of the tank changes rapidly enough to insure complete removal of the processing chemicals from the film. Ordinarily, if the water flow in 1 hour is 8 times the capacity of the tank, washing is complete in 20 minutes (with no-screen film, due to greater thickness of the emulsion, this requires 30 minutes). This is the minimum wash period regardless of how rapidly the water changes. If the rate of circulation is less, then longer wash periods are necessary. However, prolonged washing tends to soften the film emulsion, and wherever possible, the water circulation should be so regulated that washing can be completed in 20 to 30 minutes. The washing time must obviously be based on the last film put into the washing tank. The tank should be so constructed that even the tops of the film hangers are completely immersed and thoroughly washed.

Drying

Films can be dried by various methods. If the number of films handled is small, they can be dried in wall-mounted racks. Busy departments require special film driers such as those discussed in Chapter 15.

Standard Processing Technic

By summarizing one standard technique, one may obtain a clearer idea of the successive steps in processing a group of films.

1. Check temperature of developer by use of an immersed thermometer.

2. Stack cassettes containing the exposed films on the loading bench.

3. Remove required number and sizes of film hangers from their racks and place them alongside the cassettes.

4. Set the time clock at the proper developing time, but do not start it.

5. Shut all doors and windows, and turn out all lights except safelights. The darkroom is now "dark".

6. Unload cassettes one at a time and clip each film into a hanger of proper size, clipping first into the bottom clips, then turning the hanger with its handle up and inserting the film into the clips mounted on the tension springs. Tension should be equal at the four corners so that the film will not bulge.

7. Immerse the films in the developer, agitate them gently, and separate the films by placing the fingers of each hand between successive hangers.

8. Rinse hands in water and dry quickly.

9. Start the timer. Remember to agitate the films gently, about every minute.

10. Load the cassettes with fresh film and stand them against the wall, or place them in some satisfactory receptacle.

11. When the time clock rings, lift films from developer (slowly in "exhaustion" method; rapidly in "replenisher" method), and immerse and agitate them in rinse bath for 20 sec, then drain well and place in fixing bath.

12. After fixation is complete (about 2 to 3 times the clearing time, usually 5 to 10 min.) wash films in running water 20 to 30 min.

13. Dry under suitable conditions.

14. Remove films from hangers and trim the corners.

Darkroom Errors

It may be of some help to indicate the causes of the more common film defects.

Fog. There are many causes of film fogging, that is, a generalized darkening of the film. First, exposure of the film to unsafe light, such as occurs when the darkroom is not light tight, or when the safelight is unsafe from the use of too large a bulb, a crack in the safelight lamp housing, a faded safelight filter, or an incorrect filter; or prolonged exposure of the film to the safelight especially at very short distances.

Exposure to X-radiation or to Radium may cause fogging. Films should not be stored near a supply of radium, and the storage area must be adequately protected from x-rays by lead of sufficient thickness.

Overdevelopment, or development at excessively high temperature tends to cause fogging.

Developer that has become oxidized and *deteriorated* may cause chemical fog, and may also stain the film. Oxidized developer has a brown color.

Prolonged and repeated examination of the film during development may cause fog. This can be avoided by using time-temperature development which eliminates inspection of the film during processing.

Old tanks, especially of the porous type, may contaminate the developer because of the accumulation of chemicals in the walls of the tank. This causes chemical fog—usually a general grayness of the light areas on the films.

Finally, outdated films or films stored at high temperature and high humidity, may show spotty fogging known as "age fog".

Stain. Various types of discolorations may appear on the films at different intervals after processing. First is the variegated color pattern which may appear when films are improperly rinsed.

A grayish-yellow or brown tone appears when film is left in the fixer for a prolonged interval or when the fixer is old.

A grayish-white sticky scum on the film indicates incomplete washing.

It should be noted that all of these difficulties can be avoided by the use of fresh solutions and correct processing.

Marks and Defects. There are several different kinds of characteristic markings which appear when films are not handled gently.

Crinkle Marks are curved black lines about 1 cm in length which result from bending the film acutely over the end of the finger.

Static Marks are lightning or tree-like black marks on the film, caused by static electricity due to friction between two films. To avoid this, never pile films on top of each other before loading into cassettes, or after removing from cassettes. Always place the film gently into the cassette in order to minimize friction.

Water Marks. Droplets of water on the film surface may leave round spots of various sizes.

Cassette Marks. Dust particles, fragments of paper, hair, defects in the screens, etc., will leave a corresponding white spot on the film.

Reticulation Marks. These are a network of fine grooves in the film surface caused by marked differences in the temperatures of the solutions in which the films have been processed. These marks resemble grossly the reticulated pattern which is sometimes noticeable on old varnished furniture.

QUESTIONS

1. What is meant by latent image? Manifest image?
2. Of what do the black areas on a roentgenogram consist?
3. What is the purpose of development? Fixation?
4. List the ingredients of the developing solution, and describe the function of each.
5. List the ingredients of the fixing solution and describe the function of each.
6. What is meant by "time-temperature development"? Why is it preferable to "sight development"?
7. What is the "replenisher method"? "Exhaustion method"? Which would you prefer and why?
8. Name five causes of film fogging and state how they can be avoided.
9. Why should films be agitated gently when first placed in the developer and then at one-minute intervals?
10. What is included by the term "film processing"?
11. Why is it advisable to trim the corners of films after drying?

The object of any radiographic procedure is to obtain an x-ray image of the part being examined so that it is represented on the film to best advantage. The production of a radiograph of excellent quality not only affords great satisfaction to the technician, but it is also essential for accurate diagnosis. A poor radiograph may so obscure a lesion that it will not be clearly visualized.

There are four factors which determine the quality of a radiograph: *distortion, detail, density,* and *contrast.*

DISTORTION

Under certain conditions, the x-ray image of a given object is misshapen, and its component parts are not in true relationship to one another. Such radiographic perversion of the true shape of an object is known as *distortion.* Now, every x-ray image inherently has an element of distortion because the radiographic image lies in one plane only, while the object, being a solid body, has many planes. It should be emphasized that distortion tends to impair radiographic quality, so that any factor which reduces distortion is bound to improve radiographic quality.

What are the causes of distortion? The answer is readily available if one bears in mind the fact that image formation by x-rays (which travel in straight lines diverging from the focal spot) follows the simplest laws of geometry. X-ray images are really shadows, and the geometry of their formation is analogous to the formation of shadows by ordinary light. It is well known, or it can easily be demonstrated, that if an object is held between a light source and a white surface, the size of shadow enlarges as the object is placed nearer to the source of light, and shrinks as it is moved closer to the white surface. This is due to the divergence of the light rays in the beam. Referring to Figure 135, one notes that the divergent beam of light magnifies the shadow more in A than in B; that is, the shorter the distance between the object and the source of light the greater the magnification. *The size of the image is to the size of the object as the distance of the image from the light source is to the distance of the object from the light source.*

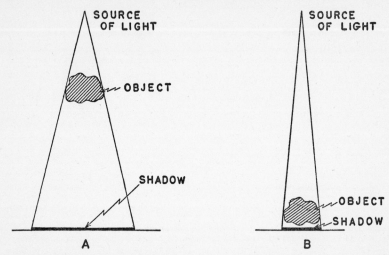

Figure 135. Image magnification. In A the shadow of the object is larger than in B, because in A the object is nearer the source of light.

Precisely the same law applies in x-ray image formation, but since x-rays *penetrate* solid objects, this law must be modified. Solid objects, such as the human body, are made up of various superimposed structures. When a part of the body is radiographed, the various organs in the body will obviously be at different distances from the film; those which are farthest from the film (or nearest the x-ray tube target) will be magnified more than those nearest the film and so their size relationship is *distorted.* This is revealed in Figure 136, which shows a cross section of an object containing a cross-hatched structure which will cast its own shadow. By measurement, the reader can easily determine that the ratio of the *image* sizes of the inner and outer structures is smaller in B, than in A where the object is farther from the film. Thus, in radiography one of the fundamental causes of distortion is *magnification, or size distortion. This type of distortion can be minimized by reducing the object-film distance, and by increasing the anode-object distance.*

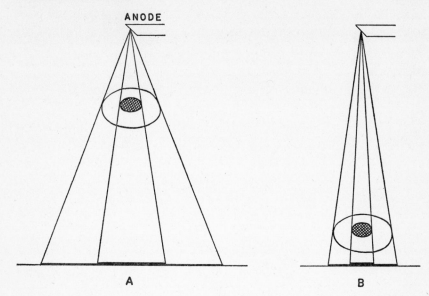

Figure 136. Size distortion. In A, with the long object-film distance, the radiographic image of the inner cross-hatched structure is larger relative to the body as a whole, than in B where the object-film distance is relatively short.

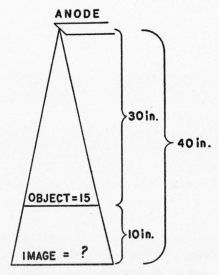

Figure 137. Magnification of the image in radiography.

The amount of radiographic magnification is determined very easily by applying the geometry of similar triangles. For example, an object measures 15 in. in diameter and lies 10 in. above the level of the film. The anode-film distance is 40 in. What is the magnification of the radiographic image? It is first necessary to find the image size. Construct a diagram as shown in Figure 137 and apply the following proportion:

$$\frac{\text{image size}}{\text{object size}} = \frac{\text{focal spot to film distance}}{\text{focal spot to object distance}}$$

$$\frac{\text{image size}}{15} = \frac{40}{30}$$

$$\text{image size} = \frac{40 \times 15}{30} = 20 \text{ in.}$$

The magnification of the image, or its enlargement relative to the size of the object, may now be expressed in one of two ways:

1. *Magnification Factor.* This is defined as the ratio of the image size to the object size:

$$\text{magnification factor} = \frac{\text{image size}}{\text{object size}}$$

In the above example,

$$\text{magnification factor} = \frac{20}{15} = 1\tfrac{1}{3}$$

2. *Percentage Magnification.* This is defined as the percentage enlargement of the image as compared with the object, and is *not a true ratio.*

$$\text{percentage magnification} = \frac{\text{image size} - \text{object size}}{\text{object size}} \times 100$$

In the above example,

$$\text{percentage magnification} = \frac{20 - 15}{15} \times 100$$
$$= \tfrac{1}{3} \times 100$$
$$= 33\tfrac{1}{3}\%$$

The same principles are employed to determine the *size of the object* being radiographed when the image size, the focal spot to film distance, and the object to film distance are known. A diagram is prepared as in Figure 137, the known values inserted, and the object size determined from the proportion. This is the basis of most methods of determining pelvic measurements of the mother in relation to the size of the fetal skull, a procedure known as *cephalopelvimetry*.

Distortion of shape is caused by improper alignment of the object with relation to the focal spot and film. Again, the analogy with the shadow cast by a source of light helps to simplify the explanation. In Figure 138, an oval object placed in the x-ray beam in such a manner that it is not parallel to the film, will cast a shadow which is almost circular. Similarly, a rectangular object can be placed in a beam so that it will cast a shadow which is almost square. If these objects are placed at right angles to the direction of the beam and parallel to the film, the images will, of course, show no shape distortion. Under certain conditions, distortion is purposely employed to bring out parts of the body that are obscured by overlying parts; for example, in radiography of the gall bladder the patient is often rotated to displace the gall bladder shadow away from the spine.

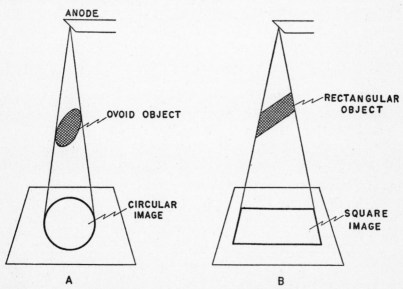

Figure 138. Shape distortion. In A the projected image of an oval object is circular because the object is not parallel to the film. In B the image of a rectangular object is almost square.

One can summarize the data on distortion as follows: *There are two types of distortion, size distortion and shape distortion. Size distortion* is due to the different degrees of magnification of different parts of an object because of varying distances of these parts from the film. The shorter the object-film distance, and the longer the anode-object distance, the less the degree of size distortion. This has practical application in determining heart size on radiographs; at a 6-foot distance from anode to film, and with the patient's chest close to the film, the ratio of the diameter of the heart to the diameter of the chest is practically the true ratio. At short distances, say 36 inches, the heart diameter is magnified more than the chest diameter so that their true relationship is distorted on the film. *Shape distortion* is due to improper alignment of the tube, object, and film. It is, of course, possible to have shape and size distortion occurring together if the causative factors of both conditions are present.

DETAIL

One may define *detail* as the sharpness of structure lines or contour lines on a roentgenogram. Good detail or definition permits the viewing eye to detect more minute changes in structure. There are numerous factors which affect radiographic detail, and these will be considered in turn.

Focal Spot Size

The size of the focal spot has a great deal of influence on radiographic detail. Again, consideration of the simplest geometric principles will reveal this influence. In Figure 139 the radiographic image is shown to consist of the image proper, or the *umbra,* and a lighter hazy area at the edge labeled P, the *penumbra.* The penumbra is caused by rays from various points on the focal spot passing tangentially to the surface (that is, skimming the surface) of the object, as revealed in the figure. The larger the penumbra, the fuzzier the margin of the image, the greater the possibility of overlapping of the images of adjacent structures, and therefore the poorer the detail. Since the penumbra decreases as the focal spot area decreases, one may conclude that *the smaller the effective focal spot, the sharper the detail.* Theoretically, a point source of x-rays would give perfect detail because there would be no penumbra, but this is impossible at the present time because of the limited heating capacity of x-ray tubes. Furthermore, even if a point source of x-rays were available, it would still give far from perfect detail because of the inherent graininess of films and intensifying screens.

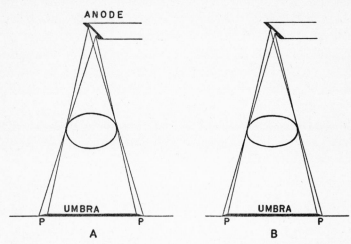

Figure 139. Effect of focal spot size on image detail. In A the large focal spot produces a broader penumbra and a less distinct image than in B where a small focal spot is used. (Umbra = image proper; penumbra = zone of blurring at edge of image.)

Anode-Film Distance

The second factor in roentgenographic detail is the distance from the anode to the film. As this distance is increased, the effect is similar to a decrease in focal spot size. From the standpoint of the film, the farther away the focal spot is, the smaller it appears. As the anode-film distance increases the penumbra decreases. This fact is illustrated in Figure 140. Therefore, *detail of the radiographic image is improved by increasing the anode-film distance.*

Object-Film Distance

Another important factor in radiographic detail is the distance from the object to the film. If the distance from anode to film remains unchanged, and only the distance between the object and

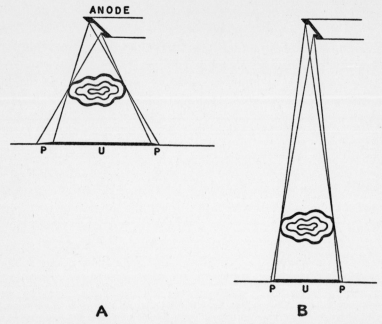

Figure 140. The effect of anode-film distance on radiographic detail. The *object-film* distance is the same in both A and B. However, in B the *anode-film* distance is greater; note that this produces a smaller penumbra and therefore a sharper image in B.

the film is altered, then by the application of the same geometric principles one finds that a decrease in the object-film distance decreases the penumbra, thereby enhancing detail (see Figure 141).

One can summarize what has been said thus far about detail as follows: there are *three geometrical factors* governing detail. These are the size of the focal spot, the anode-film distance, and the object-film distance. Detail is influenced by these factors principally by their *penumbra* effect; that is, the fuzzy borders of the image lines resulting from x-rays that originate over many points on the surface of the focal spot. Detail is improved by making the focal spot as small as possible, the anode-film distance as long as possible, and the object-film distance as short as possible. It should be emphasized that distortion and detail are influenced by similar factors: anode-film distance and object-film distance. For example, a radiograph made at a short anode-film distance or long object-film distance will have considerable distortion, and these same factors will also cause impairment of detail. Thus, *the greater the distortion of the radiographic image the poorer the detail*. The technician can readily demonstrate this principle by observing the shadow cast by a pencil on a white surface. As the pencil is moved towards the source of light, the shadow becomes larger (distortion) and also becomes more and more blurred (impaired detail).

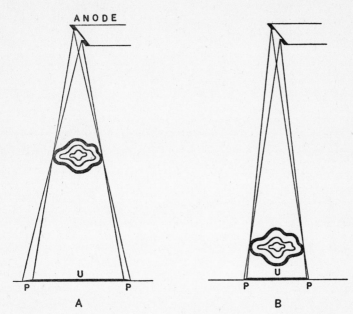

Figure 141. The effect of object-film distance on radiographic detail. The *anode-film* distance is the same in A and B. However, in B the *object-film* distance is smaller; note that this produces a smaller penumbra and therefore a sharper image in B.

As the pencil is moved nearer the white surface, the shadow becomes smaller and sharper.

There are several additional factors involved in obtaining good detail. *Motion* of the part being radiographed may be regarded as the greatest enemy of detail, since this produces a blurred image. Motion can be eliminated or minimized in three ways: (1) by careful immobilization of the part by sand bags or compression band; (2) by suspension of respiration when examining parts other than the extremities; and (3) by using exposures that are as short as possible, which requires the use of intensifying screens. The latter may decrease detail somewhat because of the factor of graininess, but this is more than compensated for by the elimination of motion.

Fogging of the film impairs detail because it reduces contrast. The types of fogging and their causes are considered in Chapter 17. Akin to this is the general haze produced by scattered rays from failure to use grid diaphragms and cones.

Cardboard film exposure holders yield images of finer detail than do screens. It will be recalled from Chapter 16 that intensifying screens increase radiographic density by virtue of the fluorescence of their crystals. Since these crystals each produce a spot of light of definite though very small magnitude, image lines are broader when produced by these crystals than when formed primarily by x-rays through cardboard exposure holders. Besides, the crystals cause diffusion of light over the active surface of the screen. For this reason, when minute detail is desired, such as in the radiography of small parts (hands, toes, wrists), it is preferable to use cardboard exposure holders rather than screen cassettes. In radiography of thicker parts, such as the skull and abdomen, screen cassettes are used with a bucky diaphragm. Screen contact must be perfect, because if there is any appreciable separation between the screens and the film, the image will be blurred, thereby impairing detail.

DENSITY

The amount of darkening of an x-ray film, or of a certain area on the film, is called *radiographic density*. It should be recalled that any region of an x-ray film which is subjected to x-rays or to light from intensifying screens becomes susceptible to the action of developer. The silver salts that have been affected in this manner are changed by the developing agent into tiny particles of metallic silver which appear black because of their finely divided state. The greater the amount of radiation that reaches the film, the greater is the final degree of blackening. Those areas which receive only a small amount of radiation, undergo little or no subsequent action by the developer so that these regions of underexposure appear transparent, or nearly so, in the finished radiograph. Thus, in the final analysis, *the density or degree of blackening depends on the amount of radiation reaching a particular area of the film and the amount of silver salts affected.* If time-temperature processing is used, then development is standardized and should produce optimum density; however, if the developing procedure is not standardized, underdevelopment may occur with resultant loss of film density.

There are five factors that are of prime importance in determining the exposure or amount of radiation reaching the film, and consequently govern its density: (1) kilovoltage, (2) milliamperage, (3) time, (4) distance, and (5) thickness and structure of part being radiographed. These will be discussed in turn.

1. *Kilovoltage.* An increase in kilovoltage applied to the x-ray tube increases both the total intensity of the emitted x-rays and the proportion of short wave length (higher energy) rays. These have more penetrating ability and are not as readily absorbed by the structures being radiographed, and therefore a higher proportion of the primary beam eventually reaches the film. Thus, increasing the kilovoltage increases the amount of radiation on the film and therefore increases the radiographic density. In general, an increase of 10 Kv over an initial kilovoltage of 60 will approximately double the exposure. At 30 Kv, an increase of about 6 Kv will approximately double the exposure. It should be mentioned that the radiographic density increases as the exposure increases, but that this relationship is not strictly proportional.

Under ordinary conditions, with equipment using grids with an 8:1 ratio or less, it is unwise to employ kilovoltages above 80 or 85 because this results in excessive secondary radiation which has a fogging effect on the radiograph and impairs its diagnostic quality. On the other hand, one must bear in mind that the efficiency of x-ray equipment is greater at higher kilovoltages because there is less of a burden on the tube (see Chapter 13) and the certainty of penetration is greater. Recent work with 100 to 130-Kv x-rays using special 12:1 or 16:1 grids is stated to offer advantages over conventional radiography, including greater latitude without significant loss of contrast and a smaller skin dose. This has come to be known as *high voltage radiography.*

2. *Milliamperage.* X-ray exposure is practically proportional to the milliamperage. This means that if the milliamperage is doubled, the radiographic exposure is doubled. If the milliamperage is tripled the exposure is tripled. (This rule does not hold precisely, but is sufficiently accurate for clinical work.) The milliamperage, which is actually the tube current, is governed by the number of electrons passing from cathode to anode per second. As the number of these electrons is increased, more x-rays are produced at the target. Note that the *milliamperage determines only the strength of the x-ray beam; it has nothing to do with the penetrating power of the beam.*

3. *Time.* An increase in exposure time causes an increase in film density, but this is not strictly proportional. However, the actual x-ray *exposure* of the film is proportional to the time. Thus, if the time is doubled the total exposure is doubled. If the time is tripled, the total exposure is tripled. The exposure time has nothing to do with the intensity of radiation (this is the amount of radiation per second) but a longer exposure time allows the radiation of a given intensity to act longer, thereby affecting more silver salt particles in the emulsion and resulting in more blackening of the radiograph. In actual practice the milliamperage and exposure time are usually multiplied and called milliampere-seconds = MaS. For example, if one has a technic set up for 100 Ma and $\frac{1}{10}$ sec, then multiplying $100 \times \frac{1}{10} = 10$ MaS. If one requires a *faster* exposure, as in radiographing a small child, and wishes to keep the density unchanged, the milliamperage can be increased to 400 and the time reduced to $\frac{1}{40}$ sec; $400 \times \frac{1}{40} = 10$ MaS. (This rule is approximate because film density is usually somewhat less at the longer exposure time, even though the MaS is the same; but the rule is sufficiently accurate under average conditions of clinical radiography.) The technician should cultivate the habit of thinking in terms of MaS because it greatly facilitates changing the established technics for special cases; in other words, it increases the flexibility of the technic chart.

4. *Distance.* The effect of distance on the strength of an x-ray beam is not as simple as some of the other factors, but it is easily

understood by keeping in mind certain simple geometrical rules. These can be listed as follows:

a. The x-ray beam originates at a point on the target (this is an assumption for practical purposes).

b. The rays travel in straight lines and diverge equally in all directions from the focal spot (except for the "heel effect," to be described later).

Note that the rays diverge or spread as they pass farther and farther from their point of origin. In other words, the width of the beam increases as the distance from the target increases. This means that the same amount of radiation is distributed over a larger area the farther this area is from the target. Obviously, if the same radiation is spread over a larger area it must be spread thinner. If, at a certain distance from the tube target, the beam were to cover completely a film of a certain size, then at a greater distance it would cover a larger film. However, the radiographic density of the latter would be less because each square centimeter of the film would have received less radiation than each square centimeter of the first film. In more accurate terms, the amount of radiation striking each square centimeter of surface decreases as the distance of the surface from the target increases. We may conclude from this *radiographic exposure decreases as the anode-film distance increases.*

It is possible to determine by simple geometry *how much* the exposure decreases as the anode-film distance increases. In Figure 142 the slanting lines represent the edges of a beam emerging from the focal spot at the target, T. Choose two planes, ABCD and EFGH at right angles to the direction of the central ray of the beam (represented by the dotted line). Both planes are assumed to be squares. Plane EFGH is at twice the distance from the target as is plane ABCD. Therefore each side of the lower plane, such as HE is twice as large as a side of the upper plane, such as DA because triangles TEH and TAD are similar and their corresponding sides are proportional. To simplify the discussion, let X equal a side of the upper plane. Then $2X$ must equal a side of the lower plane. The area of the upper plane will then be $X \times X$ or X^2, and the area of the lower plane will be $2X \times 2X$ or $4X^2$. Thus,

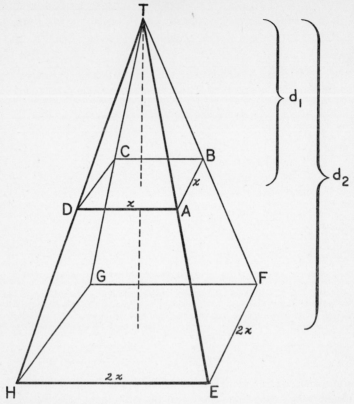

Figure 142. Inverse square law of radiation. The lower plane surface (EFGH) is selected at twice the distance from the point source of radiation (tube focus) than is the upper plane (ABCD). Each side of the lower plane (2x) is twice as long as each side of the upper plane (x) because of the spread of the x-ray beam as it proceeds away from the tube focus. It is evident from the diagram that the lower surface area ($4x^2$) is four times as large as the upper surface area (x^2), which means that at twice the distance from the target the x-ray beam covers four times the area and therefore the brightness of illumination must only be one-fourth as great.

the lower surface, EFGH has four times the area of the upper surface, ABCD.

It is evident that *when the distance is doubled, the same radiation is spread over an area four times as great.* Therefore, the brightness or illumination must be ¼ as great. This is an application of the *inverse square law of radiation,* and applies equally to x-rays and light. The law is stated as follows: *The intensity of radiation at a given distance from a point source is inversely proportional to the square of the distance.* For example, if the intensity of an x-ray beam at 20 in. from the focal spot is 100, what will it be at 40 inches? Let us set up the inverse square law in equation form:

$$I:i::d^2:D^2$$

where

> I is the intensity at 40 in. = ?
> i is the intensity at 20 in. = 100 r per min.
> d is 20 in.
> D is 40 in.

Note that the proportion is not direct, but inverse (inverted). Substitute the above values in the equation:

$$I:100::(20)^2:(40)^2$$
$$I:100::400:1600$$

The product of the extremes equals the product of the means:

$$1600\ I = 40,000$$

$$I = \frac{40,000}{1600} = 25\ \text{r per min.}$$

Thus, at twice the distance the intensity is ¼ the initial value (25 as compared with 100). This means that in radiography, if the distance is doubled, in order to keep the exposure constant, the MaS has to be multiplied by 4.

Let us consider another example. If the intensity of radiation at 60 in. is 10 r per min., what will the intensity be at 20 in.?

$$I:i::d^2:D^2$$

Let i represent the unknown intensity, at a point $d = 20$ in. from the target. Then using the data given in the above problem,

$$10:i::(20)^2:(60)^2$$
$$10:i::400:3600$$

The product of the means equals the product of the extremes,

$$400\ i = 36,000$$
$$i = 90\ \text{r per min.}$$

In other words, the distance has been reduced to ⅓ (20 divided by 60) and the intensity has increased 9 times (90 divided by 10). Thus, if a radiograph has the proper density at 60 in. and the target film distance is reduced to 20 in., in order to maintain the same density the MaS must be reduced to ⅑ the original value.

CONTRAST

In viewing a radiograph, one notes that it is made up of dark areas and light areas; that is, there are variations in the density. The difference in density between the light areas and the dark areas is known as *contrast*. The difference in darkness of two adjacent areas must be at least 2 per cent for the average human eye to perceive it. The function of contrast is to make detail more clearly visible. Moderate contrast improves detail visibility, but excessive contrast tends to impair detail, as in the so-called "chalky" film.

There are six main factors involved in securing optimum contrast: kilovoltage, scattered radiation, fogging, intensification by screens, film-processing technic, and the thickness and nature of the object being radiographed.

1. *Kilovoltage* affects contrast by its influence on the penetrating power of the x-ray beam. It has been shown in Chapter 12 that as the kilovoltage across the x-ray tube is increased, the average penetrating ability of the x-ray beam is increased. Such an x-ray beam penetrates tissues of various densities more equally than does a beam of low penetrating power. For example, in radiography of a leg, the bone structures offer a much greater hindrance to the passage of x-rays than do the soft tissues. As the kilovoltage is increased and the penetrating power of the x-ray beam is increased, the bones offer less and less of an impediment to the passage of the rays so that the contrast between the bones and soft tissues is diminished. An additional factor is that scattering increases at higher kilovoltage, but this factor is being eliminated in modern high voltage radiography by the use of grids having a high ratio.

2. *Scattered Radiation* impairs contrast because of the general graying effect on the lighter areas of the film. The scattering can

be controlled by the use of a wafer grid or bucky diaphragm, and by limiting the size of the x-ray beam with cones or cut-out diaphragms (see Chapter 19).

3. *Fogging* from any cause produces a general graying of the film so that contrast is reduced.

4. *Intensifying Screens.* It has already been stated that intensifying screens increase radiographic density for a given x-ray exposure. They also increase the contrast of a radiograph as compared with the same film exposed in a cardboard holder. The reason for the increased contrast obtained with intensifying screens is that the screen type films have more contrast for the light emitted by the fluorescent screens than they have for direct x-rays.

5. *Processing Method* may affect contrast. Within the normal range of time-temperature development, contrast is not appreciably influenced by the temperature. However, at excessively high temperatures the element of fogging enters, reducing contrast. If the films are agitated during development, contrast is improved. For optimum contrast, strict adherence to time-temperature processing is strongly recommended.

6. *Thickness and Nature of Object Being Radiographed.* The human body consists of tissues which vary in their degree of transparency or *radiolucency* to x-rays. The more rays a given type of tissue *absorbs,* the less the amount of x-ray energy left over from the primary beam to reach the film. Tooth enamel is the densest material in the body, and in decreasing order of density are bone, muscle, fat, and gas. For example, a radiograph of the abdomen shows a light zone in the center representing the image of the spine which is not as readily penetrated as the soft tissues. The various soft tissue structures are represented in shades of gray. The fat layers, most often present around the kidneys, along the psoas muscles, and in the abdominal wall, appear as dark gray or almost black lines. Finally, the gas in the stomach and intestines appears black. This difference in the degree of penetration produces the different densities in the radiograph, making it possible to distinguish various structures and to discover abnormalities in them.

In those instances where organs cannot be studied in detail because their density is too similar to that of adjacent organs, we employ *contrast media;* for example, dense media such as barium sulfate in the gastro-intestinal tract; Priodax® or Telepaque® in the gall bladder; Neo-iopax®, Diodrast®, Urokon® in the urinary tract. Or, a less dense medium can be used, such as air in the ventricles of the brain.

Most radiographic technic charts are established to correct for differences in the density of various regions of the body, and for differences in thickness of the same part of the body in different individuals. The thicker or the denser a part is, the greater the quantity, penetrating power, or the time of exposure of x-rays required. In most technic charts, the MaS and distance are maintained constant for a given part of the body and the kilovoltage is varied depending on the thickness. In recent years, there has been a trend in some quarters to choose an *optimum kilovoltage* for a given part and vary the MaS. Another trend has been toward the manufacture of radiographic equipment operating at 100 to 130 Kv, utilizing high ratio grids up to 16:1. High voltage radiography is said to produce radiographs having superb detail, wide latitude, and satisfactory contrast as has been mentioned earlier.

QUESTIONS AND PROBLEMS

1. Define the four factors in radiographic quality.
2. How can distortion be minimized?
3. An object being radiographed is located 4 in. above the film. The anode-film distance is 36 in., and the diameter of the object is 6 in. What is the size of the image? What is the percentage magnification? What is the magnification factor?
4. Define umbra; penumbra. Which of these impairs radiographic detail?
5. Name and discuss briefly the three major geometrical factors that influence detail.
6. What is the greatest enemy of detail, and how is it minimized?
7. What five factors determine density?
8. State the inverse square law in your own words.
9. At a point 50 cm from the anode, the intensity of a beam is 20 r per min. What will the intensity be at 25 cm?

10. A certain technique requires an exposure of 70 Kv and 100 MaS at a distance of 60 in. If we wish to decrease the distance to 20 in., what will be the new MaS value in order to obtain a radiograph of the same density as with the original technic?

11. A certain technic calls for 30 Ma and $\frac{1}{10}$ sec at 65 Kv. If we have an uncooperative patient and wish to reduce motion by using an exposure time of $\frac{1}{40}$ sec, what will the new Ma value be?

12. What determines the penetrating power of an x-ray beam?

13. What effect does the intensifying screen have on density? on contrast? Why?

14. List the main materials in the human body in decreasing order of their radiographic density.

CHAPTER 19 *DEVICES FOR IMPROVING RADIOGRAPHIC QUALITY*

In the preceding chapter, the various factors influencing radiographic quality were discussed. The improvement in quality of a radiograph can be attained by the use of various devices that have been designed for that purpose.

From the standpoint of actual practice, what is the main stumbling block in obtaining the ideal radiograph? It has already been pointed out that the development of modern diagnostic x-ray equipment has produced the rotating anode tube with a very small focal spot, permitting excellent radiographic detail. Furthermore, this type of tube has made it possible to utilize high milliamperage with very short exposure time, thereby reducing the factor of motion, the greatest enemy of detail. In other words, the inherent construction of modern equipment should allow the production of radiographs of superb quality, but certain auxiliary devices are needed to overcome the remaining obstacle, *secondary radiation*. This still remains the chief problem to be solved in securing the best possible radiographic quality.

Secondary Radiation

It should be recalled from Chapter 12 that a roentgen ray beam, when it emerges from the tube focal spot as the primary beam, is a heterogeneous mixture of rays of various wavelengths. The primary beam is made up of *primary rays* resulting from the conversion of the energy of the electrons as they are stopped by the target; and *characteristic rays* which are emitted by the target metal due to excitation of its atoms. When the primary beam reaches the patient and passes through him, *secondary radiation* is produced by interaction of the primary beam with the atoms in the patient's body. Secondary radiation is also emitted as the beam passes through the table top. It may be recalled that the greater proportion of the secondary rays (1) is softer than the primary rays; and (2) is scattered in various directions. This multi-directional scattering of the primary beam impairs radiographic quality in two ways. First, it tends to diffuse x-rays over the surface of the film, darkening the entire radiograph and thereby reducing contrast. In the second place, it impairs detail by blurring fine structural lines. The scattering effect is illustrated in Figure 143. This shows how the primary beam sets up many secondary

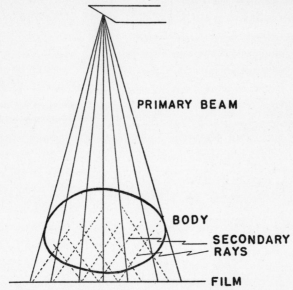

Figure 143. Deleterious effect of scattered and secondary radiation on radiographic quality.

centers of radiation in the body. These centers emit rays in various directions, represented by dotted lines in the diagram, producing a graying or fogging effect on the film emulsion. This scattering effect increases as the volume of irradiated tissue increases. Thus, it is most pronounced in radiography of the abdomen and least pronounced in radiography of small parts such as the hands and feet.

REDUCTION OF SECONDARY RADIATION BY USE OF THE GRID

Since secondary radiation cannot be entirely eliminated because of the very nature of x-rays and their interaction with matter, we can only hope to reduce it to a minimum. This is particularly important in radiographing large anatomic areas such as the abdominal viscera, because of the greater amount of scattering by such a large volume of tissue. The most effective devices available today for this purpose are the *stationary wafer grid* and the *Potter-Bucky grid diaphragm*. Although the latter is by far the more frequently used of the two, the stationary grid will be discussed first because of its relative simplicity.

Stationary Grid

The most popular type of stationary grid is the so-called wafer grid. It is a flat, thin, rectangular device the same size as the film, and it is placed between the patient and the cassette for the purpose of reducing the amount of secondary radiation reaching the film. The grid, although it resembles a sheet of metal externally, is actually composed of alternating parallel strips of lead and wood (or bakelite). These strips are vertically disposed, as shown in Figure 144. The strips of lead and the alternating strips of translucent material are extremely thin. How does such a device func-

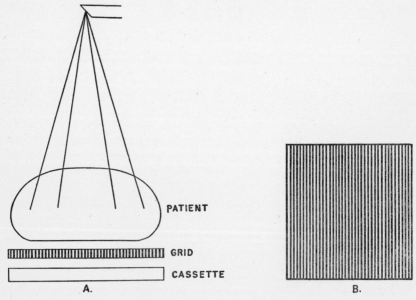

Figure 144. Stationary grid, seen in cross section in A, and top view in B.

tion? Figure 145 shows a small section of the grid greatly magnified. The rays in the primary beam which pass straight through the narrow spaces will reach the film. Since the scattered rays are for the most part directed at various angles, they will strike the lead strips and be largely absorbed, so that they will

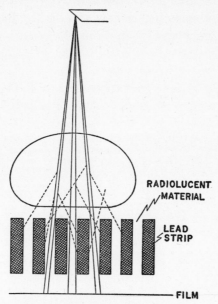

Figure 145. Principle of the lead grid. The secondary radiation, represented by the dotted lines, proceeds in various directions and is absorbed in large part by the lead strips. The rays that pass straight down through the x-ray-transparent (radiolucent) material between the lead strips reach the film.

have little or no effect on the film. Such a grid absorbs as much as 90 per cent of secondary radiation and results in a startling improvement in detail and contrast of the radiograph. The stationary grid has one disadvantage, and that is the fact that the lead strips cast shadows on the radiograph as thin white lines; however, at the usual viewing distance the lines are only faintly visible on the radiograph so that their presence is more than compensated for by the improved quality of the radiographic image. Because of the interposition of the grid with its lead strips in the x-ray beam, a great deal of the energy is absorbed and therefore the exposure must be increased three or four times over the non-grid exposure.

The efficiency of a grid in removing secondary radiation is dependent on the *grid ratio, defined as the ratio of the depth of the lead strips to the space between them.* For example, if the lead strips are 2 mm deep and the translucent spaces between average 0.4 mm, then the grid ratio is $2 \div 0.4 = 5$. This is usually stated as a 5:1 grid. Note that as the depth of the grid increases relative to the translucent spaces, the efficiency increases, as represented by an increase in the grid ratio.

These grids can be obtained in various sizes, depending on the size of the cassette to be covered. If a grid larger than the cassette is used, a wooden frame must be placed around the cassette to avoid bending the grid when a heavy part is placed over it. Since the grids are extremely light, they are very convenient to use in portable work, and also in the radiography of thick parts in the upright position.

Usually, grids are employed with intensifying screen cassettes because of the relatively heavy exposures that would otherwise be required. However, certain parts of medium thickness, such as knees, shoulders, and ribs can be radiographed with non-screen plus grid technic; this produces radiographs with remarkably fine detail and excellent contrast, superior to the conventional screen plus grid technic. The grid is very thin and therefore does not appreciably increase the object to film distance, so that it causes no distortion of the radiographic image. There has recently appeared on the market a *grid cassette* which has a built-in grid forming the front of the cassette. It is much more convenient to use than an ordinary cassette with a separate grid.

Most wafer grids are *not focused;* that is, the lead strips are all vertical. If such a grid is used at a very short anode to film distance, the beam will be too divergent and the outer portion of the beam will strike the lead strips, therefore causing underexposure of the periphery of the radiograph (see Figure 146). If the beam is not exactly perpendicular to the grid, and is tilted across the direction of the lead strips, a larger proportion of rays will be

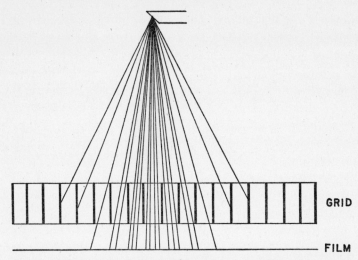

Figure 146. The effect of excessively short target-film distance on grid efficiency. The x-ray beam is sharply divergent, and a large proportion of the peripheral rays are absorbed by the lead strips, with reduction in density near the outer margins of the radiograph.

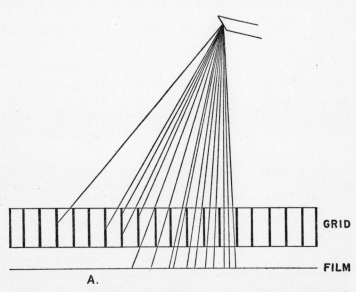

Figure 147. The effect of having the x-ray beam inclined towards the grid. One portion of the radiograph will be underexposed, as indicated at A.

absorbed on one side of the beam, and therefore one edge of the film will be lighter. This is shown in Figure 147. If the beam is tilted parallel to the length of the strips, there will be no variation in density across the film surface.

The Potter-Bucky Diaphragm

This is essentially a grid which *moves* between the patient and the cassette during the exposure. It is named after the two doctors who invented it. The grid consists of alternating strips of lead and wood, but these can be coarser than those in the wafer grid, be-

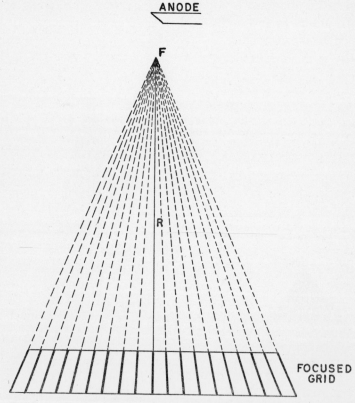

Figure 148. Potter-Bucky focused diaphragm. The lead strips are inclined so that their directions, indicated by the broken lines, meet at a specified imaginary point above the grid, F, called the *grid focus*. (Note that this point is not the same as the tube focal spot.) The vertical distance from the center of the grid to its focus is called the grid radius, R.

cause the motion of the grid during the exposure prevents the appearance of the lead shadows ("grid lines") on the radiograph. There are two main types; the curved diaphragm which is now almost extinct, and the flat type.

Most flat diaphragms are *focused;* that is, the lead strips are tilted more and more towards the edges of the grid as shown in Figure 148. If one extends the directions of these tilted strips upwards, these imaginary lines will be found to intersect at a definite distance above the grid. The vertical distance between this imaginary point of intersection and the center of the grid, represented in the diagram by the letter R, is called the *radius* of the grid. In actual practice, the grid is efficient if the target to film distance is no greater than the radius plus 25 per cent, and no less than the radius minus 25 per cent. Thus, if the radius is 40 inches,

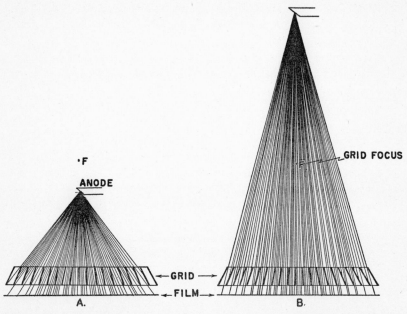

Figure 149. The effect of anode-film distance on the efficiency of a focused grid. In A the anode-film distance is less than the grid radius minus 25 per cent, and more and more rays are absorbed by the lead strips near the edge of the film. In B the anode-film distance is more than the grid radius plus 25 per cent, and again there is relatively greater absorption of the beam at the edges of the film. In either case, the outer portions of the radiograph will show reduced density.

one can use target to film distances of 30 to 50 inches. Distances smaller or larger than this will result in relatively greater absorption at the periphery of the beam with consequent decrease in density away from the center of the film. This is illustrated in Figure 149.

As in the case of stationary grids, the tube must not be tilted across the direction of the lead strips or there will be decreasing film density towards one edge of the film. The tube can, however, be tilted in a direction parallel to the strips without causing density variation. In actual practice, the Potter-Bucky diaphragm is placed under the table top with the lead strips oriented parallel

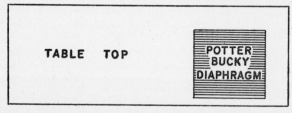

Figure 150. Top view of a radiographic table equipped
with a Potter-Bucky diaphragm. Note that the lead strips
are parallel to the long axis of the table.

to the long axis of the table, as shown in Figure 150. Consequently, the tube may be tilted along the long axis of the table, but should not be tilted across the table.

The tube must be centered to the central axis of the grid, for maximum efficiency. If the tube is off-center, across the direction of the lead strips, the *effect on radiographic density depends on the anode-film distance relative to the grid radius.* If the tube target is off-center and at a distance above the grid equal to the grid radius, there will be uniform reduction in density of the film, as indicated in Figure 151A. This can be readily proved by elementary geometry. If the anode is at an appreciable distance *above* the grid focus, and is at the same time off-center, the area of the film directly beneath the anode will be lighter than the remainder of the film. If the anode is *below* the grid focus and off-center, then the area of the film directly below the anode will be darker than the rest of the film. These relationships are illustrated in Figure 151.

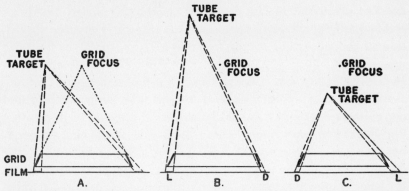

Figure 151. The effect of off-center position of the anode, on the efficiency of a focused grid. In A the tube target is off-center but level with the grid focus. The projections of the lead strips on the film are equal in size, but are broader than they would be if the tube were not off-center. Therefore, the radiographic density is uniformly decreased over the entire radiograph.

In B the target is off-center but is *above* the level of the grid focus. The projection of the lead strip lying more directly under the target is broader than that of the corresponding lead strip on the opposite side (L is broader than D). Therefore the radiograph will show less density on the side towards which the tube is shifted.

In C the target is off-center but at a level below the grid focus. The result is opposite that in B. L = lighter. D = darker.

The focused type of grid has a "tube side" and a "film side." In all the above Figures, the grid is shown correctly with the tube side towards the tube target. If the grid is inserted reversed, as in Figure 152, the tilted strips at the outer regions of the grid will absorb a great deal of radiation, with corresponding underexposure of the peripheral areas of the radiograph.

Mention must be made of the grid ratio in Potter-Bucky diaphragms. In common use are grids with ratios of 6:1 or 8:1. These absorb enough primary and secondary radiation to require an increase of about 15 Kv, or multiplication of the MaS by 4 in order to compensate for the resulting loss of film density. Diaphragms with a grid ratio of 16:1 are available for use in modern high voltage radiography. Because of the absorption of radiation by any type of grid, it is essential that intensifying screens be used in radiography of the thicker anatomic regions.

As we have stated before, the Potter-Bucky diaphragm moves during the x-ray exposure. This is accomplished by "cocking the

Bucky," which means that it is pulled to one side of the table by a lever which puts tension on a spring. When the diaphragm is released (either by a string or by an electromagnetic tripping device), the spring pulls it across the table and its motion is cushioned by a piston acting against oil in a cylinder device so that the diaphragm moves smoothly and evenly. The oil is forced from the cylinder through a small channel into a second oil chamber,

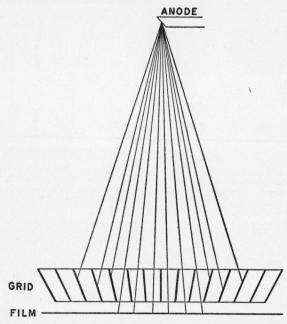

Figure 152. The focused grid is inverted, with the "tube side" away from the tube target. Therefore, the outer regions of the radiograph will have decreased density.

by the pressure of the piston. When the diaphragm is cocked again, the piston draws the oil back into the cylinder. A timing device regulates the speed of travel of the diaphragm by varying the size of the channel between the cylinder and the second oil chamber. A simplified version of this mechanism is indicated in Figure 153.

The relationship of the speed of the diaphragm to the exposure time is very important in preventing the appearance of grid lines.

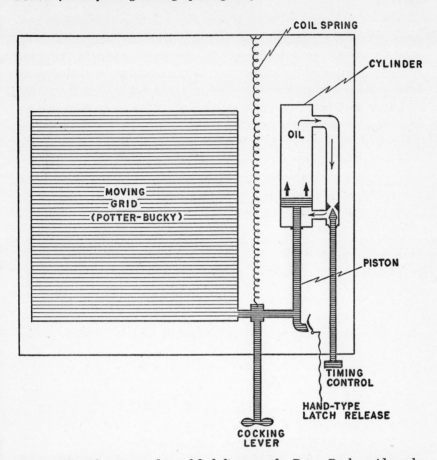

Figure 153. Schematic and simplified diagram of a Potter-Bucky grid mechanism. The latch has been released and the spring pulls the grid and piston in the direction of the heavy arrows. As the piston moves in the cylinder, oil is displaced through the connecting chamber in the direction of the thin arrows. The oil cushions the motion of the grid and piston. When the cocking lever is pulled out, the grid and piston are pulled along with it, and the latch holds the mechanism ready for the next trip. Note that when the piston is pulled back through the cylinder the direction of the oil movement is reversed. The timing mechanism controls the size of the opening in the small oil chamber, and thereby controls the speed of travel of the piston when it is released. The smaller the hole, the greater the resistance to the flow of oil and therefore the slower the travel of the piston and the attached grid. In modern equipment, the latch mechanism is more complicated than shown here, and is tripped by an electromagnetic relay which is automatically activated when the exposure is made.

The average distance the diaphragm travels is 2 inches. It reaches full speed after it has traveled about 0.2 inch, and at this instant the x-ray exposure should start. The exposure should be completed while the diaphragm is moving at a steady speed, and before it has completed its full travel. If the exposure starts before the diaphragm has reached full speed, or if the exposure is completed after the diaphragm has stopped, grid lines will appear on the radiograph as alternating white and dark strips. On the other hand, if the diaphragm moves too long after the exposure is completed, this means that the tube target could not have been centered to the grid during the exposure and there may result uneven film density, as described above. Ordinarily, the grid should not travel longer than 20 per cent more than the x-ray exposure time. Fortunately, this relationship is established at the time of installation so that the technician has only to set the Bucky timer and the exposure timer and the correct relationship is established automatically. However, the Bucky diaphragm timer should be checked occasionally to rule out the possibility that it may be out of adjustment.

There are two main types of Potter-Bucky diaphragms with reference to speed. The standard type can be adjusted for exposures of ½ second to 30 seconds. The high-speed type covers an exposure range of ⅒ second to 30 seconds, or ⅒ second to 40 seconds.

There are several causes of grid lines appearing on the film in addition to the relationship already discussed, of grid travel and exposure duration. Since moving grids have relatively thick lead strips, the appearance of these grid lines in the radiograph is especially objectionable. It may be of advantage here to list the common causes of grid lines when a Potter-Bucky diaphragm is used:

1. Exposure starting before grid has reached full speed.
2. Exposure continuing after grid travel has slowed down or stopped.
3. Uneven movement of the grid, such as jerky motion resulting from improper entrance of the piston into the oil cylinder, or from air bubbles in the oil. To eliminate this, oil of the proper type should be added to the cylinder.

4. Target of tube not centered to the center of the diaphragm.
5. Synchronism. This requires explanation. It has been indicated in Chapter 12 that the x-ray beam is not generated continuously, but in intermittent showers corresponding to the peaks in the voltage applied to the tube. If the travel of the grid is such that a different lead strip always happens to be below a given point at the same instant that a kilovolt peak is reached, the images of the lead strips will be superimposed on the same point on the film, even though the grid is moving. The net effect is the same as though the grid were stationary. This is most apt to occur with short exposures and at certain settings of the Bucky timer (not the x-ray exposure timer). To eliminate this, once the setting that produces synchronism is found, the Bucky timer should always be set slightly beyond this point.

Recently, there has been developed a reciprocating Potter-Bucky diaphragm which requires no separate timer and does not have to be cocked. It oscillates continuously during the exposure and operates without producing grid lines at exposure times of $\frac{1}{20}$ second or longer. This type of Bucky diaphragm is more efficient in removing secondary radiation than is the conventional single-stroke type.

The Bucky diaphragm has its greatest application in the radiography of thick parts. Since relatively long exposures are required, cassettes with intensifying screens are ordinarily used. However, exceptionally fine radiographs are obtained of shoulders, knees, and ribs when non-screen film technic is used in conjunction with the moving diaphragm; of course, the exposure must be increased by 15 Kv, or the MaS must be increased 4 times to compensate for the absorption of energy by the diaphragm when the grid ratio is 6:1.

REDUCTION OF SECONDARY RADIATION BY MODIFICATION OF THE PRIMARY BEAM

It is possible, to some extent, to modify the primary x-ray beam so that there will be less secondary radiation produced. This depends on two well-known facts. First, it is generally recognized that *an increase in the kilovoltage to a high value with conven-*

tional equipment increases the amount of secondary radiation. Therefore, the radiographic technic should be established so that the kilovoltage for a given part is sufficient to penetrate it adequately. Excessively high kilovoltage should be avoided, unless grids with a high ratio are used (12:1 or 16:1). Under ordinary conditions, with a grid ratio of 6:1 or 8:1, the kilovoltage should not exceed 85.

In the second place, *the amount of secondary radiation increases as the volume of irradiated tissue increases.* This means that the larger the area being radiographed, and the thicker the part being radiographed, the greater will be the amount of secondary radiation and therefore, the greater will be the impairment of radiographic quality. The practical lesson to be learned from this is that the size of the field must be restricted to the smallest possible diameter that will still include the anatomic area of interest. This can be accomplished by the use of *cones* or *cut-out diaphragms* which are placed in the path of the primary beam, as close to the x-ray tube as its housing will allow. These devices are most effective when they narrow the field to a diameter of less than 6 inches, especially in non-grid radiography. However, when large areas such as the abdomen are to be radiographed, the grid is the most efficient means of removing secondary radiation and a cone influences the quality of the radiograph very little under these conditions.

The effect of the cut-out diaphragm is shown in Figure 154. It is obvious from this diagram, that the cut-out will have a beneficial effect on radiographic quality by decreasing secondary radiation, thereby diminishing its fogging effect. However, it must be kept in mind that about 50 to 75 per cent of the density of a radiograph may be due to the secondary radiation that reaches the film, and therefore when the primary beam is limited by a cut-out diaphragm, the primary beam x-ray exposure must be increased to compensate for this loss in density. This increase in exposure must be determined by trial in each case. It is essential, in setting up a technic chart, that the size of the cone or cut-out be indicated for each technic. Whenever the beam is further restricted or enlarged, the exposure must be increased or decreased, respectively.

The radiographic *cone* or *extension cylinder* is similar in prin-

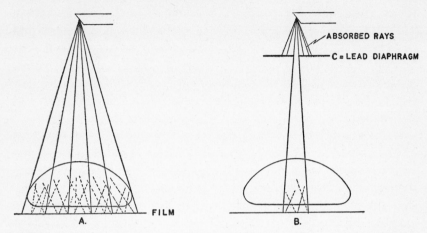

ABSORBED RAYS

C = LEAD DIAPHRAGM

FILM

A.   B.

Figure 154. The effect of cut-out diaphragm C on the volume of tissue irradiated and the resulting secondary radiation. In A there is no restriction of the x-ray beam, a large volume of tissue is irradiated, with resulting abundance of secondary radiation. In B the cut-out diaphragm narrows the beam, a small volume of tissue is irradiated, and there is less secondary radiation.

ciple to the cut-out diaphragm. The cone is a conical tube of metal placed in the x-ray beam to narrow its diameter. However, these devices, because they consist of a length of metal in the path of the x-ray beam, contribute a definite amount of secondary radiation to the primary beam, if the *lower* opening is too small and narrows the beam. Since this secondary radiation emerges in many directions, it reduces the effectiveness of the narrowed beam. If the *upper* aperture narrows the beam, there is relatively little scattering from the sides of the cone. This is illustrated in Figure 155. The cut-out diaphragm, consisting of a sheet of lead with a hole cut in the center, does not present an appreciably large scattering surface and is therefore a more desirable means of limiting the field. However, the advantage of using a cone is that it facilitates accurate centering.

Recently, there has appeared on the market a new type of device which combines the best features of the cone and the diaphragm, the Videx Cone. This is a relatively short cone provided with a lead iris diaphragm that can be easily opened and closed to delimit a beam of desired diameter. There is attached a

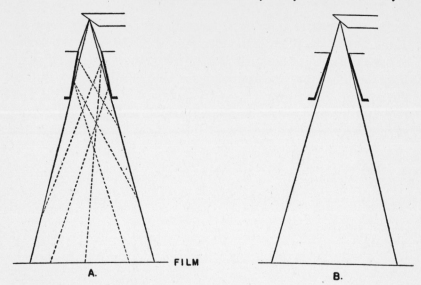

Figure 155. In A the lower opening of the cone narrows the beam, and scattered radiation from the inner surface of the cone decreases the effectiveness of the cone. In B the upper opening narrows the beam and scattering is minimized; this type of cone is therefore more efficient.

centering rod which projects a small spot of light onto the patient so that alignment of the focal spot with the part being examined is extremely accurate. This cone is so easily adjustable that it can be left in the tube housing practically permanently; otherwise, a set of cones of various sizes is required for different anatomic areas.

Since these beam-limiting devices reduce the size of the beam, one must know how large a film will be covered by a cone or cut-out of given size at various focal spot to film distances. This can be determined by referring to tables in radiographic technic manuals, but the technician can easily compute the film size covered by a given cone by application of simple rules. This calculation requires the following data:

1. Distance from focal spot to cut-out.
2. Distance from focal spot to film.
3. Diameter of cut-out.

The method of determining the film coverage by a beam limited by a cut-out diaphragm is not difficult. In Figure 156, the cut-out is 1 in. in diameter and is 4 in. from the focal spot. The focal-film distance is 40 in. What is the diameter of the beam at the surface of the film? In the diagram, it is to be noted that the beam diverges from the focal spot and continues to diverge as it passes through the cut-out. This forms a large triangle with its apex at the focal spot and its base on the film; and a small triangle with its apex at the focal spot and its base at the cut-out. These triangles are

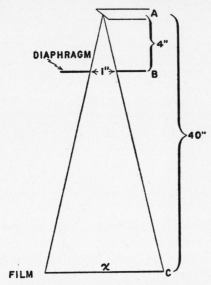

Figure 156. Method of calculating film coverage with a given cut-out diaphragm. In this case $x:1::40:4$. Therefore, $4x = 40$ and $x = 10$.

similar, so that by the application of a simple, geometrical principle, we obtain the proportion:

$$AB:AC::d:x$$

where AB = focal spot to cut-out distance.

AC = focal spot to film distance

d = diameter of cut-out.

x = diameter of film surface covered by beam.

Substituting the numerical values in the proportion,

$$4:40::1:x$$

The product of the extremes equals the product of the means:

$$4x = 40$$
$$x = 10 \text{ in.}$$

Therefore, the x-ray beam at the level of the film is a circle having a diameter of 10 in. This will obviously be too small to cover a 10 in. x 12 in. film. Will it cover an 8 in. x 10 in. film? It will obviously cover the long and short sides of the film but the diagonal of the film measures 12.8 in. so that the corners of the film will be cut short (see Figure 157). The diagonal of the film can be found by measurement or by calculation.

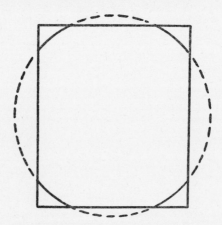

Figure 157. The x-ray beam cuts the
corners of the film.

When using a cone, one applies the same principles, but one must be certain to choose the correct measurements to introduce into the calculation. As we have seen above, a cone should be so constructed that the upper opening narrows the beam, in order to reduce secondary radiation from the sides of the cone. In Figure 158, the upper aperture (opening) limits the size of the beam, and therefore the calculations can be made as though a diaphragm were at that level, and the lower opening can be completely disregarded.

When a cylinder is used, it is usually the lower aperture that limits the size of the beam (see Figure 159), and therefore the calculations are made as though a cut-out diaphragm were present

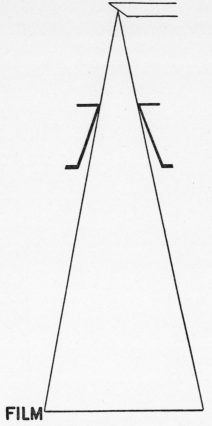

Figure 158. The upper aperture limits
the field when a properly constructed
cone is used.

at the level of the lower opening. In Figure 159, the data permit
us to set up the following proportions:

(target to top of cone + length of cone) : target to film distance : :
diameter of lower aperture : x

$$(3+10):40::4:x$$
$$13:40::4:x$$
$$13x = 160$$
$$x = 12.3 \text{ in.}$$

Thus, an 8 in. x 10 in. film will have ¼ in. cut off all corners by
the beam under the stated conditions.

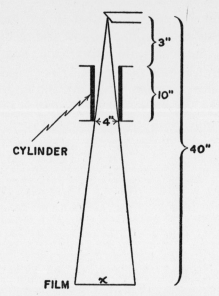

Figure 159. The effect of a cylinder in
limiting the size of an x-ray beam.

OTHER METHODS OF ENHANCING RADIOGRAPHIC QUALITY

The Heel Effect

The primary x-ray beam, as it leaves the tube target, does not have a uniform distribution of radiation. Thus, towards the cathode side of the beam, the intensity is about 105 per cent of the intensity at the center, while at the anode side of the beam, the intensity is about 75 per cent of the center, when the target-film distance is 40 inches (see Figure 160). This has a very important application in radiography and is called the *heel effect*, which is defined as the variation in intensity of the x-ray beam at different points along the long axis of the tube. In radiographing a part of the body which has a wide range of thicknesses, one can take advantage of the heel effect by placing the thicker part towards the cathode end of the beam (where the intensity is 105 per cent) and the thinner part under the anode side (where the intensity is 75 per cent). This results in more even film density, and actually irons out varying thickness of the radiographed object. For example, in radiography of the abdomen supine for the study of the kidney areas, the patient should be placed on the table with his head towards the cathode end of the tube and his feet towards the anode. On the other hand, examination of the thoracic spine in the anteroposterior view requires placing the patient with his head towards the anode, and his feet towards the cathode, since the upper part of the thorax is thinner than the lower part. It should be noted that the heel effect becomes more

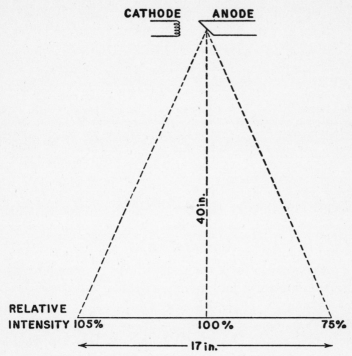

Figure 160. Intensity distribution of an x-ray beam.

pronounced, the shorter the target-film distance. Thus, at a distance of 30 inches, the anode side of the beam is about 60 per cent of the cathode side at the edges of a 17-inch film.

Compensating Filters

Various filtering devices have been introduced to aid in the radiography of parts of the body that differ markedly in thickness or density, so that these regions can be represented in satisfactory density on one film. These materials include aluminum and various barium-plastic compounds. An illustration of this principle is the use of an aluminum wedge in radiography of the foot in the anteroposterior projection. The thickest part of the wedge is placed under the toes and the thinnest part under the heel; this produces radiographs of more uniform density. The disadvantage of such a system is the increased object to film distance resulting in distortion and its attendant decrease in detail. This may be avoided by the insertion of a compensating filter in the filter slot of the x-ray tube housing. This arrangement is particularly useful in the radiography of long segments of the spine and in the examination of the pregnant uterus.

QUESTIONS AND PROBLEMS

1. How does a cut-out diaphragm diminish secondary radiation?
2. A cut-out diaphragm measuring 2 in. in diameter is located 6 in. below the focal spot. What will be the diameter of the beam at 36 in?
3. A cylinder measuring 12 in. in length is used to narrow an x-ray beam. The lower opening of the cone is 15 in. from the focal spot. What is the smallest standard film that will be completely covered at an anode-film distance of 40 in.?
4. Describe the principle of a radiographic grid.
5. What is meant by grid ratio? What is the relationship between grid ratio and grid efficiency?
6. What is meant by the focus of a grid? The radius of a grid?
7. What causes decreased density of the edges of a radiograph when a grid is used?
8. Name five causes of grid lines with a Potter-Bucky diaphragm and state how each can be corrected.
9. What is the most effective method of eliminating secondary radiation in radiography?
10. What is meant by the "heel effect"? How is it influenced by the target-film distance?

CHAPTER *20* SPECIAL PROCEDURES

I n recent years there have been developed modifications of radiographic procedures for special purposes. The most important of these include stereoscopic radiography, body section radiography, roentgenkymography, and photofluorography. These will be described in order.

STEREOSCOPIC RADIOGRAPHY

Stereoscopy is the process of "seeing solid"; that is, seeing in three dimensions. An ordinary photograph has only two dimensions, lacking depth. That is because the camera has "one eye" and projects the image on the film in only two dimensions. A pair of human eyes, on the other hand, views the same subject and the brain perceives the impression of solidity or three dimensional appearance. How is this brought about? Each eye views the object from a slightly different angle depending on the distance of the object and the distance between the pupils of the eyes (see Figure 161). These slightly different images are formed on the retina of the respective eye and are carried separately over the optic nerves to the brain. Here these images are fused into one which has three dimensions—height, width, and depth. Another very important function of stereoscopic vision is that it permits us to judge distances. This can be determined readily by trying to touch an object with one eye closed, and then trying to do the same thing with both eyes open. However, it is possible for a person with one eye to develop the ability to judge distances fairly well, although stereoscopy is impossible.

We are not born with stereoscopic vision but develop this faculty in infancy. Dr. Batson at the University of Pennsylvania has shown that individuals differ in their ability to fuse stereoscopic images, and that in many instances this ability can be improved by corrective glasses, exercise, and practice.

It is possible, and indeed desirable in many cases, to obtain stereoscopic effects roentgenographically. In doing so, one must attempt to duplicate the various steps in the process of seeing stereoscopically under ordinary conditions.

First, one must obtain two views of the same object at two slightly different angles. Thus, the x-ray tube takes the place of the eyes and it exposes two separate films in slightly different

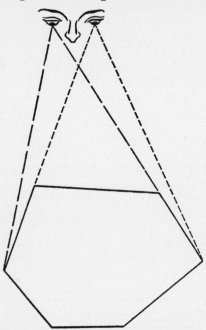

Figure 161. Stereoscopic vision. Each eye sees a slightly different view of the solid object. These two images are blended in the brain to give the impression of one image having a solid appearance; that is, height, width, and depth.

positions. The part being examined is maintained immobilized while the tube is shifted in order to obtain these two films. This step is shown in Figure 162.

The question now arises "how far must the tube be shifted in order to obtain a satisfactory pair of stereoradiographs?" In order to answer this, we must consider the means by which these films are to be viewed. There are several types of devices on the market that answer this purpose. They require two illuminators, one for each film. In addition, they must have some mechanism whereby the image from each film is cast separately on the retina of each

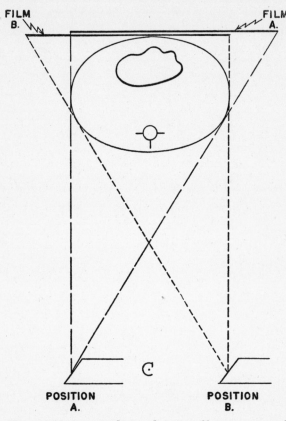

Figure 162. Stereoradiography. Two films are exposed separately, one with the tube target at A, and the other with the target at B. Note that the object is not moved. The target positions are at equal distances from the center C.

eye so that the brain can readily fuse them into a single stereo-scopic image. The most commonly used devices are *mirrors* and *prisms*. The mirror method is used in the Wheatstone stereoscope and since it is simpler to understand, it will be described in detail. The film that was exposed by the tube in the left position is viewed by the left eye and the film that was exposed in the right position is viewed by the right eye (see Figure 163). The images from both view boxes, as reflected in the mirrors, lie straight in front of the observer and are superimposed. Under ideal conditions the stereoscopic image should lie about 25 to 28 inches in front of the eyes. Furthermore, the focal spot to film distance should also be 25 to 28 inches, and the tube shift should approximate the distance between the pupils of the observer's eyes. The interpupillary distance varies among individuals, but averages about 2½ inches.

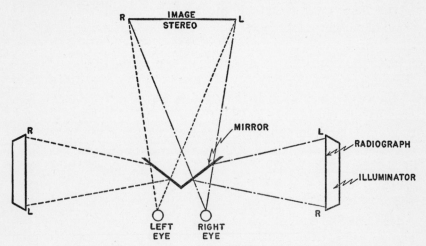

Figure 163. Principle of the Wheatstone strereoscope.

In actual practice, one seldom uses such short target to film distances. When the more conventional distances are employed (36 to 40 inches for table top radiography, 72 inches for chest radiography), the tube shift must be increased proportionally. Theoretically, if one uses a target to film distance of 40 inches, the total tube shift can be obtained from the following proportion:

Tube : Target-Film :: Interpupillary : Viewing
Shift   Distance   Distance   Distance
x :   40   ::   2.5   :   25
$$25x = 100 \text{ in.}$$
$$x = 4 \text{ in.}$$

It is evident from this proportion that the tube shift is theoretically *one-tenth the target to film distance, when the viewing dis-*

tance is 25 inches. In most cases this ratio will yield excellent stereoradiographs. However, as has already been mentioned, some individuals have difficulty in fusing stereoscopically and the 1:10 ratio may produce stereo pairs which cannot readily be fused by such observers. In such instances, the tube shift will have to be reduced to a ratio of 1:13 or even 1:16 at short target to film distances in order to reduce eyestrain, but the apparent depth of the image will necessarily be diminished as compared with the larger shift ratio of 1:10.

The *direction* of the tube shift relative to the anatomic area is of some importance. In general, the tube is shifted at right angles to the dominant lines; thus, a chest stereo requires a tube shift crosswise to the ribs. When the tube is shifted across the direction of the Bucky grid lines, there should be no difference in the density of the two radiographs if the tube is correctly centered to the grid. When the tube is shifted parallel to the Bucky grid lines, there may be a difference in the density of the films because of the heel effect; and there will also be a difference in the detail of the two radiographs because the size of the effective focal spot will be different in the two positions. This is shown in Figure 164.

One must be careful that the cone is large enough to cover the film in both positions of the tube. If a small cone is used, the tube will require tilting in order to cover both films. In most cases where stereoradiography is used, the cone may be removed entirely, without significantly impairing the quality of the roentgenograms.

The subject of stereoradiography may now be summarized by enumerating the steps required in obtaining the films and viewing them.

1. Center accurately the part to be radiographed.
2. Determine the total shift of the tube for the given focus-film distance. Suppose this shift to be 3 in.
3. Determine the correct direction of shift (across the dominant axis).
4. Now shift the tube one-half the total required shift, away from the center. In this case, $\frac{1}{2} \times 3 = 1\frac{1}{2}$ in. Now make the first exposure.

5. With the patient immobilized in the same position, change the cassette. (For chest stereoradiography, respiration must be suspended.)
6. Now shift the tube the total distance, in this case 3 in., in a direction exactly opposite the first shift, and make the second

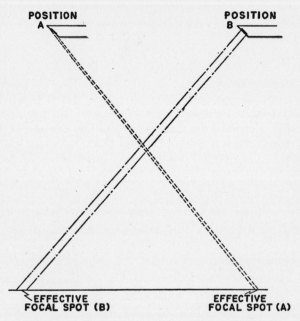

Figure 164. Difference in size of the effective focal spot when the tube is shifted parallel to the long axis of the tube. Note that in position A the effective focal spot is smaller and therefore the detail is better than in position B. The density of the radiograph will be greater in position B because of the heel effect. In modern installations the tube shift should be across the table whenever possible.

exposure. (This is the same as shifting the tube one-half the total distance to the opposite side from the center point.) The exact method of making the shift is shown in Figure 165.

7. Process the films simultaneously and dry.
8. The films are now ready for viewing. They must be placed in the illuminators correctly so that they will give proper per-

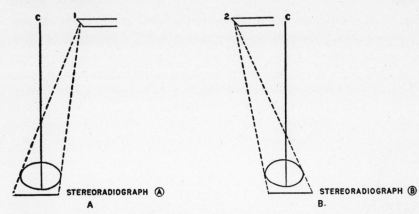

Figure 165. Method of shifting the tube in stereoradiography. In A the tube has been shifted one-half the total distance to one side of the center C for the first exposure. In B it has been shifted the full distance in the opposite direction for the second exposure.

spective and avoid giving an "inside-out" appearance. This is very important in localizing lesions or foreign bodies correctly. In using the Wheatstone stereoscope:

a. Hold the films up so that the side which faced the x-ray tube now faces the eyes, and at the same time in such a position that the tube shift is horizontal.
b. Now turn the films around horizontally, since the mirrors in the stereoscope will reverse the images.
c. It will be noted that the image on one film is closer a given edge than is the image on the other film. The film with the image closer to the right hand is placed in the right illuminator, and the other film is placed in the left illuminator.
d. The viewing distance is adjusted to 25 in.
e. The mirror, with its faces maintained at an angle of 90 degrees to each other, is slid forwards or backwards, or is tilted, in order to make the images fuse.
f. If the stereoscopy is correct, an anteroposterior film will appear anteroposterior stereoscopically, and a posteroanterior film will appear posteroanterior in the stereoscope. Thus, if a chest was radiographed in the con-

ventional PA position, it will appear in the stereoscope that the anterior ribs lie farther from the observer than do the posterior ribs. This verification can be simplified by attaching the identifying marker to the cassette changer or the table top so that its images will fuse in the stereoscope; since it will lie in the same plane as the anatomic part farthest from the tube it will appear to be farthest from the observer if stereoscopy is correct.

In using the Stanford stereoscope, one must modify the above procedure by omitting step (b) and placing the film with the image *farther* from the *right* hand in the *right* illuminator, and the film with the image *farther* from the *left* hand in the *left* illuminator.

The frequency with which stereoradiographs are made varies widely in different departments, depending on the preference of the individual radiologist. It has its greatest value in localizing lesions more accurately and in giving a better perception of the shape, structure, and relationship of a lesion to adjacent anatomic areas.

BODY-SECTION RADIOGRAPHY

In an ordinary roentgenogram all of the structures throughout the thickness of the anatomic part are superimposed. At times, this makes it difficult to visualize an area of interest adequately because of the confusing multiplicity of structures. One of the outstanding advances in radiography was the invention of a device in 1922 by Bocage, which permits the making of radiographs of a desired layer of the body, at the same time blurring out structures in front of and behind this layer. The general term for this process is *body-section radiography*, and the various methods of accomplishing it are known as laminagraphy, planigraphy, and tomography, among others. In this country, the device was first perfected by Jean Kieffer in 1929.

The principle is essentially the same in all these methods, and can be greatly simplified by a brief description of a moving beam of light and the shadow which it casts when an opaque body is placed in its path. This discussion can easily be followed by the student, using a flashlight, a pencil, and a white surface. As shown in Figure 166, if a pencil is placed in a beam of light and the light is moved, the shadow of the pencil will move in the opposite direction. *In effect, the relationship of the light, the pencil, and the shadow, is as though they were connected by a rigid rod which pivots about the pencil.* If a photographic film were placed so as to receive the shadow image, and if this film were to move in the same direction and at exactly the same speed as the shadow, then there would be practically no blurring of the image since the shadow would always fall on the same area of the film. In effect, this would be the same as if the light source, the pencil, and the film were all stationary. If all three were connected by a rigid rod which pivoted around the pencil, the film would move in a direction opposite to the direction of the light source and the shadow would always fall on the same film area as in Figure 166B.

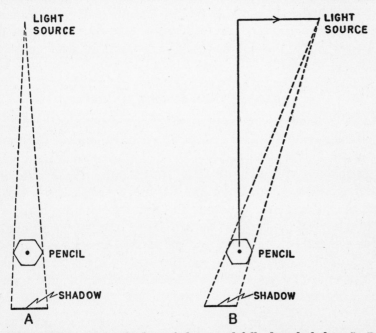

Figure 166. In A the shadow of the pencil falls directly below. In B the light has moved to the right and the shadow has moved to the left. If the shadow were to fall on a film which moved at the same speed as the shadow, then there would be relatively little blurring of the image.

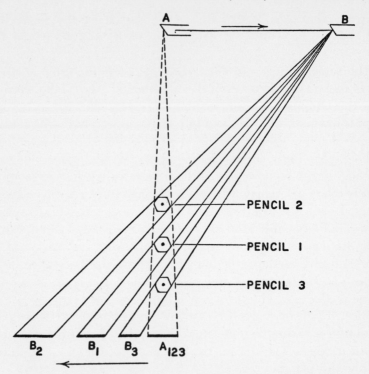

Figure 167. The effect of motion of the light source on three objects, one of which marks the pivot level. If pencil 1 marks the pivot level, and if the film is moved to the left at the same speed as shadow B_1, this shadow will remain sharp. The shadow of pencil 2 moves faster than the film and is blurred out. The shadow of pencil 3 moves slower than the film and is also blurred out.

Let us see now what would happen if two additional pencils were placed in the beam, one above and one below the pencil which marks the pivot level. This is shown in Figure 167. At position A the shadows of all three pencils are superimposed and fall at A_{123}. If the light source is moved to B and at the same time the photographic film is moved at such a speed that the shadow cast by pencil 1 maintains a constant position on the film at B_1, this particular shadow will maintain a fairly sharp outline. On the other hand, the farther the light is moved from A toward B, the more the shadows of pencils 2 and 3 are separated from that of pencil 1, and therefore the corresponding shadows B_2 and B_3 are blurred. Similarly, if pencil 2 were chosen as the pivot level the shadow B_2 would be sharp whereas B_1 and B_3 would blur out.

The same principle applies in radiography. In some anatomic areas such as the first cervical vertebra, the larynx, the sternum, and the temporomandibular joint, it is very difficult or actually impossible to obtain a radiograph of the desired part without confusing shadows from superimposed structures, by conventional radiography. Body section radiography permits us to radiograph a "slice" of the body of certain thickness, so that its image on the film is relatively sharp. Structures in planes outside this slice are blurred out. The application of this principle in radiography is shown in Figure 168. Study of the diagram reveals that only structures in plane A, which is the level of the axis of rotation of the tube and film carrier will remain relatively sharp—said to be "in focus." The farther some other plane such as B is from the desired plane A, the more the former will blur out. The nearer B is to A, the less it will blur out. The longer the excursion of the tube, as from 0 to 1 in the diagram, the thinner will be the plane that remains in focus. The shorter the excursion of the tube, the thicker will be this plane.

In actual practice the x-ray tubehead is connected to the film carrier—the Bucky pan—by means of a metal rod. The pivot point of the rod is *adjustable* for various heights above the table top, and the rod and pivot mechanism are behind the table so that they do not lie in the x-ray beam. To obtain a body section radiograph, one must first position the patient on the x-ray table as for routine radiography. The pivot point is then adjusted at various heights above the table, corresponding to a series of layers through the patient. *At each level a separate film is exposed while the tube and Bucky tray are in motion.* The relation of the tube and cassette is shown in Figure 169. There results a series of radiographs which are in focus at different levels. In one of these films the desired structure will appear in sharpest detail. The pivot height above the table at which this particular film was exposed will represent the distance of this structure above the table, and hence its distance from the anterior abdominal wall if the patient is lying prone. For example, in obtaining a series of body section radiographs of the second cervical vertebra, one of these will show the odontoid process in sharpest detail, the structures in front of and behind this being blurred out.

There are various kinds of motion that can be used. The simplest is *rectilinear;* that is, the tube moves in one direction while the

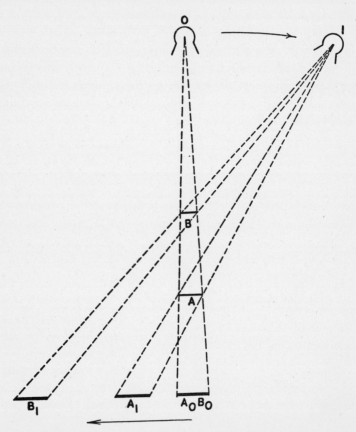

Figure 168. The principle of body section radiography. At position 0 the images of structures B and A are superimposed on the film at A_0B_0. When the tube is shifted to 1 and the film carrier moves in the opposite direction such that the axis of rotation (pivot) is at level A, the image of A, A_1, will have a constant position on the film and will not blur out. A_1 and A_0 will fall on the same spot on the film. The image B_1, however, will shift relative to A_1 and will blur out. (In practice, the tube is moved from position 1 through 0 to a corresponding point on the opposite side of 0, during the exposure.)

cassette moves in a diametrically opposite direction. Although this method is usually quite satisfactory, it imparts streakiness to the radiographic image because structural lines which lie parallel to the direction of motion are not completely blurred. A better method employs *circular* or *spiral* motion of the tube and Bucky pan; this produces equal blurring over the film surface of the out-of-focus layers and minimizes streakiness.

The apparatus should be activated by a motor which moves the tube and Bucky pan during each exposure. This can be performed at the control stand, thereby preventing exposure of the technician to x-rays. The simplest device allows the tube and Bucky pan to be moved manually, but this exposes the technican to radiation and is therefore undesirable.

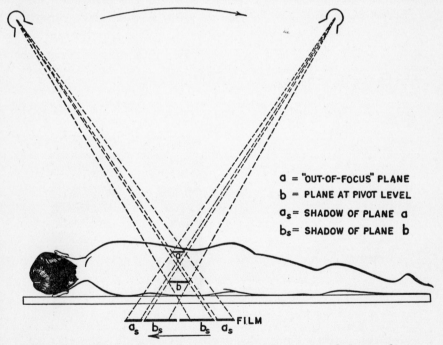

a = "OUT-OF-FOCUS" PLANE
b = PLANE AT PIVOT LEVEL
a$_s$= SHADOW OF PLANE a
b$_s$= SHADOW OF PLANE b

Figure 169. Body section radiography. The tube is moved during the exposure in the direction of the curved arrow, while the film moves in the opposite direction. The pivot level is selected at the same level as *b*. The shadow of *b* (*b$_s$*) moves with the cassette and always falls on the same spot on the film. The shadow of *a* lying in a plane above *b*, falls on different areas of the film during the exposure and is consequently blurred.

Because a larger depth of tissue is irradiated in body section work, the exposure must be increased. This may amount to 20 per cent or more, depending on various factors.

This procedure has been an extremely valuable addition to radiography and can reveal the correct diagnosis in many instances where it would otherwise be missed.

ROENTGENKYMOGRAPHY

It is possible to analyze the motion of an anatomic structure, such as the heart, by means of a device known as a *roentgen kymograph*. This consists of a sheet of lead $\frac{1}{16}$ in. thick and about 16 in. x 20 in. in dimensions, having multiple parallel slits 0.4 mm wide and 18 mm apart. This is called the *kymographic grid*. In order to study the movements of the heart, one places the grid between the patient and the film, with slits horizontal. During the exposure, a mechanism moves the film vertically over a distance of 17 mm; that is, just less than the space between the slits. Since the x-rays can reach the film only through each slit, they produce a series of parallel horizontal bands on the film, each one containing a wavy line representing the motion of that particular portion of

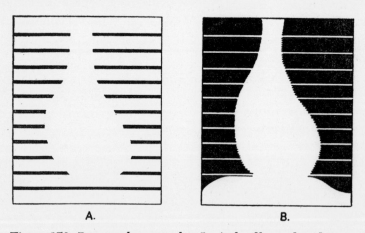

A.					B.

Figure 170. Roentgenkymography. In A the film and grid were stationary and the images of the grid slits appear as black lines. In B the film has moved past the grid slits, so that each grid slit delineates the motion of the heart border within the area that it scans. The heart border is represented as a sawtooth margin because of cardiac pulsations during the exposure.

the heart border during the exposure. These bands are produced by the x-rays passing through a given slit while the film moves through the distance of 17 mm. Figure 170 shows the films produced when the kymograph is stationary and when it is in motion. In areas where the heart pulsations are impaired, the sawtooth margin of the kymogram is flattened.

It must be noted that only the cardiac motion which is at right angles to the direction of the film movement will be recorded. Any component of the heart's pulsation which is parallel to the film movement will not be recorded. It is obvious that the slits in the kymographic grid must be at right angles to the motion of the film.

PHOTOFLUOROGRAPHY (PHOTORADIOGRAPHY)

In recent years there has been a tremendous amount of field work done in *mass surveys of the chest* for the detection of tuberculosis. This has been made possible physically and economically by the development of equipment permitting the rapid exposure of films that are much smaller than the conventional 14 in. x 17 in. film.

The principle of this method of radiography is relatively simple. The x-ray beam is passed through the patient's chest and strikes a special fluoroscopic screen (see Figure 171). This is connected by means of a light-tight hood to a high speed camera which photographs the fluoroscopic image on a small film. When the film is developed it bears a miniature image of the patient's chest. The accuracy of *detection* of chest lesions by this method is very high and is therefore of inestimable value in the survey of large groups of people at low cost.

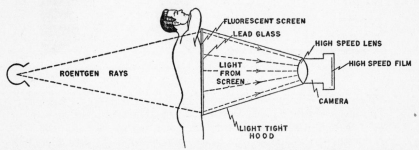

Figure 171. Essential components of a photofluorographic unit.

The essential components of a satisfactory photofluorographic apparatus include the following:

1. *X-ray Control, Transformer, and Tube.* This must have a capacity of at least 200 Ma and preferably 500 Ma at 100 Kv. A rotating anode tube with a high rate of heat dissipation is essential because of the large number of exposures made per hour. A phototimer is desirable to increase the efficiency of photofluorography in mass surveys.

2. *Fluorescent Screen.* This must have a high degree of brightness, and is usually of a type which produces blue fluorescence when activated by x-rays. The high speed is necessary in order to provide sufficient intensity of light to reach the film in the camera and give a satisfactory rendition of the fluorescent image. The screen measures 14 in. x 17 in. and is backed by lead glass to absorb x-rays passing through the screen, at the same time allowing the light from the screen to pass to the camera.

3. *Light-tight Hood.* This is placed between the fluorescent screen and the camera. The hood is shaped like a truncated pyramid, larger where the screen is attached and tapering back towards the camera.

4. *High-speed Camera.* This receives the light from the fluorescent screen. The lens has an extremely great light-gathering ability (aperture) because at best the light coming from the fluorescent screen is not of a high order of brightness.

5. *Photographic Film.* This is loaded into the camera to photograph the fluorescent image. If the screen is blue-fluorescent, then one must use special, high speed, blue-sensitive film. Various sizes of films are available. The most commonly used are 35 mm, 70 mm, 4 in. x 5 in., and stereoscopic 4 in. x 10 in.

The speed of the equipment is such that excellent films are obtained by exposures of $\frac{1}{10}$ to $\frac{1}{2}$ second. The grain of the fluoroscopic screen would be undesirable, but it is effectively reduced by the minification of the image, since the film image is much smaller than the fluorescent screen image.

The advantages to be gained from this type of apparatus include (1) the large number of patients that can be radiographed in a very short time; (2) the excellent quality of the films; (3) the small storage space required for the films; (4) the transportability of the equipment (it can be mounted in a truck or bus); and (5) the economy in using a small film size.

QUESTIONS

1. What is meant by stereoscopic vision?
2. What determines the correct tube shift in stereoradiography?
3. List the steps in making and viewing a pair of stereoradiographs.
4. Describe the principle of body section roentgenography.
5. Of what value is laminagraphy?
6. Describe the principle of roentgenkymography.
7. Show by diagram, completely labeled, the essential parts of a photofluorographic unit for mass chest radiography.
8. What are the advantages to be gained by chest photofluorography?

CHAPTER 21 RADIOACTIVITY AND RADIUM

One of the most amazing discoveries of the last century concerned the ability of certain elements to give off penetrating radiations spontaneously. In 1896, Henri Becquerel reported his experiments showing that the heavy metal *uranium* emitted rays which passed through paper and darkened a photographic plate in a dark room. Soon after this, Marie Curie and her husband, Pierre, began their search for other elements that might have similar properties. In 1898, after great hardship and personal sacrifice, they announced their discovery of *radium,* a new element which has the property of emitting penetrating radiations. The result of this discovery not only opened new fields to conquer in medicine, but also greatly extended our knowledge about the structure of matter.

RADIOACTIVITY

Unstable Atoms

What happens when an atom of an element such as uranium or radium emits radiation? There are two important phenomena associated with this sort of atomic behavior: first, the nucleus of the atom disintegrates, undergoing a change in its structure; and second, penetrating radiations are given off.

Why do some elements undergo such spontaneous breakdown? The precise answer is unknown, but one may speculate as to the reasons. It is known that the atomic nucleus contains closely packed protons and neutrons. The naturally occurring radioactive elements all have an atomic weight greater than 208 and atomic number greater than 83. This means that the nuclei of such atoms have a superabundance of neutrons and protons, with which are associated terrific electrical stresses and strains. Such nuclei are unstable and tend to explode, throwing out certain radiations, and changing to simpler nuclei. Which particular nucleus will explode at a given moment is uncertain, but statistically, a constant percentage will break down per second.

The ability of certain elements, such as radium, to undergo nuclear breakdown spontaneously and at the same time to give rise to penetrating rays is known as *natural radioactivity*. In contrast to this, there is a host of elements which are ordinarily not radioactive, but which are rendered unstable when their nuclei are subjected to bombardment by subatomic particles such as neutrons or deuterons, in special physical devices such as the cyclotron and the atomic pile. These elements are then said to be artificially radioactive. *Artificial radioactivity* may be defined as the breakdown of nuclei of atoms associated with emission of penetrating radiations, after the nuclei have been rendered unstable by atom-smashing devices.

The artificial radioactive elements are designated as *radioactive isotopes*, and they constitute a tremendous array of material to be used in medical and biologic research. Their potentialities in industry and warfare are almost unlimited.

Radioactive Series

The naturally occurring radioactive elements can be grouped in three series or families, based on the following parent elements: (1) Thorium, (2) Uranium, (3) Actinium. Each of these gives rise, by spontaneous nuclear decay, to a series of successive elements characteristic of that series. The chain of breakdown of the successive elements always occurs in exactly the same way, and at a fixed rate. Some of the daughter elements last for a very short period before they disintegrate and are therefore difficult to isolate; others, such as radium in the uranium series, have a relatively long life and can therefore be obtained in pure form. At present, radium is the most widely used radioactive element in the medical field. The uranium family has been the most important one for radiology because radium and its offspring are the last descendants of the uranium series. The radium series is really a subdivision of the uranium series.

RADIUM

Properties

Since radium is extensively used in therapy, and since its behavior exemplifies that of the other radioactive elements, the discussion will center mainly about this element. It is a heavy metal having a silvery-white appearance when pure, and behaving chemically like barium and calcium. It is a member of the uranium radioactive series. Radium has atomic number 88, and atomic weight 226. Since its radioactivity is not affected when it is combined with other elements, it is usually sold in the form of a salt, *radium bromide*. This salt is more easily and more cheaply obtained than the pure metal.

Radioactive Radiation

There are three entirely different types of rays that are emitted by radioactive elements in any of the radioactive series. A given element may emit all three of these radiations, or may emit only one or two of them. These are the only known types of radioactive emanations that we have to consider: (1) alpha particles; (2) beta particles; and (3) gamma rays. Various members of the radium series as will be shown below, give off one or more of these radiations.

1. *Alpha Rays*. These are, strictly speaking, particles. They leave the nucleus at high speeds, up to 20,000 miles per second but do not penetrate matter to any appreciable depth. For example, they are stopped by a sheet of ordinary paper. The alpha particles are really *helium ions* carrying two positive charges. When they collide with an atom of some other element, they accept two electrons and become a neutral atom of helium.

$$\text{alpha particle} + 2 \text{ electrons} = \text{helium atom}$$
$$\text{He}^{++} + 2\,\text{e}^- = \text{He}$$

Thus, an atom of radium produces an atom of an entirely different element, a phenomenon which is called *radioactive transformation of matter*. Because of their relatively large mass (compared to other radiations) and because of the fact that they carry two positive charges, alpha particles are strongly ionizing; that is, when they encounter other atoms, they ionize them readily in great numbers.

2. *Beta Rays.* These, too, are more correctly spoken of as beta particles since they consist of high speed *electrons*. They are ejected from the nucleus at speeds approaching the velocity of light rays. They are able to penetrate matter to a greater depth than alpha rays. They may penetrate 1 cm of tissue. In fact, beta rays require 0.5 mm of platinum, or 1 mm of lead for complete stoppage. Since they penetrate so well, they are useful in therapy, especially for superficial skin lesions in small areas. Beta rays are strongly ionizing, but less so than alpha rays.

3. *Gamma Rays.* These are electromagnetic waves and photons. They travel with the speed of light and are much more penetrating than alpha or beta radiation. Gamma rays resemble x-rays, but gamma rays have more energy because their average wave length is shorter than that of roentgen rays generated *under ordinary conditions*. Since they are electromagnetic waves, they are not deflected by a magnetic field and have all the other properties in common with x-rays. The application of radium in therapy is most often based on gamma radiation, the alpha and beta particles usually being removed by appropriate absorbing filters.

The Radium Series

When an atom of radium disintegrates, it is not completely destroyed. Rather, it is changed to another element. Let us "look into" an atom of radium and see what happens during its radioactive breakdown. The atom ejects an alpha particle which has an atomic weight of 4. Since the atomic weight of radium is 226, then the atomic weight of the atom after emission of an alpha particle is $226 - 4 = 222$. The atomic number of radium is 88 and the charge on an alpha particle is $+2$. Therefore, the atomic number of the new nucleus is $88 - 2 = 86$. Thus, we have left a new atom with atomic weight 222 and atomic number 86: this element is *radon*, the first breakdown product of radium.

$$1 \text{ radium} \longrightarrow 1 \text{ radon} + 1 \text{ alpha particle}$$

Radon is a gas, and it is also radioactive because all elements having an atomic number greater than 83 are unstable. The radon

		ALPHA	ALPHA	ALPHA	BETA GAMMA	ALPHA BETA GAMMA	
URANIUM.....	RADIUM-->-	RADON-->-	RADIUM A-->-	RADIUM B-->-	RADIUM C.....	LEAD
ATOMIC NO.	88	86	84	82	83	82
ATOMIC WT.	226	222	218	214	214	206
HALF LIFE	1590YRS.	3.8 DAYS	3 MIN.	26.8MIN.	19.7 MIN.	STABLE

Figure 172. The successive disintegration products of radium, shown from left to right. These constitute the Radium Series, which is a portion of the Uranium Series. The data on Radium D, E, and F have been omitted. Radium G is lead, and is stable.

atom disintegrates to another atom, which in turn breaks down to a fourth atom, and so on. This chain of disintegration continues until a stable atom is left; in this case, a metal, *lead*. Figure 172 shows the radium series. It is included mainly to illustrate certain points, and not as a memory exercise. First of all, it should be noted that the element radium does not, itself, give off all three types of radiation. Radium emits alpha particles. Beta and gamma rays are not produced until Radium B and C appear in the series. Since a piece of radium within a container after a definite period of time reaches a state of equilibrium with its descendants, and then actually consists of a mixture of these descendants, we speak loosely of radium as emitting all three types of radiation. It is more correct to say that the *radium series* emits all three types of radiation. Whether we start with radium or radon gas there is soon a sufficient accumulation of Radium B and C to give appreciable intensities of beta and gamma radiation. That is why radon can be used in therapy.

Half Life

In Figure 172 there is a caption "half life." This is a term which indicates the length of time required for one-half the initial amount of radium to disintegrate. Another way of considering this is as follows: suppose we have 1 gram of radium at the start. Referring to the diagram, we note that its half life is 1590 years. This means that the intensity of radiation from this piece of radium will be one-half as great 1590 years from now as it is at present; or, in 1590 years, there will be only ½ gram of radium left. In another 1590 years, it will again be reduced by one-half; that is, it will be one-fourth the original amount. It is interesting to note that the half life is constant for any given radioactive element, and that the half lives of various elements show wide variation. Thus, the half life of radon is 3.8 days, that of Radium A is only 3 minutes. In the radioactive series which consists of a mixture of all the off-spring of the parent element, the quantity of any one of the elements is greater if its half life is greater. Thus, radium which has the longest half life in its series will be present in greatest amount, whereas radium A with a half life of 3 minutes will be present in smallest amount.

As we have already indicated, there is no way of predicting which atom of radium will explode at a given moment. However, we know statistically that in 1590 years one-half the atoms in a given amount of radium will have exploded. Thus, the half life is really a statistical concept indicating the time it takes for disintegration of one-half the atoms on the basis of pure chance.

RADON

When an atom of radium emits an alpha particle, an atom of radon remains:

1 radium — 1 alpha particle = 1 radon

Radon is an element existing under ordinary conditions as a colorless, heavy gas. It is radioactive and has a convenient half life (3.8 days) so that it can be used in therapy. In practice, the radon is pumped from a container of radium, purified by passage through an intricate system of glass tubes and chemicals, and collected in thin glass or gold capillary tubes. The tube is pinched off and sealed at short intervals. After several hours, the radon reaches equilibrium with its offspring elements since they are all sealed in the tiny capillary tubes. Consequently, the preparation now emits alpha, beta, and gamma rays. The intensity of radiation given off by any such preparation can then be determined by the physicist.

RADIATION DOSAGE

The effect of penetrating radiations on a given tissue depends on the amount of radiation absorbed by the tissue, and this, in turn, is related to the quantity of radiation to which the tissue is subjected. In order to specify radiation exposure, or *dosage* as it is more commonly called, we must have certain precisely defined units which provide all the essential information. Such a system of dosage must be sufficiently accurate so that it permits comparison of various treatment methods and evaluation of treatment results. Furthermore, it provides the radiologist with the means whereby he can exchange information with his colleagues.

The first step in obtaining radiation dosage is the determination of the *time-intensity factor*. In the case of radium, this consists simply of multiplying the time by the number of milligrams of radium in the applicator. Thus, if 10 milligrams of radium element are applied for 24 hours, the time-intensity factor is $10 \times 24 = 240$ milligram-hours (usually abbreviated mg-hr). The radium does not lose any appreciable amount of strength during any practical treatment period because of its very long half-life. However, *radon* deteriorates relatively rapidly and one must take into account the progressive loss in the intensity of radiation from it during a treatment period lasting more than a few hours. Thus, with a radon treatment applicator the strength of the radon drops to one-half the initial intensity in 3.8 days, and to one-fourth in 7.6 days. The intensity reaches a negligible level at the end of one month.

The time-intensity factor for *radon* therapy requires the use of a different unit, the *millicurie*. This is defined as that amount of radon such that a specified proportion of it—to be exact, 37 million atoms—disintegrates per second. In more practical terms, 1 millicurie of radon is equivalent in therapeutic value to 1 milligram of radium, provided correction is made for the spontaneous decay of the radon. This means that if 1 milligram of radium were applied to a given area of the skin for 1 hour, the amount of radiation emitted would be the same as if 1 millicurie of radon were applied under similar conditions. However, when applied over periods of time longer than a few hours, the gradual decay of the radon necessitates the use of a dosage table for dosage calculation. One millicurie of radon, when it has completely disintegrated, is equivalent to 1 milligram of radium acting for 133 hours. Thus,

1 millicurie (mc) radon destroyed = 133 mg-hr radium

After determination of the time-intensity factor, that is, the number of mc-hr or mg-hr of radon or radium, the radiation exposure at the site of the lesion must next be found. The radiation exposure depends not only on the time-intensity factor, but also on the *distribution* of the radium in the tissues, the *volume of tissue irradiated,* and the *filtration* of the applicator. In the case of surface treatment, one must consider the *area* of the surface, its *shape,* the *distribution* of the radium in the applicator, the *distance* of the applicator above the surface, and the *filtration* of the applicator. It has been found experimentally by physicists that the intensity of gamma radiation at a distance of 1 cm from a point source of 1 mg of radium filtered by 0.5 mm platinum is 8.4 gamma roentgens per hour. This observation has enabled the physicist and radiologist to express radium and radon dosage in terms of roentgens. If the radium in a surface applicator or in needles inserted into the tissues is distributed according to certain plans, such as those of Paterson and Parker or of Quimby, the minimum number of gamma roentgens delivered to the lesion per 1000 mg-hr or mc-hr exposure can be found from the tables provided by these authors. This determination is in the province of the physicist or radiologist, but the technician should be aware of the existence of these methods.

There is one method of expressing radiation dosage which is falling into disuse. This is based on the *threshold erythema dose,* defined as the smallest radiation exposure that will cause faint reddening of the human skin. This is an empirical method and is subject to a wide variety of errors, so that it is a far less accurate unit than the gamma r. It has been found that approximately 1000 gamma r at one sitting will deliver a threshold erythema dose. To obtain the same result with x-ray, one must expose the skin to 680 r with 200 Kv, 0.5 mm copper filtration; or 270 r with 100 Kv, 1 mm aluminum filtration (these doses are measured on the skin and include backscatter).

TYPES OF APPLICATORS

There is a great variety of applicators that can be employed to administer radium or radon treatment. The arrangement and actual administration of such therapy is the direct responsibility of the radiologist, but since the technician sometimes aids in preparing the applicators, it may be advantageous to describe briefly some of the more frequently used forms.

At the present time, most radium applicators are made of metal: monel, brass, silver, gold, or platinum. These metals serve two main purposes: (1) they act as filters, and (2) they permit the application of radium in a particular form.

Filtration

It has been mentioned that the radiations from radium differ in their penetrating ability. Any metal container will absorb all alpha particles because of their poor penetrating power. This is desirable because the alpha particles are strongly ionizing and would produce severe local reactions without reaching very far into the lesion being treated. The beta rays are more penetrating and if it is desired to treat a very superficial lesion, the radium may be placed in a container with filtration of monel metal 0.05 mm thick. If one wishes to use gamma radiation only, this can be attained by absorbing all the alpha and beta radiation by the use of 0.5 mm platinum or gold; or 1 mm of lead or silver; or 2 mm of brass. The various containers which will be described can be obtained with a wall thickness to provide the proper filtration. Heavier filtration than that required to remove all the beta radiation tends to harden the emergent gamma rays by absorbing some of the softer gamma rays, much as the filter in an x-ray beam absorbs relatively more soft than hard x-rays, but the practical value of such heavy filtration in the case of radium is of doubtful advantage.

Containers

The various types of containers for radium and radon will now be considered.

1. *Implants* ("seeds"). These are tiny sealed capillary tubes containing radon. The dimensions of these "seeds" are usually about 0.75 mm by 3 mm and they have a wall thickness of 0.3 mm gold. The strength of the radon content is determined by a physicist so that the proper dosage can be calculated. Implants are usually left in the tissue permanently, since the radon loses practically all of its strength in about one month, and the dosage can be established on this basis. The gold is relatively innocuous to the surrounding tissues. In some cases, removable implants may be used, being left in the tissues for a predetermined time.

2. *Needles.* These are hollow tubes with a point at one end and an eye for threading at the other. Within the hollow shaft of the needle is sealed the radium, to form the *permanent type needle.* There is another type called the *sheath needle* which is so designed that the tip may be unscrewed (see Figure 173). The

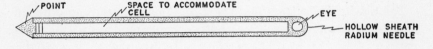

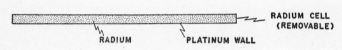

Figure 173. Sheath type of needle and radium cell. The point of the needle is unscrewed and the radium cell is inserted into the hollow shaft of the needle. The point is then replaced.

radium, sealed in removable platinum cells, can be inserted into the hollow needle. The total filtration of the needle and cell usually equals 0.5 mm of platinum. By the use of sheath needles one may have cells containing different amounts of radium, and needles of different lengths so that a very flexible treatment system is available. The sheath type of needle can also be used with radon tubes of such dimension that they easily fit into the needle. It should be pointed out that the actual or active length of the radium is always less than the length of the needle.

3. *Tubes.* These are similar to needles except they are rounded at both ends. Tubes are usually made of 0.5 or 1.0 mm platinum-iridium alloy which is harder than platinum and less easily damaged. Tubes are so constructed that one end is removable by unscrewing. Radium can be placed in the tube either in the form of cells or needles. Radon can be loaded into tubes in the form of gold or glass capillary tubes sealed at both ends.

4. *Plaques.* These are flat applicators which are hollow and have one face made of thin monel metal (0.05 mm) on the inner

surface of which is permanently spread a layer of radium. These plaques can be obtained in any desired strength. Filters can be added to remove beta radiation. Plaques are usually employed in the treatment of very superficial skin lesions.

PROTECTION

The problem of protection of personnel from radium rays is considered in greater detail in Chapter 22. However, it must be emphasized that the best protection is *distance*. No radium applicator should ever be picked up in the fingers. All loading of applicators, or other manipulations, must be performed by the use of long forceps. The radium should be stored in a lead container of correct thickness; and should be transported in a lead-lined carrying case provided with a long handle.

LOSS OF RADIUM

In some cases, the technician may be held responsible for the transportation or storage of radium. This requires constant checking, since lost radium is expensive to trace. A trained physicist must be employed to locate any lost radium, and he uses for this purpose a *Geiger counter*. This is an electronic instrument which clicks rapidly when it is brought into the vicinity of radioactive material. It is very important that lost radium be found, not only because it is so expensive—about 20 dollars per milligram—but also because it is dangerous to persons unaware of its presence. Nurses and other personnel are always to be instructed that no dressings from patients who are receiving radium therapy should be discarded without first consulting the radiologist.

QUESTIONS

1. Define radioactivity. By whom was it discovered?
2. Why are some elements radioactive? Where do the penetrating radiations arise?
3. What is the diffence between natural and artificial radioactivity?
4. Of what radioactive series is radium a descendant?
5. Why is radium of value in radiology?
6. Name and describe briefly the three types of penetrating radi-

ations emitted by the radium series. Which one does radium itself produce?

7. What is the main purpose of the filter in a radium applicator?
8. Define "half life." Why is this important in therapy?
9. Describe the physical properties of radon.
10. What is a millicurie?
11. What are the four main types of radium or radon applicator?
12. Why is it important to find lost radium?

CHAPTER 22 PROTECTION IN RADIOLOGY

In the days when Radiology was still an infant science, practically nothing was known about the dangers of the radiations emanating from the roentgen tube and from the radioactive elements. It was no small wonder, therefore, that the pioneer physicists and radiologists incurred the serious general and local injuries which all too often led to a fatal outcome. These men and women were martyrs to a new branch of science and the vast majority of them received neither financial gain nor personal glory.

Since that time, we have accumulated very precise information about the proper means of avoiding radiation injury to personnel, and one need not assume that conditions are safe without first investigating them. There is still considerable negligence on this score, and that is why there are frequent papers on this subject at meetings of radiologists and technicians.

Every technician should have in his possession, and should read carefully, the handbooks prepared by the National Bureau of Standards, Washington, D. C.:

H23 Radium Protection
H41 Medical X-ray Protection up to Two Million Volts

What is the safe limit of exposure to radiation beyond which there is danger of temporary or permanent injury? An attempt will be made to answer this question, as well as to point out steps that can be taken to eliminate the risk of overexposure. The problem of protection will be taken up only as it affects the *technician* and the *patient* and not as it pertains to the radiologist since there are special aspects that involve the latter only. However, some attention will be directed to the use of radium. Brief consideration of electrical hazards will also be included.

THE PERMISSIBLE DOSE

It is obvious that before we can discuss the safety of a given radiologic installation, some sort of standard must be established so that one can judge when conditions are safe. This standard is the so-called *permissible dose*, which is defined as the maximum amount of x-ray or gamma ray energy that a person may receive continuously or at repeated intervals without suffering any perceptible damage to the blood or reproductive organs, insofar as can be determined. It should be pointed out immediately, and strongly emphasized, that this definition implies *whole body radiation* received by the individual.

It has been found in large radiology departments, such as Memorial Hospital in New York, that personnel exposed to amounts of radiation not exceeding 0.1 roentgen per day over long periods of time will suffer no demonstrable untoward effects. Thus, the tolerance limit of 0.1 r a day is purely an estimate and not an experimental result. The most recent publication of the United States Bureau of Standards gives a lower safe tolerance limit—0.3 r per 48-hour week of uniform exposure. This amount of radiation is equivalent to about *0.05 r per day* if one assumes that the working week is 6 days. Thus, the new permissible dose is about one-half the old one, and it is the safe limit that is now being generally accepted.

PROTECTION FROM WHOLE BODY EXPOSURE

Let us consider the problems arising from the fortuitous whole body irradiation of x-ray personnel during the working day. These will be considered under three headings:

1. Determination of the safety of the working conditions in a given radiology department.

2. Deleterious effects to the individual resulting from excessive exposure.

3. Methods of eliminating dangerous conditions if they exist.

First, the determination of the safety of the working conditions in a given department can be undertaken without any specialized training, although this can be done much more accurately by a physicist experienced in this field. Several methods are available.

The most precise is that employing an ionization chamber of the thimble type, sensitive to $\frac{1}{200}$ roentgen. This type of measuring device is called a *minometer*. However, this instrument is not readily available in many radiology departments and its extreme degree of sensitivity renders it so liable to unforeseen errors that it should be used only by those who have had adequate experience with it.

A simple method, and one which can be adapted for practically any situation is the *dental film method*. A dental film is worn on the chest with the tube side out for a period of 3 weeks. The use of a long test period such as this contributes to the accuracy of the method. At the end of this time, a *second* dental film of the same type is exposed to 1 roentgen of x-rays at the greatest kilovoltage and filtration to which the technician may be subjected during his routine daily work. This quantity, 1 r, is the total permissible dose for 3 weeks (approximately 3 × the weekly permissible 0.3 r). This is the *calibration* film. Both films are now developed together at 68 F for 5 minutes and compared. The film that was worn on the chest should be no darker, and should preferably be lighter than the calibration film, if the technician has been exposed to no more than 1 r in the 3-week period.

If it is impossible to obtain a calibration film, an alternative method is to wear a film (radiatized) for 8 full work days. The film is then developed in rapid x-ray developer for 5 minutes at 68 F. If it is dark enough to obscure newspaper print, more careful tests should be carried out since it indicates that conditions probably are unsafe.

What are the harmful effects of overexposure of the whole body? If the technician is exposed to radiation in excess of 0.3 r per week for long periods of time, he may not be aware of untoward reaction until irreversible damage has been done. Not every individual has the same degree of susceptibility to radiation. Thus, some people may absorb amounts in excess of the permissible dose for many years and never suffer ill effects. However, some individuals are definitely susceptible to injury by amounts appreciably greater than the permissible dose. Since the individual technician cannot be certain as to his own susceptibility it seems reasonable that one should take every possible precaution. There is usually a latent period during which the individual appears to be in good health. When radiation injury finally appears it may affect the *blood-forming organs,* causing certain changes in the blood count. One of the earliest signs is a change in the ratio of lymphocytes to granulocytes; radiation damage causes a rise in the number of lymphocytes and a fall in granulocytes. The white blood count may be decreased, or in some instances may be increased over normal values. It has been found recently that the platelets in the circulating blood decrease as the result of excessive radiation. Changes in the red cell count are relatively late and indicate severe injury.

Excessive exposure to penetrating radiations may also involve the *generative organs,* leading to reduced fertility or sterility. An interesting sidelight to this problem is the damage that may occur to the chromosomes in the sex cells, which may lead to mutations or freaks in later generations. Such freaks have actually been produced in fruit flies by the famous geneticist, Dr. H. J. Mueller.

When detected early, the above-described changes are usually reversible. But what concrete steps can be taken to correct the situation? First, the individual so affected should be removed from the vicinity of the harmful rays until he returns entirely to normal. Second, a trained physicist should be engaged to survey the radiology department to determine the source of the unsafe conditions and to recommend the best means of correcting them. It should be emphasized here, however, that even if conditions are absolutely safe, the individual technician must observe certain rules of conduct. In other words *even in the most modern, well-protected department, the technician is subject to over-exposure if he does not make full use of the available protective facilities at all times.*

It is advisable to use, wherever possible, rayproof tubes; that is, tubes which the manufacturer has surrounded by a sufficient thickness of lead to eliminate stray radiation. This can be determined by referring to the proper table in the Handbook of X-Ray Protection. For the average diagnostic tube, this is 1.5 mm lead ($\frac{1}{16}$ inch). All x-ray rooms, except the outside walls, should be lined with lead or other material equivalent to the correct thickness of lead for the maximum Kv used. This can be found in appropriate tables in the Handbook. For ordinary diagnostic work, 1.5 mm lead is adequate, and for 200 Kv therapy, 4 mm lead is required. Such lead sheeting or other protective barrier should have overlapping seams, and if nailed, the nailheads should be covered with the right thickness of lead. Detailed instructions for shielding such walls are given in the United States Bureau of Standards Handbook H41 mentioned earlier. The control booth for diagnostic installations should be lined similar to the walls and should be at least 7 feet high; the lead glass window must be overlapped by the wall of the booth, and have the same lead equivalent as the remainder of the booth. All rays should scatter at least twice before reaching the operator. In fluoroscopy, the technician should wear a lead rubber apron of 0.5 mm lead equivalent, and when not actually assisting the radiologist, should stand either in the control booth or back of the radiologist. Note that the above recommendations apply mainly to the reduction of *stray* or *scattered* radiation reaching the technician. Direct radiation can be eliminated simply by never standing in the path of the x-ray beam.

Following are some figures to indicate the amount of radiation reaching the technician in various procedures if no protection is used. Dr. Braestrup found that with a mobile unit, the operator at 1.5 meters (roughly 1½ yards) received 0.004 r per 100 milliampere-second, and with a cysto unit at the position of the cystoscopist, 0.02 r per 100 MaS. With a dental x-ray unit, the operator is bombarded by 0.1 r, more than the entire day's tolerance dose, during 8 full-mouth dental examinations of 10 films each. In general, it is well to remember that *approximately 0.1 per cent of the main beam is scattered at right angles to the beam 1 meter from the patient* (Glasser and others). One can readily see from the above figures that the dangers are not being exaggerated.

A few simple rules of conduct in the presence of adequate protection in the physical setup, will aid greatly in reducing the hazard.

1. Never remain in the radiographic or radiotherapy room while an exposure is in progress; remain behind a safe barrier as specified above.

2. Never hold a patient for treatment or radiography, since it takes but one 200-r treatment of 200 Kv therapy, or several film exposures at this position to exceed the day's tolerance dose for the technician.

3. Give yourself the same degree of protection that you would give a loaded cassette.

Nothing has thus far been said about local protection, particularly of the hands, because this sort of danger is almost negligible in x-ray work, unless the technician is careless enough to hold patients for therapy or radiography. This should not be permitted under any circumstances. If a patient must be held during x-ray exposure, this should be done by some person who is not habitually exposed to these radiations.

PROTECTION FROM EXPOSURE TO RADIUM

Just as with x-rays, the problem of inadvertent exposure by personnel to radium involves general *body radiation* and *local radiation*. These two aspects of the radium problem will be considered separately.

Protection from Whole Body Exposure

Whole body exposure to radium may occur during:
1. Storage
2. Manipulation
3. Transportation

The *storage* of radium can be made relatively safe by providing containers of the proper lead equivalent, according to the tables in the Handbook on Radium Protection, previously mentioned. *Lead* and *distance* are the two best means of protection that we have. However, large thicknesses of lead are required because of the marked penetrating powers of gamma rays.

In the Handbook, there is a chart prepared by Dr. Failla showing the wall thickness of lead containers for the storage of various amounts of radium at various distances from the departmental personnel. For example, if 100 mg radium is kept in a container that completely surrounds the radium with lead of 2 cm thickness, the personnel at a distance of no less than 4½ feet will be exposed to no more than 0.1 r in an 8-hour working day. However, this is based on the old tolerance dose. To convert the data to the *new permissible dose,* one may apply the inverse square law. Thus, 100 mg radium inclosed by 2 cm lead will be safe at a distance of no less than 6¼ feet in an 8-hour working day, during which time the personnel will receive a maximum of 0.05 r. In general, the larger the amount of radium to be stored and the shorter the working distance, the greater the thickness of lead required to reduce the exposure to the permissible dosage level. But the lead thickness required for protection is not strictly proportional to the amount of radium; for instance, under the above conditions, 200 mg radium would require 3 cm of lead for equivalent protection.

During the manipulation of radium, as in loading needles, capsules, or other applicators, considerable whole body exposure can be accumulated. This can be reduced to a safe limit if a wide, L-shaped lead block at least 2 inches thick is placed between the radium and the operator. This should be provided at the top with an inclined lead glass visor, equivalent to at least 3 mm lead (see Figure 174).

Protection from Local Exposure

For protection of the hands from *local injury,* the above general measures should first be carefully observed. Then, the additional precaution of handling radium only with long-handled forceps should be strictly adhered to. Speed of handling is as important as distance, since both reduce the dose at the skin. *Never, under any circumstances, should radium be picked up in the fingers.* One should always use forceps or some similar instrument. Lead rubber gloves offer no protection worth mentioning as far as radium is concerned, because it is impractical to line gloves with sufficient lead thickness. The local injury by radium may take years to manifest itself, depending, of course, on the dose. It consists, in the early stages, of reddening and dryness of the skin. Later, there is brittleness and splitting of the nails, followed by keratoses, atrophy, and ulceration of the skin. Finally, cancer may develop in the ulcerated areas.

Transportation of radium should be accomplished by means of

long-handled containers lined with sufficient lead, according to Bureau of Standards specifications. For example, 100 mg radium should be carried in a container lined with 2 cm lead suspended by a handle 45 cm long; or, the container may have a 1 cm lead thickness and a handle 60 cm long. Transportation should be as fast as possible, and should preferably be done by someone who does not regularly handle radium or x-ray equipment if the radium is to be carried about frequently.

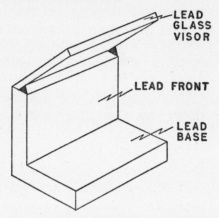

Figure 174. L-shaped lead protective block for preparing radium applicators. This is the rear view. The operator stands on the opposite side of the block so that the upright lead section protects his body and the inclined lead glass visor protects his face.

PROTECTION OF THE PATIENT FROM RADIATION

Some consideration must be given to the problem of protecting the patient from excessive radiation in the course of diagnostic procedures. The development of a skin reaction as a result of *fluoroscopy* or *radiography* is inexcusable, and in many states, has been ruled in the courts as evidence of malpractice.

It is in fluoroscopy that the greatest danger exists. Before any patient is subjected to this type of examination, a careful history should be taken to ascertain the recency and number of previous fluoroscopic studies. X-ray exposures are cumulative over many years and further exposures must be governed by what has gone before. There are several precautions that may be taken to minimize the danger of excessive radiation in roentgen diagnosis.

1. *Dark Adaptation.* The radiologist, before starting fluoroscopic examination (in a room which should be as light-tight as the darkroom) should sit in a dark room or wear special dark adaptor goggles for 20 to 30 minutes. This permits the retina of the eye to attain maximum sensitivity to the relatively dim fluoroscopic image. Such careful dark-adaptation is necessary to make a more *rapid* and more *accurate* examination.

2. *Intermittent Fluoroscopy.* It is good practice to use intermittent activation of the fluoroscopic tube rather than a long-continued one. During the brief dark intervals, the eyes have an opportunity to rest and re-adapt. This, incidentally, also prolongs tube life. Intermittent fluoroscopy definitely decreases the patient's exposure.

3. *Restriction of Field Size.* The size of the fluoroscopic field is limited by lead shutters placed between the tube and the patient. As we have seen, the larger the size of the field, the greater the depth dose, and also, the greater the backscatter to the skin. The size of the field should be limited to the smallest area that will include the part being studied. At the same time, this serves to protect the personnel from excessive radiation.

4. *Correct Operating Factors.* Dr. Russell H. Morgan has shown experimentally that, as the tube kilovoltage is increased, screen brightness is increased. If, then, the milliamperage is reduced and filtration is increased so that screen brightness is maintained constant, the patient will actually receive *less* roentgen exposure per minute than at the lower kilovoltage. In other words, fluoroscopic efficiency as far as the patient's exposure is concerned, improves under these conditions. The improvement above 100 Kv is not appreciable, and Dr. Morgan recommends a range of 85 to 100 Kv, 4 Ma, and 3 or 4 mm Al filter in clinical work. The *target-to-screen* distance is not of great importance provided it is not less than about 15 inches. At distances greater than 15 there is further decrease in exposure for a given degree of screen brightness, but this improvement is small and of doubtful value.

5. *Filtration.* As noted earlier, one can increase the hardness of an x-ray beam by the use of a suitable filter. This removes relatively more soft than hard rays, thereby decreasing the amount of radiation absorbed by the skin. In fluoroscopy, most installations use a 1 mm Al filter in front of the tube aperture. Dr. Morgan has shown that heavier aluminum filtration is more effective in decreasing the patient's exposure. When filtration is increased from the customary 1 mm Al to about 3 or 4 mm Al, there is surprisingly little impairment of screen brightness, and this can be restored by a slight increase in tube milliamperage.

6. *Maximum Permissible Exposure.* During fluoroscopy and radiography, the patient is exposed to radiation which would cause skin reaction if sufficient in quantity. To avoid this serious complication, one must know the roentgen output of the particular x-ray installation under actual operating conditions. This may be determined by a roentgen-meter, and the maximum dose that the patient receives should be the smallest possible fraction of the erythema dose. In Table V are shown the maximum permissible exposures at various distances and with different filter thicknesses. The table is approximately accurate for an average installation. It includes a safety factor of 50 per cent; is based on the roentgen output of the average x-ray unit; and assumes an erythema dose of 275 r. However, it should be emphasized again that for strict accuracy, each unit should be checked with an r-meter. The table applies to the average skin area, but because of the sensitivity of the hair follicles, the values shown in the table must be reduced by 25 per cent in head exposures.

To use Table V, select the appropriate operating factors first, then obtain the corresponding maximum MaS from the table. For example, if total filtration is 1 mm Al, distance 14 in., and kilovoltage 85, the maximum permissible exposure as shown in the table is 1000 MaS. If the tube is operating at 3 Ma, divide 1000 by 3, which equals 333 seconds or 5.5 minutes; this is the maximum allowable exposure. If the milliamperage is 4, then $1000 \div 4 = 250$ seconds, or 4.2 minutes, is the maximum allowable.

Table VI shows the modification of the maximum permissible exposures at various kilovoltages, if the filtration and milliamper-

TABLE V

Maximum permissible exposure in milliampere-seconds at 85 Kv, excluding the head. The exposure should be reduced 25 per cent in head examinations. (Data quoted by Files.)

Target-skin Distance inches	Total Filtration 0.5 mm Al	Total Filtration 1.0 mm Al	Total Filtration 1.5 mm Al
10	265 MaS	510 MaS	810 MaS
12	380	730	1090
14	520	1000	1500
16	680	1300	1950
18	870	1650	2500
20	1060	2050	3000

TABLE VI

MODIFICATION OF MAXIMUM PERMISSIBLE EXPOSURES OF THE PATIENT AT VARIOUS KILOVOLTAGES

Kv	Change in Maximum Permissible Exposure Obtained from Table V
100	Reduce MaS by 25%
90	Reduce MaS by 8%
85	No change
80	Increase MaS by 10%
70	Increase MaS by 35%
60	Increase MaS by 80%

age are kept constant. For example, if the maximum exposure is 1000 MaS at 85 Kv, then at 70 Kv it would be 1000 + (35% × 1000) = 1350 MaS. If one were to use, instead, 100 Kv, then the maximum permissible exposure would be 1000 − (25% × 1000) = 750 MaS. Note that the data in these tables are presented in a different manner from those obtained by Dr. Morgan, but they

really are not contradictory. His results are based on the main-
tenance of constant screen brightness at the higher kilovoltages by
a compensating increase in filtration and decrease in tube milliamperage; under such conditions, the patient's exposure per
minute is actually decreased at the higher kilovoltage values. On
the other hand, if the milliamperage and filtration are kept constant and the kilovoltage alone is increased, screen brightness
increases and the patient's exposure also increases; under these
conditions the data in Tables V and VI apply and one notes a decrease in the maximum permissible exposure at a higher kilovoltage.

In any x-ray diagnostic procedure, the patient's history should
be checked for previous x-ray exposures; *the total exposure in the
preceding month plus the present exposure must not exceed the
maximum permissible shown in Table V.* This is why it is so essential that a careful record be kept on all patients undergoing x-ray
study. Note should be made on the patient's permanent record, of
each exposure, including the area exposed, Kv, MaS, filtration,
and target-film distance or target-skin distance. Each patient
should be questioned routinely about previous fluoroscopic and
radiographic examinations in order to ascertain the safety of additional exposure.

The problem of protection of the patient in *therapy* is entirely
different from that existing in diagnosis. Depending on the lesion
being treated, the radiologist varies his x-ray dosage to obtain the
desired effect. In some instances, the dosage needed is small
enough so that no skin reaction is anticipated. At the other extreme
lies the treatment of certain malignancies requiring heavy exposure which may even lead to blistering of the skin. Various size
cones or diaphragms are used to delimit the size of the field being
treated, since one should avoid producing skin reaction beyond
the actual treatment field. Frequently, the treatment field is de-
limited by lead shields which are placed so as to protect the
tissues lying directly beneath the shield. The thickness of such
lead barriers depends on the Kv and filtration of the roentgen
beam. Such data are available in the article by Trout and Gager.
From these data, one can determine the thickness of lead needed,
with beams of various half-value layers, to reduce the amount of

radiation to a certain percentage of its initial value. Table VII is based on this article, and gives the necessary information for the more commonly used treatment factors. The last column in the table indicates the nearest lead thicknesses that are ordinarily available, and that may safely be used with the beam of given half-value layer. These lead thicknesses will protect the underlying tissues to the extent that they will allow no more than 0.5 per cent transmission of the quantity of that particular primary beam. The original paper should be consulted for more detailed information.

TABLE VII

Thickness of lead required to reduce the incident radiation to 0.5 per cent of the initial intensity, with beams of various degrees of hardness

Kv	Half-value Layer	Thickness of Lead for 0.5% Transmission		Usual Thickness of Lead Available
		mm	in.	
60	0.5 mm Al	0.21	0.008	1/100 in.
100	1.0 mm Al	0.68	0.026	3/100 in.
140	0.5 mm Cu	1.52	0.06	1/16 in.
200	1.0 mm Cu	1.97	0.08	5/64 in.
220	2.0 mm Cu	2.77	0.11	1/8 in.
250	3.0 mm Cu	3.45	0.14	5/32 in.

ELECTRICAL PROTECTION

In recent years, most radiology departments have been equipped with shockproof equipment for therapy and radiography, but there is still widespread use of non-shockproof installations for fluoroscopy. The latter is usually grounded for protection from the sparking-over that occurs frequently, especially in damp weather.

The best protection against non-shockproof equipment is *distance*. One must always maintain a distance, from high tension cords or conduits, greater than the sparking distance in order to avoid sparking-over to the patient or technician. A non-shockproof fluoroscope must be grounded adequately to a *water pipe* so that if spark-over occurs, the high voltage will pass directly to ground and not harm the patient or fluoroscopist. Sparking is most apt to occur at sharp angles or bends in cord reels or conduits because electric charges tend to concentrate at such points. This has already been pointed out in Chapter 5. This phenomenon is manifested by *corona* at such sharp bends, consisting of a bluish-violet, hissing discharge due to the ionization of the surrounding air by the accumulated electric charges. The ionization of the air causes a chemical change in the oxygen of the air, producing *ozone,* a gas having a characteristic pungent odor due to its reaction with the moisture in the nose to form hydrogen peroxide.

With modern shockproof equipment, the shock hazard has been practically eliminated, provided the ground connections are intact and the cables are in satisfactory condition. These should be inspected periodically.

Oddly enough, one of the commonest sources of electrical danger arises in the darkroom. All exposed electric outlets should be grounded. The technician should always observe the *one hand rule:* never reach for an electric fixture while the other hand is submerged in the processing tanks, or touches another conductor.

High voltage and low amperage shock tends to "throw" the victim, whereas low voltage high amperage shock tends to "hold him." In the latter instance, do not grasp the victim directly, but first either open the main switch or remove him by means of a dry board, a dry wad of newspaper, or a dry rope. Then apply artificial respiration and seek medical aid if shock is severe.

Closely allied to the electric hazard is the *danger of explosion.* When certain gases, such as some types of anesthetics, reach a sufficiently high concentration in the atmosphere, they may ignite explosively if a spark occurs either in the electrical contacts of the equipment or from a static electrical discharge. Modern x-ray equipment is shockproof, but it is not necessarily *sparkproof.* To minimize the danger, all equipment should be carefully grounded. Sparkproof electric outlets and sparkproof x-ray illuminators should be used in all operating rooms. If such precautions cannot be taken, then it is essential that non-explosive anesthetics be used. The anesthetics that are most commonly used, constitute the greatest explosion hazard and include ether-nitrous oxide mixture, ether, ethylene, and cyclopropane.

HYGIENIC CONSIDERATIONS

Assuming that all of the above safety factors have been followed and the technician has been very conscientious in observing the rules of conduct, one may rightly ask, "Are there any unforeseen sources of danger, or may there be individual hypersensitivity so that the generally accepted permissible dose may be unsafe in a given case? If so, how can one determine any untoward effects?" This can be decided fairly easily. Since the blood-forming organs are the most sensitive in the body, and since the circulating blood so conveniently reflects the state of the bone marrow and lymph nodes, a regular blood count including a platelet count, is an excellent indicator of excessive subjection of the body to harmful radiation. When a technician accepts a new appointment, a complete blood count (as well as a complete physical examination) should be done before work is started. Thereafter, monthly counts should be made for about four months. If there is no significant drop in the white cell and platelet counts, no alteration appears in the differential count, and no anemia occurs conditions are probably satisfactory. However, blood counts should be done routinely every three to four months as a precautionary measure. Radium workers should have their hands inspected by a radiologist or dermatologist at frequent intervals.

It is advisable to institute certain hygienic policies. The technician should have at least two, and if possible, four weeks' vacation each year, with at least two weeks consecutive and in the summer. The vacation should be spent out-doors and, of course, completely away from roentgen and gamma radiation. The working schedule should conform to an average 8-hour day with at least one full day off each week. As much time as possible should be spent out-doors after working hours. Radiologic rooms should be well-lighted and well-ventilated.

It is reasonably certain that if proper protective measures are taken to make conditions safe; if the technician is always careful to make full use of the available protective equipment and takes proper personal precautions against careless exposure; and if proper hygienic measures are undertaken as outlined above, the danger from these radiations is practically non-existent. This is attested to by the fact that it is rare for a careful technician to incur radiation injury

QUESTIONS

1. What is meant by "permissible dose"? What is the maximum permissible dose in r for an 8-hour day? For 1 week?
2. Describe two methods by which one may determine the amount of whole body radiation he is receiving in his radiology department.
3. What are the effects of excessive whole body exposure to penetrating radiations? How soon do these effects manifest themselves?
4. What material is widely used in protective barriers? What thickness of this material is required for the walls of ordinary radiographic rooms? What thickness is required for 200 Kv x-rays?
5. How can one avoid the local deleterious effects of x-rays? Of radium?
6. What are the six main factors in protecting the patient during fluoroscopy?
7. Assume that the conditions of your x-ray department are safe from the standpoint of penetrating radiations. State three rules of conduct on your part that will help eliminate the hazard of exceeding the permissible dose.
8. Why should x-ray equipment be grounded? Does an ordinary steam-heating pipe afford a satisfactory ground connection? A gas pipe? A water pipe?
9. What is the best means of protection from radium radiations?
10. What is the "one hand rule"? Why should it always be observed?

APPENDIX   *RADIOACTIVE ISOTOPES AND ARTIFICIAL RADIOACTIVITY*

I t may be recalled from Chapter 4 that all matter is made up of extremely small particles called *atoms*. The structure of the atom has been the subject of a tremendous amount of scientific investigation, and it may be summarized as follows. The atom consists of a center called the nucleus, in which is concentrated almost the entire mass of the atom. Surrounding the nucleus are orbits or paths in which electrons are in continual motion. The nucleus, for our purposes, may be considered as having two constituents, protons and neutrons. A proton is a positively charged particle weighing nearly 2000 times as much as an electron. A neutron has practically the same mass as a proton but has no electric charge.

All matter is made up of one or more chemical constituents called *elements*. The atoms of each element have a characteristic and distinct number of positive charges or protons in the nucleus, and an equal number of electrons in the orbits around the nucleus. The number of nuclear positive charges is called the *atomic number*. It must be emphasized that the atomic number is specific for a given element; all atoms of any one element have the same atomic number. Atoms of different elements have different atomic numbers.

The mass of an atom is concentrated in its nucleus, which is composed of protons and neutrons. Therefore, the mass of any atom is designated by the term *mass number* which is defined as the total number of protons and neutrons in the nucleus of that atom. For example, hydrogen has one proton in the nucleus, so its mass number is 1. Helium has 2 protons and 2 neutrons in the nucleus, so its mass number is 4.

Isotopes. If we were to take any sample of a given chemical element, we could show by appropriate studies that all of the atoms in that sample would have the same atomic number and therefore the same chemical properties. (It should be recalled that the atomic number of an element is equal to the number of positive charges, or protons, in the nucleus.) Curiously enough, it would be found that all of the atoms in the sample would not necessarily have the same mass number or total number of protons and neutrons in the nucleus. It must be realized that there is not an unlimited range of mass numbers in the sample; there may be only two or three or several as they occur in nature, and the proportion of the atoms of different mass numbers is relatively constant for the element being studied. Such atoms of an element, having the same atomic number but differing in mass number, are called *isotopes*. Since all the atomic isotopes of an element have the same atomic number, they have the same chemical properties. The gas, hydrogen, for example, has two naturally occurring isotopes: hydrogen with atomic number 1 and mass number 1; and deuterium (heavy hydrogen) with atomic number 1 and mass number 2. These two forms of hydrogen have identical chemical properties but differ in mass.

Radioactive Isotopes. In recent years, physicists have been able to prepare new isotopes artificially, isotopes which heretofore had been completely unknown. More interesting still is the fact that many of these isotopes are radioactive, disintegrating into entirely different elements with release of energy. These radioactive isotopes have the same chemical properties as their non-radioactive relatives, differing only in their mass number and in their property of radioactivity.

The artificial radioactive isotopes are produced by bombarding the atomic nuclei of certain atoms by means of sub-atomic particles such as neutrons or deuterons in a cyclotron or atomic energy pile. A neutron, it will be recalled, is an uncharged sub-atomic particle having mass number 1. A deuteron is a heavy hydrogen nucleus having a positive charge and mass number 2. The nucleus of the bombarded atom captures a neutron or a deuteron, becoming unstable and exhibiting the property of spontaneous breakdown known as *radioactivity*. This, in general, resembles the disintegration of the natural radioactive elements such as radium.

An example of the transmutation of an ordinary element to another element which is radioactive will make the above process more easily understandable. Ordinary sulfur is converted, during neutron bombardment, to radioactive phosphorus:

$$\text{Ordinary} + \text{Neutron} \rightarrow \text{Radioactive} + \text{Hydrogen}$$
$$\text{Sulfur} \qquad\qquad\qquad \text{Phosphorus}$$

$$_{16}S^{32} \quad + \quad _{0}n^{1} \quad \rightarrow \quad _{15}P^{32} \quad + \quad _{1}H^{1}$$

In each term of the equation, the lower number or subscript represents the atomic number, and the upper number or superscript represents the mass number. Since the atomic number of phosphorus is always 15, radioactive phosphorus is usually abbreviated P^{32}. When P^{32} is formed, its nucleus is unstable because of the extra neutron (ordinary non-radioactive phosphorus is P^{31}) and disintegrates to ordinary sulfur, emitting a beta particle (negative electron) in the process:

$$_{15}P^{32} \rightarrow {}_{16}S^{32} + \text{beta particle}$$

At the present time, there is no way of altering the type of radiation emitted by a given radioactive element, natural or artificial.

Artificial Radioactivity. The nuclear instability resulting from neutron capture, while it is constant for any given radioactive isotope, varies tremendously among the different isotopes. The degree of instability is designated by the half life, just as in the case of radium. Half life is defined as the time required for the disintegration of one-half the atoms in a given sample of radioactive isotope. This is the same for all samples of any one isotope and cannot be changed by any known means. The half life ranges from a fraction of a second for some isotopes, up to millions of years for others.

The amount of radioactivity of a radioactive material is measured in terms of a unit called the *curie.* For practical purposes in radiology a smaller unit is more convenient; this is one thousandth of a curie, known as a *millicurie.* One millicurie is that quantity of a radioactive element, natural or artificial, that undergoes 37 million disintegrations per second, which means that 37 million nuclei will have decayed to some other element in one second. The atoms of most of the commonly used radioactive isotopes emit, during their disintegration, gamma rays or beta particles or both. The radiations emitted by any selected isotope are always the same and cannot be altered by any known means. Thus, P^{32} always emits beta particles. Some isotopes emit positively charged electrons known as positrons. Only isotopes of atomic weight greater than 205 emit alpha particles.

Practical Use of Isotopes. The radioactive isotopes have been widely used in research, in medicine, and in industry. Of greatest interest to the x-ray technician is their application in medicine. In general, there are three main fields of usefulness. First the radioactive isotopes are of outstanding importance in tracer studies. In the past, it has been difficult to determine how the body handles certain drugs and foodstuffs because of the almost insurmountable problem of tracing the course of these substances and their breakdown products through the various tissues and organs. Now chemists can prepare compounds containing in their chemical structure a radioactive isotope which labels this compound so that it can be followed by certain instruments, such as the Geiger counter, during all the changes that it undergoes in the body. Selective uptake of the compound in certain organs can also be determined. Since the body cannot differentiate chemically between the ordinary compound and the one containing the radioactive isotope, it handles them both identically, thereby affording us a means of investigating the chemical processes going on in the body.

The second field of usefulness of radioactive isotopes is in medical diagnosis. This is really a practical application of the tracer method. For example, radioactive iodine (I^{131}) can be used to determine the state of functional activity of the thyroid gland: in the overactive gland there is excessive uptake of ingested iodine which can be detected by the Geiger counter. Another example is the selective uptake of certain iodine-containing dyes (chemically related to mercurochrome) by some types of brain tumors. If radioactive iodine is substituted for ordinary iodine in one of these dyes and given to the patient internally, its presence in excessive amounts in a brain tumor can be detected externally by means of a Geiger counter. This method of localizing brain tumors is highly accurate and shows great promise.

The third application of radioactive isotopes is in treatment. The goal, something which has not yet been reached except in a limited way, is to obtain an isotope preparation that is selectively taken up by a diseased organ which can then benefit directly from the radiations emitted by the isotope. Thus, in the case of hyperthyroidism where the thyroid gland is overactive, I^{131} can be given in suitable form internally. It concentrates in the thyroid to a marked degree and the radiations from the I^{131} suppress the activity of the gland. However, the application of this principle to malignant disease is thus far extremely limited.

TABLE VIII

SOME ISOTOPES OF MEDICAL INTEREST

Isotope	Half Life	Radiations Emitted	Use in Medicine
Phosphorus 32	14.3 days	beta	Treatment of polycythemia, leukemia, skin cancer. Used in tracer studies to determine red cell volume.
Iodine 131	8 days	beta and gamma	Treatment of hyperthyroid disease and certain thyroid cancers. Tracer studies in locating brain tumors and thyroid cancer metastases.
Iron 59	46.3 days	beta and gamma	Tracer studies to study formation of hemoglobin in red blood cells, and iron metabolism generally.
Cobalt 60	5 years	beta and gamma	Radium substitute in needles, wires, etc., and in external radiation.
Sodium 24	14.8 hours	beta and gamma	Mainly as tracer in blood circulation studies and in sodium metabolism.
Gold 198	2.7 days	beta and gamma	Treatment of tumor masses by direct injection of the isotope in colloidal suspension.
Strontium 90	25 years	beta	Treatment of lesions on surface of eye.
Carbon 14	5600 years	beta	Only in long term animal and plant experiments because of long half life. Tag for tracer studies of various organic compounds.

ISOTOPES IN MEDICINE

It may be of interest to summarize briefly the present status of a few of the more important medical isotopes.

Radioactive Iodine. This is abbreviated as I^{131}, the most commonly used radioactive isotope of iodine. It is called iodine 131, has a half life of 8 days, and emits beta particles and gamma rays. It is obtained by the transmutation of the element tellurium in the atomic energy pile. Iodine 131 is used in the diagnosis and treatment of diseases of the thyroid gland, and in the localization of brain tumors. The therapeutic effect of this isotope, as in treatment of hyperthyroidism or certain thyroid cancers, depends largely on the beta particles. The localization or tracer studies depend on the gamma rays which are much more penetrating than the beta particles and can be detected outside the body with a Geiger counter.

Radioactive Phosphorus. Phosphorus 32 has a half life of 14.3 days and gives off beta rays. It is prepared by neutron irradiation of sulfur in a cyclotron or atomic energy pile. After administration by mouth or by injection in suitable form, P^{32} tends to concentrate in the bone marrow, spleen, liver, and lymph nodes. It can therefore be used, to a limited extent, in the treatment of certain blood disorders. Its greatest value is in the treatment of a disease called polycythemia rubra vera, in which the bone marrow produces an excess of red blood cells. P^{32} can be used to check this overproduction of cells. This isotope has also been used to a limited degree in the treatment, by surface application, of certain skin diseases including superficial skin cancer.

Radioactive Sodium. Sodium 24 has a short half life, 14.8 hours, and emits beta particles and gamma rays. It tends to be distributed fairly uniformly in the body fluids, but, has thus far been of little or no value in therapy. However, it is of some value in diagnosis; when injected into a blood vessel, the state of the circulation can be determined. Na^{24} has been widely used in research in the study of the manner in which the body handles this element.

Radioactive Iron. Of the two radioactive isotopes of iron, that having mass number 59 is more suitable for research in medicine. Iron 59 has a half life of 44 days and emits gamma rays so that it can be employed as a tracer to study the absorption, distribution, storage, and elimination of iron in the body. Such studies have taught us, for example, that the body retains iron avidly in its storage depots to be used in the production of hemoglobin in the red blood cells, and that the body absorbs iron from ingested food only when it is needed.

Radioactive Cobalt. Fairly large amounts of cobalt 60 can be produced in the atomic energy pile. This isotope has a half life of 5.3 years and emits gamma rays comparable in wavelength to 2 million volt x-rays and with more uniform quality of radiation than x-rays. Cobalt 60 can be made in a variety of forms—needles, beads, plaques, wires, etc. and offers great promise as a radium substitute. Large cobalt 60 irradiators have been designed for use in external irradiation.

There is a host of other radioactive isotopes that may provide more efficient means of treating malignant disease, but only time will tell to what extent these will replace the present methods of irradiation.

BIBLIOGRAPHY

Batson, Oscar V., and Carpentier, Virginia E.: Stereoscopic depth perception. *Am. J. Roentgenol., 51:*202–204, 1944.

Braestrup, C. B.: X-ray protection in diagnostic radiology. *Radiology,* 38:207–216, 1942.

Crabtree, J. I., and Henn, R. W.: Developer solutions for x-ray films. *Med. Radiog. & Photog.,* 23:2–12, 1947. (Published by Eastman Kodak Co., Rochester, N. Y.)

Files, Glenn W.: *Medical Radiographic Technic.* Springfield, Ill., Charles C Thomas, Publisher, 1945.

Glasser, Otto: *Medical Physics.* Chicago, The Year Book Publishers, Inc., 1950.

Glasser, O., Quimby, E., Taylor, L. S., and Weatherwax, J. L.: *Physical Foundations of Radiology.* New York, Paul B. Hoeber, Inc., 1950.

Kieffer, J.: Analysis of laminagraphic motions and their values. *Radiology,* 33:560–585, 1939.

Medical X-Ray Protection up to Two Million Volts, *Handbook 41.* U. S. Department of Commerce, National Bureau of Standards. Superintendent of Documents, Washington, D. C.

Radium Protection, *Handbook H23.* U. S. Department of Commerce, National Bureau of Standards. Superintendent of Documents, Washington, D. C.

Sante, L. R.: *Manual of Roentgenological Technique.* Ann Arbor, Mich., Edwards Brothers, Inc., 1950.

Taft, R. B.: Stray radiation under actual conditions. *Am. J. Roentgenol., 46:*373–376, 1941.

The Fundamentals of Radiography, Eastman Kodak Co., Rochester, N. Y.

Trout, E. D., and Gager, R. M.: Protective materials for field definition in radiation therapy. *Am. J. Roentgenol., 63:*396–408, 1950.

Weyl, C., and Warren, S. R., Jr.: *Radiologic Physics.* Springfield, Ill., Charles C Thomas, Publisher, 1951.

INDEX